After Ext

Dirty Leeds Uncut

by Robert Endeacott

PDG Books Ltd, 2012

After Extra Time – Dirty Leeds Uncut is published by PDG Books Ltd,
email pdgbooks@btinternet.com
Registered company number 5334818

ISBN 978-1-905519-11-8

Printed by Charlesworth Press

Acknowledgements

There are certain people no longer alive who naturally I haven't been able to personally thank for building or being a part of something very special to many of us, namely the football club. Some of them are men who had more influence in the growth of Leeds as a team and as a city than has been properly recognized. Those men undoubtedly inspired this novel.

Included in that group are John Charles and Billy Bremner, two of the greatest footballers of ANY generation, and Harry Reynolds, the ex-chairman and 'founder' of the reincarnated Leeds United. There is too a man of whom many won't have heard but who is prominent within this tale: Ces Burroughs. Actually, I hardly knew him myself as I was only a nipper but he was a very good friend to my Dad while they were on the Elland Road ground staff together, and he helped with the development of some of the great Leeds players as well.

And talking of groundsmen and great men, there is one man I am deeply indebted to, a man who not only was a fine friend of the Endeacotts - and countless other folk - but also the main source of help and encouragement for this book: that man is of course John Reynolds.

Alas, John died early April 2012 and we lost an absolute gem of a person as a result. His death came just eight months after the death of my Mum, Moyra, and I am not embarrassed to admit that barely a minute passes by without my thinking of her. But when I'm 'in a good place' I'm at least able to think of all the pleasure she brought to our lives. She is terribly missed, as is John of course. Any of you reading this and in the vicinity of your mum, go and give her a hug and a kiss, there's never a wrong time to do it. Well obviously there IS, but you get my meaning...

Above all, the man who I have to thank for inspiring this book is without doubt Don Revie OBE. And yes I did meet him when I was 8 or so years old and he did tell my Mum that the correct way to pronounce his surname was/is 'Reevi'! But counter that with just about every Leeds player of the day pronouncing it 'Revvi' and we have an eternal puzzle. However, what is not in doubt is that we had a fantastic football team &

coaching staff thanks to the deeds of Don Revie, and he and the team never received the plaudits and recognition (nationally) they deserved. But WE know, we know how fantastic his and his men's achievements are. I hope I've delivered truth and justice to the legend as well as put a few 'mistakes' right.

Big thanks to Beeston Hill Historical Society, Beeston Library (Jane Smith & co.), the British Film Institute, BBC Radio Leeds, BBC TV, the National Museum of Football, Waterstones, the forums LUFCTalk, Gelderd Calling and OneMickJones, as well as Facebook, Twitter, Linkedin, YouTube and not forgetting Leeds United AFC of course.

Special Acknowledgements to Chris & Adele Archer, Keith & Dot Archer, Graham Barnes, Paul Birch, Craig Bradley, Vicky Bradshaw, Jack Bray, Rick Broadbent, Dave Brydon, Jim Cadman, Anthony Clavane, Pete Cluderay, Dave Cocker, Mick Cotter, Gary Edwards, James Ellis, Graham Endeacott, Paul Eubanks, Graeme Garvey, Sam Gibbard, Gayle Graham, Julian Hardcastle & family, Tony Hill, Peter Holme/Gordon Small, Phil Hodgson, Harry Hogg, Ben Hunt, Alwyn Hutchinson, Colin S Jeffrey, Neil Jeffries, Steve 'Johna' Johnson, Gary Kaye, Nick King, Thom Kirwin, Bogdan Leonte, Peter Lorimer, Johnny Lorrimer, Fraser Marr, Lance McCrickard, Hugh Neill, Andy Oddy, Kevin & Lynda O'Rourke, Tom Palmer, Brian Passmore & family, David Peace, Dean Plews, Adam Pope, Brian Revis, Stephen & Maureen Reynolds, Steve Riley, Deborah & Peter Robinson, Joseph Ross, Tom Rowe, Steve Swift, Margaret & Peter Veitch, Stu Wheatman (of course!) and Sam & Sophie Emery (even more of course!).

A big part of my reasoning for bringing out the 'director's cut' of Dirty Leeds was to enable myself to do a bit for charity, and Candle Lighters seems the perfect cause I think. So of every new copy of this book that is sold, approximately 10% is going to Candle Lighters. It's not a big deal but I hope it helps in some small way and if I'm not destitute as a result then I'd like to do it again.

Dedicated to our Mum, Moyra, always a Leeds fan and always a beautiful person.

Chapter contents

'... the Disciplinary Committee considered the list of clubs whose players had been cautioned or suspended, censured or fined during the 1963-'64 season. Ipswich Town and Sheffield United had the best record and Leeds United the worst...'

The *FA News*, summer, 1964-'65 pre season.

And so the myth began, *dirty Leeds*...

Chapter 1: 1961 - 'Maybe we'll meet up again'

1 i

Eamonn Andrews should have been a spy. How he always manages to spring that bloody red book on his victims without them suspecting it is like proper *Callan* stuff. A big fella he is too, I never realised until seeing him in real life while I was loitering without much intent in town. Thirteen years and one month before and I'd been hanging around for ages waiting for the footballer Don Revie, freezing my small assets off. Thirteen years one month later, three or so miles away from Elland Road, and I'm hanging around for ages for him all over again. But at least it's warm tonight, and I'm wearing proper trousers this time and not school shorts.

My grandma always said Eamonn Andrews was dashing. Well, he was dashing tonight alright, all over the place, making sure the filming all went exactly to plan. Even I was bricking it, and I had nothing at all to do with the programme or the supposed Sportsmen's Dinner being held at the Queens Hotel. I'd been invited to that but could I hell as like afford a dinner jacket and chuffing bow tie. Ces didn't go either. John and Ray did, and John even got on the telly, right at the start of the programme, a big white smile underneath his big black moustache. He offered to pay for the hire of a suit and stuff but I couldn't accept the gesture. Besides, it all sounded way too posh for my liking. Too many portly 'sportsmen' there who'd never kicked a football in their life, counting money and chewing food was more their game. No, I'd have been right out of place, big style.

I stood around the hotel main entrance in City Square, thinking I'd at least get my face on the box. Even that didn't happen. Andrews turned up, microphone in his hand, camera crew filming him. I was lurking behind one of the hotel pillars - there was a kid already in prime position for the cameras. He got on the telly alright, with his bloody parka and big autograph book, the little weirdo. Not that I really had anything against him for collecting autographs, I'd been doing exactly the same thirteen years ago, in 1961, when it all really began. March 1961 to be more precise, a time when they didn't seem to really like entertainment in Leeds. They'd just knocked down the Empire Palace theatre to replace it with a shopping arcade, even though no one asked for one. And the football club, well that was all just a bad joke with only a few of us supporting them. We deserve a big bundle of credit for it, for sticking with them through thin and thin.

Anyway, back to April 1974: I was suddenly more interested in having a drink than I was waiting for The Gaffer so I walked off for a pint in the Scarbrough Taps round the corner from the hotel. Truth is, generally speaking I was in a right mood, as dark as the streets around the Square: narked, feeling left out, lonely and a failure, I was nearly 25 years old but felt more like a 65 year-old OAP.

1 ii

April 1974. the Queens Hotel, Leeds, a special occasion organized by the chairman of the city's Variety Club, Marshall Bellow, to pay tribute to one of Yorkshire and England football's greatest achievers. It is a sportsmen's dinner, taking place in the vast dining room of the renowned hotel. Famous names from sport, the media and the arts are here, with luminaries from the world of local business too. Some of the men are in cahoots with Bellow in order to make the night an even grander event - were that possible - for their unsuspecting guest.

The Queens Hotel is white underneath its filthy, blackened coating. Connected to one of the country's busiest railway stations, it possesses a high reputation for the quality of its accommodation and restaurants and Art Deco interiors. That reputation is preserved, despite the neglected exterior of the building. On the hotel steps stands television host Eamonn

Andrews, directly in front of one of the large, comparatively clean pillars guarding the main entrance. A drone of motor traffic and a hum of voices indicate a busy City Square, though only a few members of the public are in camera range around Andrews. One of those people, a teenaged boy with lank hair, wearing a parka coat with a fur-edged hood, smiles at the camera and clutches a well-used autograph book in his hands. He hasn't got the Irishman's signature yet and he will have quite a wait before a chance arises. And then Andrews receives a signal...

With microphone in his left hand, Eamonn Andrews talks to the TV camera - in a couple of nights his image will be addressing an audience of millions. His renowned brogue and that most famous introduction will charm and captivate the viewers of Great Britain and keep them in suspense for just a few minutes: who is this week's famous 'victim'?

'This is *This Is Your Life*,' he begins, softly. 'Tonight we're in the north of England inside this hotel where a celebration dinner is about to begin. Although there are many famous faces, the man I'm after is only just about to arrive because he is the Guest of Honour of the Variety Club here at Leeds... Now he's so respected and so well-known that stars from many fields have come here to pay tribute.... There's *Man at the Top* Kenneth Haigh, soccer manager Joe Mercer, television personality Michael Parkinson, playwright and actor Colin Welland, that great character of show-jumping Harvey Smith, and others...' Amongst those 'others' are cricketer Freddie Trueman, footballer Derek Dougan, the 'Super Leeds' team and staff, wrestler-cum-actor Paul Luty...

'...There's an extra guest - me and this,' Andrews continues, indicating his microphone. 'I've got to move very quickly because he's on his way in now, and make sure I'm right behind him and his host Marshall Bellow as he's welcomed into that dining room.'

The oak double doors swing open on cue. Inside, another camera pans over the seated and dinner-suited guests. The room is packed, no spare seats tonight, folks. A score or so of long, white-clothed tables are lined up in canteen fashion, with hundreds of men dressed to the nines seated around them. Men mill around on foot too, anxious to find their places. Dinner jackets, bow ties, frilled and plain shirts, white and coloured collars, cuffs. Long hair, sideburns, moustaches, beards. Balding heads, some with hair combed over.

On each side of a tiny area at the front of the room are two small rows of cream, chic chairs for the *This Is Your Life* subject and his surprise guests. Surprises to him at least. Mauve walls, dazzling, burnished pink curtains, a wooden-cased television positioned nearby, and the beiges, creams and greens of the patterned carpet give a distinctly colour un-coordinated look to the proceedings. There are fine sportsmen here, with fine sporting achievements to their name, and there are many non-sportsmen in attendance too, their reputations made not from sporting prowess but from business acumen and financial power. A stench of cigarette and cigar smoke hangs over the wealth and influence, this room and its adornments will need a thorough cleaning after this evening has passed.

Loud applause and boisterous cheering fill the air as the principal guest approaches the dining room doors. Andrews is nowhere to be seen. Hiding. Then, quietly, unassumingly, Don Revie OBE enters the scene with Marshall Bellow at his side. They walk slowly to the doorway and then pause. Revie - dark blue dinner suit, black trimmed lapels, a yellow silk handkerchief peeking out of the breast pocket and a big black bow tie over a proud frilled shirt - is momentarily wide-eyed with pleasant surprise at such a fervent welcome. Proud but remaining calm, he complies with the press cameramen as they request their shots. The presence of television cameras too doesn't perturb him - as the manager of one of the most successful football teams in the world, he is used to having them around. The enthusiastic applause continues...

Behind him, a tall Dubliner stealthily enters the room, practically unnoticed. And to Revie's right, another dinner-suited man - uncannily similar in looks to Bobby Moore - hands a new microphone to the cat burglar Andrews. Gesturing to the crowd to hush, Andrews begins to speak, 'Gentlemen, gentlemen...' he says, with Revie still smiling and still oblivious to any deception, '... I know that you've arranged a very special night for your Guest of Honour...'

Revie realises an official is making an announcement nearby, and the man's voice sounds curiously familiar. His pleased expression turns to a mild frown and then to one of worry and concern, as he recognises the voice. The owner of the voice reaches Revie's side. Revie turns to look at him and he grins when he sees who it is. Even then though, he has not entirely grasped the situation... then his grin freezes as his eyes take in the large red book in Andrews' hands. And at that very instant, Don Revie looks petrified. Unperturbed, Eamonn Andrews carries on, he is in full flow and there is no turning back, just as there is no turning back or escape for Don Revie despite the urge to do so.

Eamonn Andrews - '... but I have your chairman's permission to add one extra touch and say... DON REVIE, TONIGHT, THIS IS YOUR LIFE.'

1 iii

Shrinking and shivering in the winter sun, the mad things you do when you *really* want something, specially when you're a kid in short trousers. A March 1961 morning and I was off school for some or other reason, and I must have been waiting over two hours and my knees were tingling big time. They felt like I'd lost all feeling there in fact. Freezing, lead clouds all over, a grey dull day with my kneecaps blue and the backs of my knees red. Real brass monkey's weather with a proper biting wind to boot, I was hoping it'd snow to warm it up and make it slightly less uncomfortable. It didn't. And I was on my own, the only chump dateless enough to be there.

Then it's *clack clack clack* and it's about time too! - the Leeds players and coaches after their training session on the Fullerton Park pitches. Slicked back hair, black muck, dark looks, brown marks, no smiles. I had my little pale blue autograph book with me, nice and full of signatures. I had too many to count - there was Freddie Goodwin's and Grenville Hair's, big Jack's, little Billy's, black Gerry Francis'. The backroom staff's and all: Jack Taylor's; Syd 'IOU' Owen's, Les 'The Shocker' Cocker's,

'Smiling' Bob English's, 'Warm Face' Cyril Partridge's, Maurice 'The Gent' Lindley's. And all the time I used to be thinking, non-stop, hoping and planning – *One day people will be asking for my autograph. Mine, one day, when **I'm** a Leeds United player...*

The rubbish you think of when you're nearly eleven.

Clack clack clack. The best autograph in my collection was King John's, I got it before he left to join the Itie's. The greatest player ever to play for Leeds, for any Yorkshire team most likely. My grandma took me all the way up to his house in Middleton to get it, it must have been 1957 or thereabouts. It was the furthest I'd ever walked, and that hill was a right pain for my little legs and feet. I'll have had a good whinge and then forgotten all about it, once I'd realised that the aching feet were worth it. 'Charlesy', *the* John Charles, actually came to his front door to see us and have a chat, smiling, ruffling my hair, stuff like that. He even gave me a banana. And the thing I remember the most, clear as day, is that he was a giant, massive, lengthways and across as well.

He signed my book *To Jimmy, Best Wishes John Charles* - and it's always been like a piece of treasure to me. I had other old, important Leeds players' too - Wilbur Cush, Georgie Meek and the nicest Jock footballer I ever met, Jimmy Dunn who lived near us, just up the street opposite the Elland Road gates in the Heaths, lovely, big semi-detached houses with front *and* back gardens and sheds and garages and indoor toilets. The Heaths are like palaces compared to the Hoxtons where me and my grandma were. All the houses around there were redbrick, except the Hoxtons were older and the bricks more black and brown than red, because of the traffic and the factories.

There was one Leeds player's autograph I didn't have - I didn't have Don Revie's. I'd never even had the chance to get it before. *Clack clack clack.* The studs of twenty or so Leeds players' boots, down the crumbly steps from the Fullerton pitches. The team was doing rubbish and had just given manager Taylor the push. Halfway down Division Two, we had no chance of promotion back to the First but the way we'd been performing, there was definitely chance we'd get out of the division, by relegation to the Third. There weren't many Leeds United supporters, that's a fact, and this lot of players probably didn't deserve them anyway.

Clack clack clack they came, down from the pitches on to the black shale. I'd watched them train from behind the wire fencing at the top of the embankment. Any stray balls that came over, I was their unofficial ballboy, running up and down the hillock, whacking them back over the fence from the shale below. I'd been fagging balls nearly all morning. Sodding sodden wet balls with the laces loosening, not in good nick at all, and weighing a ton, especially for a kid like me, a weed. And did anyone say thank you? Did they bollocks.

As the players made their descent, I skidded down the incline towards them. A procession on to the shale they came and it was crunch time for me. Them buggers didn't even look slightly cold, because they had layers of wool on over their training gear. It made them look more like fishermen than football men. Syd and Les had silly wool hats on and all, making them look a bit simple in my opinion. Not that I'd ever let on, you didn't cross the Leeds coaches if you could help it, I learnt that early on. Les would 'shock' you and Syd would make you pay, it was as simple as that, they were right hard taskmasters and it wasn't worth upsetting them. Unless you were like Jack Charlton maybe, hating being told what to do and liking a quarrel or two.

The Leeds players, all in blue, ugly blue, caked in cold, wet mud, training bottoms dark brown more than blue. And then I see him, Don Revie, and even he's got himself dirty. He must have slipped or been clattered or something because getting stuck in was never his style, he couldn't tackle for toffee. He was my target and like a missile I homed in on him, book poised. Snaking my way through the others, dodging them like I was a sparring boxer.

'Don, Don… can I have your autograph?' He didn't hear me, he was too busy talking to Jack Charlton. Or maybe he was ignoring me because I was being a bit impolite.

'Mister Revie, will you sign us this?' He still didn't seem to hear me, they were both still talking, and arguing in fact. In Jack's case, everyone always said that he could start an argument in a Trappist monks' monastery, or cause a fight in an empty room. And he was never wrong, nothing was ever his fault. He was cussing at Don Revie, dead angry, nearly shouting, on about *not* having a chip on his shoulder and mentioning Revie *not* being able to drop him from the team. 'You're not the bloody manager, so what the hell!' he said, glancing down at me too. For a split second he looked quite sheepish, like he was embarrassed at his behaviour in front of a boy. But he didn't say anything else and just walked off, big giraffe strides towards the changing rooms.

I switched my attention to Don Revie again. 'Don… Mister Revie… can you sign us this?' And *he* looked down at me then as well, though it wasn't from as high up as Jack Charlton. His face was red, and I realised it probably wasn't the best time of asking, possibly even the worst. And then he says, right snotty, 'It's Mister Revie, pronounced Ree-vi.'

Everyone I knew had always pronounced it 'Revvie' and not 'Ree-vie'- my grandma, Ces, John, Mr Hatfield at school, the radio - how was I to know? Maybe he was pulling my leg or putting an act on. Or maybe he was in fact a weird split personality type. Or maybe he was just being contrary. I was confused - I often was - and a couple of the other players went by, laughing, making me feel more embarrassed.

I only wanted his autograph for God's sake, so I asked again, right deliberate like, 'Can I have your autograph then, Mister Ree-vi?' And he didn't like that, it was obvious. 'No you can't,' he said, 'Come back when you've learnt some respect and better manners.' And off he walked, he just ignored me and left. Don bloody Revie or *Revvie* or however you bloody well pronounced it, the cheeky, miserable sod. It was the first time I'd ever met him and spoken to him, in my life, and that's the sort of reception I get! It put me in my place but it wasn't right and I couldn't just let it finish like that.

So I blurted at him, 'I don't want it anyway - you're past it!'

He stopped walking. And he turned around, looking at me with a right rotten stare. There was no one else around now and I'm suddenly a worried I'm in big trouble. And then he said, 'What did you say?' He didn't shout but he was angry. Not that that stopped me - it was his fault I was annoyed and I couldn't let go, I couldn't stop myself, 'Even my grandma says so, you're past it. *And* she's quicker than you!' and before he could react I'd scarpered by him like a proper little coward, belting off up through the rusty gates, on to Elland Road. That had showed him. Well, not really, not at all in fact.

A hundred yards sprint, by the petrol station and garage and the Old Peacock car park, past the terrace houses, cross Wesley

Street, round the corner into Hoxton Street where we lived. It was another 'Trafalgar Day' as I'd christened it, washing lines strung across the street, all the way up, with sheets and clothes hanging down, wafting in the breeze, looking like an armada of tall ships.

The smoke and fumes made me cough, as usual, and my throat and lungs throbbed because of the cold air. I felt like I'd won a race but I had a cold churning in my stomach at the same time, like I was ashamed, like I'd done something bad and which I'd live to regret. I was half worried Revie would be after me, trying to find out where we lived. He'd know his way round our streets, because Jack Charlton for one had lived there some time ago, and then Revie would tell my grandma so's she'd be able to bollock me as well.

1 iv

As the *This Is Your Life* signature tune blares out, Eamonn Andrews leads Don Revie to his seat and in to the spotlight at the front of the Queens Hotel dining room. Revie feels more akin to a prisoner being led to the dock. He sits down and crosses his legs, leaning forward like a man awaiting excruciating dental treatment.

Andrews - 'We caught you on the hop Don, I think?'

Revie - 'Very much so,' but then he quips, 'Where's Marshall Bellow?'

Louder now, Eamonn Andrews - 'Well Don Revie, This Is Your Life and tonight these distinguished guests are paying tribute to your tremendous career which began in Bell Street, Middlesbrough, where you were born. Your first soccer pitch was right outside your own back gate on a cobbled alley where you played as a boy with a pair of Wellington boots as football boots and a ball made of rags. But that humble beginning was to put you on the road to lasting fame. And tonight, this audience is honouring your achievements. They're all men, but behind your success has been a woman and I know she's your number one fan - your wife Elsie.'

Elsie Revie emerges from behind the curtains, greeted with loud applause and the customary fanfare of music. Her reddish hair immaculate, she is wearing a glorious green, white and violet patterned dress and a broad smile on her face. Pleased to be there and relieved that the harmless conspiracy has all gone according to plan, husband Don would be proud of the meticulous planning and organization that has gone in to producing the programme. Still in a state of mild shock however, Don looks at his wife with a trace of annoyance in his eyes - he has been tricked and he does not like surprises.

'And of course with her, two more members of the Revie family - nineteen year-old Duncan and fourteen year-old daughter Kim.' More loud applause and music as they appear through the curtains and walk a few steps to sit down next to Elsie. Again, Don Revie appears rather unimpressed, perhaps realising that his offspring have been involved in the scheming too.

Elsie tells the audience about her husband's career, stacked as it is with achievements, and that another landmark is approaching too, their silver wedding anniversary in October. With her gentle Scottish accent noticeable, she jokes that she is hoping to get a 'proper' invitation to that celebration, and then she tells of how football brought them together in the late 1940's, through her dad Johnny ('Jocky') Duncan and Uncle Tommy Duncan's connections with Leicester City, Don's first professional club. And then Elsie talks of domestic matters: 'Don's pretty marvellous we think. We have my mother, two aunts and my uncle, and in spite of being in the most insecure job in the world, he's provided a home and bought a large house so that we can all live together. Because he believes that as well as looking after the young, you must look after the old people. And he certainly HAS looked after my old people!' Eamonn Andrews then welcomes '80 year-old Jean Duncan and 76 year-old Jenny Duncan, and of course 86 year-old Willie Duncan.' Jenny is the spokesperson for the trio, telling the audience of their huge gratitude to Don.

Son Duncan Revie, studying Law at Cambridge University, tells of his dad watching him play football for his school team - on just the one occasion. Dad's analysis of son's performance? 'Fair skill but I could turn a double decker bus quicker.' Kim reveals, hardly surprisingly, that they are all ardent Leeds fans and that their house is full of them. Their father meanwhile, looks like he wishes he was anywhere but there, this really is an ordeal and he easily understands why Danny Blanchflower walked out of the very same show when he had been chosen as a recipient in 1961. February 1961 in fact, just a few weeks before Revie began his Leeds United managerial career. As the event progresses, Revie looks humble and sad, as if criticised rather than praised. But then Eamonn Andrews mentions Don Revie's elder, twin sisters, Joyce and Jean, and he brightens up immediately, jumping to his feet to greet them as they appear through the curtains. These are the sisters who helped to look after him when he was twelve, and fill the void left by the death of their mother in 1939.

Jean tells how fourteen year-old Don missed her wedding to play for boys' team the Middlesbrough Swifts, saying 'Well I'm off, see you after the match.' And when he turned professional, she recounted that the most relieved people were the neighbours as they knew they weren't going to get a football through their window every five minutes. And it had been a good thing their dad was a joiner otherwise there wouldn't be any windows left in Bell Street! Andrews then tells how Don Revie was instructed by Revie senior to secure his future by learning a proper trade as playing football wasn't exactly a safe profession.

Andrews - 'What was that trade, do you remember?'

Revie - 'Yes, apprentice bricklayer.'

Andrews - 'And you worked hard at it?'

Don Revie - 'Yes I did.'

The next surprise guest will be Bill Sanderson, a fine old fellow and Revie's first official manager at Middlesbrough Swifts. Before he comes on, a recording of his voice plays, describing Don Revie as a boy sneaking into the Swifts manager's house to hear and watch his team-talk and tactical instructions set out in diagrams on the wall. Eamonn Andrews then introduces Sanderson, and mentions that whilst Don Revie had been involved in various record transfer fees, Sanderson's Swifts were the first club to pay a fee for his services. Sanderson - 'Probably for an all-time low, Eamonn - for five bob...' and amidst great merriment, 'In cash.'

Andrews - 'Don, it was while playing with Middlesbrough Swifts that your dreams come true with an invitation to join

Leicester City as a part-time professional. At sixteen you pack your bags and leave home for the first time. How did you feel then?'

'Er... very, very lonely because I'd never been there before... erm... only as far as Redcar on a day out.'

*

March 1961, new days bring with them new battles. Military coups and brutal revolutions cause bloodshed the world over, countries are ripped apart by power lust, corruption and greed while plans for a Wall are afoot in central Europe, which will divide more than just a nation and its people. Nazi trials still take place while the main victors of World War Two endure more hardship than the guilty defeated. And spies defect, spies are jailed, spies are tortured, executed, murdered. There is the Pill, and Ban the Bomb, and the science-fiction of rockets and satellites and animals in space. There are riots in London and other cities, in the name of peace, while for months Cuba and the Bay of Pigs has simmered, with Kennedy, Khrushchev, Castro, posturing and sparring, and not in the name of peace.

And March 1961 saw Don Revie dropped from the Leeds United first team. This was bad news, especially as, at 33 years of age, the stamina and fitness were waning. The superstitious Revie should have known all along that his Leeds career was doomed - his conviction that birds brought bad luck was bolstered by the Leeds coat of arms containing three owls and the club's nickname being the Peacocks. A player of his calibre - England international, a Cup and award winner - in the Reserves, having to prove himself all over again! Or maybe the truth was colder than that, maybe Leeds United didn't want him to prove himself, maybe they didn't want him at all, trying to force him out of the club. Never mind a thinner pay packet, there was a distinct possibility of no pay packet at all.

Football was Revie's livelihood and his main consideration in life. He needed football and he was confident football needed him, even if it wasn't at Leeds United. Life at the club, with so much player indiscipline, lousy training methods, lousy facilities, lousy attitudes from unprofessional professionals, was grossly unsatisfactory. Throw in frequent arguing amongst the players, disrespectful behaviour towards the manager and coaches, numerous lousy performances and results, Revie knew it was time to leave. It was a run down, no hope, Second Division, second-rate club, manned by players who didn't seem to care and run by men who hadn't a clue of how to repair the situation, even with a man like Harry Reynolds on the board of directors. Reynolds was a self-made millionaire who enjoyed a good rapport with Revie, he was astute, enterprising and ambitious. They were similar characters and got on well but the reality was, the club was severely on the slide.

He was intent on leaving behind him all the stress, the unclean south Leeds air, the polluted Elland Road atmosphere. Time for a fresh start, a fresh challenge, fresh fields. Fresh air! He would escape the melancholia that hung over the city of Leeds like a charcoal cloud - it had always been the Don Revie way to get out before being forced out, this time would be no different. Besides, Leeds United didn't deserve him any longer.

He had aspired to move in to football management for some years now, and Bournemouth & Boscombe Athletic had invited him to apply for the job as player-manager. Chester and Tranmere Rovers were interested too. Even a club in Sydney was keen, though their plans involved only a part-time position. The Australians had offered to fly the wife and family out there too, find them a new home, help Elsie get a teaching job, look after the kids, make them all very comfortable. But England was where his home and heart belonged. He wanted the Bournemouth job and in his mind he had already accepted it and was planning the move down to the south coast.

Harry Reynolds could be forthright and tough, but a self-made millionaire probably had earned the right to be that way. He aimed to take over from Sam Bolton as Leeds chairman when the time was right, and he wanted to spend more of his time and money on the club. He had lots of both to spare since retiring two years before. Though Harry Reynolds - 'Mr Leeds United' - had wealth and power, he was a trustworthy man. But if you crossed him, it could cost you an ally for life. A typical Yorkshireman some would say, he was hard but fair, and he recognized the importance of treating employees right. He had agreed to a meeting with Revie - Revie had expected to receive a reference letter from Reynolds, in order for him to take the Bournemouth job. Revie had assumed that the meeting would be brief, ending with a firm handshake and the sincere best wishes of all at the club too as he departed for the south coast. The morning of the meeting, Revie was to learn an important lesson, that in business as well as in life, it is often wrong to make assumptions.

Reynolds, genial and uncomplicated, quickly informed Revie that he had written the reference letter but almost immediately decided 'To hell with that!' and torn it up. Don Revie, Reynolds declared, would not be allowed to leave Leeds, at least not without a fight. That 'fight', Sam Bolton and the directors had agreed, would be a £6,000 fee. Six thousand pounds for a man four months away from his 34th birthday. Revie was exasperated and perplexed as to why they were trying to ruin such a good opportunity for him. After all, he had served them well and it was quite clear they didn't want him there anymore.

Realising that there was a serious misunderstanding brewing, Reynolds explained that they did indeed want him to be player-manager - their player-manager, Leeds', Reynolds told him he was ideal for the job. Revie however felt nowhere near as confident, the job would be too big to take on, there were too many wrongs at the club needing to be put right. Jack Charlton for one. Reynolds, who used to have the plaque *If it's difficult, do it now. If it's impossible, it'll only take a little longer* on his office wall in his Holbeck Arches scrap metal days, casually dismissed the new and not particularly well-paid Leeds player-manager's concerns.

*

All smiles in the Leeds players' changing room before the morning's training session, with the local press there to photograph and report on the hiring of a new boss. Even Jack Charlton looks pleased; he and Revie shake hands. Jack Charlton wishes Don

Revie well because, for all his faults, Jack Charlton is a transparently honest man.

From now on, Revie asks of them all, they should call him 'Gaffer', 'Boss' or 'Mister Revie'. Preferably 'Gaffer' and definitely not 'Don' anymore. He tells them that the conditions at the club will improve and that it will be 'First class from now on' with regards to travel and accommodation for games, plus improved facilities and equipment at the club. There will be better, more enjoyable and innovative training methods as well, and any man not working hard enough in training, would be awarded with a yellow jersey with a wooden spoon sewn into it. 'If everybody is Leeds United-minded and pulls together, from the directors right down to the ladies who do the cleaning and the washing, then the club will get somewhere.' There were words of warning too - if he ever heard of anyone talking about him or his methods behind his back, that person would be sacked, because Revie didn't intend allowing the morale of the club to be destroyed by niggling and petty jealousies. Everyone employed at Leeds United must be in it together - side before self - and they would all start afresh on the Saturday, away at Portsmouth. He set about making changes off the pitch straight away, with his secretary instructed to rid her new boss's office of all purples and greens, as they were unlucky colours, and any pictures of birds within the club to be thrown out.

The new manager retained the services of the coaching personnel. To a man they backed him from the start, all committed to smartening the place up and dragging the club out of the quicksand depression it had found itself in. No job was too small for the coaches, even to the extent of painting the changing rooms. And nailed on the 'home' room wall, the sign KEEP FIGHTING.

Les Cocker and Syd Owen would train and coach the first team squad. Cocker was regarded as Revie's main right-hand man or 'lieutenant' as well as physio for the first team during matches. Owen focused on the tactics and set-piece plays, of the opposition too, and was seen as the bigger thinker of the two coaches. Both were highly adept at assessing player strengths and weaknesses, an aspect which would prove invaluable. Maurice Lindley would be the club's chief scout as well as assistant to Revie with everyday management work. The scouting network was already in place and Revie was well aware of its importance, an essential tool for the development of the club which reached across the British Isles. Bob English and Cyril Partridge would coach and train the Leeds Reserves, Juniors and youth players, whilst all the coaches would help with the sessions of massage and physiotherapy.

Small, wiry, tough and supremely fit Les Cocker, from Stockport, had played for Accrington Stanley and coached at Luton Town with Syd Owen as his manager in the fifties. Near fanatical about football, he was an early recipient of the Football Association's Coaching Certificate and had built up a strong reputation in the game. With his wartime experiences in the army, footballers discovered he could be as tough and abrasive as a drill sergeant, yet players and managers found there were few more loyal and genuine allies around.

Tall, fair-haired, Birmingham-born Syd Owen had a fine career as a centre-half for Luton, leading them to the FA Cup final in 1959, the year in which he received the Football Writers' Footballer of the Year award. He won three caps for England too while at Luton, and he managed the club for one season before joining Leeds in 1960. While Les Cocker could be described as 'near' obsessed with football, Owen *was* obsessed! And he was a hard taskmaster too, perhaps too intolerant and impatient at times but if ever a lad with the right attitude and spirit to succeed arrived, Syd Owen selflessly aimed to help him achieve his ambitions.

Maurice Lindley, from Keighley, played at Everton before a spell of coaching and then managing at Swindon Town. His time in management was 'educational' if not entirely a fulfilling experience. Tall, slim and dapper, he maintained the appearance of an easy-going gent able to cope with just about any job put his way. Perhaps he gave the impression of being so laid back he was almost horizontal, but Lindley's support would prove crucial many times over. Cyril Partridge, who had played for Queens Park Rangers, was asked by Revie to increase his working hours from part-time to full. Revie had grand plans for the young players at the club and Cyril Partridge and Bob English were the ideal men to make those plans succeed.

Like the other co-stars of this intended Leeds United renaissance, Bob English had been in the game for years. A small man, close in height to Les Cocker but broader, it may have surprised some to learn that he had played football for the Army, and hockey and basketball, and even boxed and fenced for them too.

Taking into account suggestions from the backroom team, as well as the obvious boredom of the players (himself included of course) Revie changed the training methods immediately. There would be variety, every day - sprints, cross country runs, jumps, skipping, physical jerks, England v Scotland five-a-side tournaments - also known as mini-wars - plus rounders, golf, cricket and table tennis matches and Olympics-style contests. And in addition to the customary five and seven-a-side matches, three-a-side games on quarters of a pitch were held. Anything that could increase healthy competition and improve team spirit was used. The venues for training would vary – if not on Fullerton Park then the parks in Roundhay or Farnley were utilised, while occasional mini-marathons from Elland Road, through Beeston and up to Middleton were staged. The new introductions worked like a dream - players actually looked happy after training, savouring especially the 'in house' tournaments and competitions.

On the playing side, in March 1961, Revie knew the structure of his team should be based around the strengths of the chosen players and the jobs they could do, not what he *hoped* they could do. Some players were more versatile than others and, of course, some were more skilful and better trained. Revie would make the formation 4-2-4 (changeable to 4-4-2 when emphasis on defence was needed) and on occasion 4-3-3, depending on the manpower available. He also had in mind which players he wanted to keep and which were surplus to requirements, but so late in the season and so early in his managerial career, this was not the right time to make sweeping changes.

Floyd Patterson's world title win over Ingemar Johansson was much more significant for the nation's sports columns. *The*

Times read simply: 'D Revie, the Leeds United inside forward, was yesterday appointed team manager of the club in succession to Mr J Taylor. He has been given a three-year contract. Revie will go on playing as long as he can.' Don Revie and Leeds United were not at all important, and his first match as boss also received scant coverage. Not such a bad thing, Portsmouth beat them 3-1. In the match, not unlike Major Buckley's employment of Charles during the '50s, Revie used Jack Charlton at centre-forward instead of centre-half, as an emergency measure. However, Charlton was nowhere near as good as Charles, in either position, and he knew it. He hated playing in attack, he wasn't good enough for the role even though he did score the goal at Portsmouth. Humiliatingly, defenders marking him soon recognized his limitations, and some would even laugh at him, they actually laughed at him. His intention was not to cause trouble for Revie but, unsurprisingly given his reputation, he did air his grievances regularly. Revie was sympathetic but desperate times warranted desperate measures. Portsmouth were fighting hard against relegation and their players scrapped for every ball as if their futures depended on it. A stern lesson which the Leeds players had better heed, as they were not safe themselves yet. True, relegation was highly unlikely but it wasn't impossible. There were now eight games remaining. Eight games to steer Leeds away from the threat of the Third Division.

1 v

I'd never get his autograph after that, I just knew it. Me cheeking him off was one thing, now they'd only gone and made him the sodding manager! I'd probably get banned from watching the team training now and all, thanks to Don bloody Revie. Served me right, according to my grandma, like I needed telling. She'd laughed though when I told her what I said about Revie being slower than her. It wasn't a long laugh mind you, and the next thing she was telling me off about my being too cheeky for my own good and asking for a belt-whack, just like my father. I couldn't work her out sometimes, she had more faces than Leeds Town Hall clock. Truth is, my 'father' pissed off to God knows where when I was born and when my mum died, Rest In Peace, so I didn't get how I could take after him. I was a good runner, maybe that's what she meant. Without a yellow stripe down my back, of course, unlike him.

After a bit of thinking I decided to try and make up for being cheeky to Don Revie, even though it was my honest belief that he'd asked for it. I'd go and say sorry, and hope he'd accept my apology. Maybe he'd just been in a bad mood and none of it was anything to do with me. Leeds were doing abysmally, he'd been out injured I think as well *and* he was getting his ear chewed off by big Jack, I bet I'd turned up at the worst possible moment. Anyway, I needed his autograph, that was the point, my collection was incomplete without it.

My main reason though trying to get in his good books was because I wanted to play for Leeds when I was old enough. Apprenticeships started at fifteen so I had about four years to wait. 'Forever' in my grandma's book - mine was all just a little *Billy Liar* dream, and football wasn't important anyway she'd say, between coughs, even though everyone else was always saying how good I was at it. I'd show her, all those people weren't having me on and they couldn't all be wrong. My grandma doubting me made her one of my best motivations and that's the truth. She wasn't that mean, I should own up, it was more to do with her worrying about me failing at school - you supposedly got nowhere in life without qualifications. In her mind, probably in most grown-ups' minds, football wouldn't get me paid work, which is really what life is all about when you think about it. I understood that, but Mr Hatfield at school (Cross Flatts) was always telling me that I could do well as long as I tried my hardest and never gave in. *Keep working hard, keep trying your best, keep at it. Win that ball, it's yours for the winning – win it, keep possession, use it wisely. Show for it back, always be in position to help your team-mates. Never hide. Football is for the eleven, not for your self.*

He knew what he was on about, he'd been sports teacher at the school for years and I think he taught Paul Madeley there a while back so he knew it when he saw a good player. All I wanted was to follow the path of Paul Madeley, it was as simple as that. Leeds United scouts had kept their eye on him and eventually signed him from local non-league team Farsley Celtic. He was brilliant at football but he really had to work at it, Mr Hatfield said. For one thing, he wasn't that quick over short distances, he had good 'natural' ability but to make it to professional you needed a lot more than just that. Tons of stamina and pace, plus strength, and good luck of course - you needed luck on your side if you were going to escape serious injury. I could be as good as Paul Madeley, Mr Hatfield said, as long as I kept training and built myself up, got some proper meat on me. Putting weight on wasn't easy, it was like rationing was still on in our house.

It was early and I'd been running. Not long before Don Revie became boss, I'd begun a morning routine to get myself properly fit. My grandma, with her morning cough, would get me up at seven and out I'd go, rain or shine, dark or light. It was better at that time of a morning, the air felt clearer and cooler, even though it often felt like a cold blade going right down my throat and into my chest, like it was punching my lungs and purifying them at the same time. A painful but good sensation too. My legs always ached a bit – running downhill more than up, I never rightly understood that. And talking of confused, it was about that time when the local newspapers were going on about the city council's promise of 'Clean Air by 1975.' They'd make sure the factory chimneys were made higher and that new rules came in about incinerators and what was good and bad stuff being burnt. So what the hell were we breathing now? Clean Air by 1975 - only fourteen years to wait - and it obviously didn't matter that much to them in charge what the air was like in 1961.

I preferred it when hardly anyone was around early mornings to see me running - that way they couldn't be thinking I was barmy or even up to no good, out burgling or something. Course I wasn't a thief and course I wasn't mad, though if anyone ever heard me singing on those runs they might have got on to the asylum straightaway. It was nothing special, I wasn't singing pop singles, I just made up lines to help spur me on. A bit like reciting multiplication tables except I was using Leeds players' names. And I didn't make mistakes here either. I'd step out of our house, right foot first every time, for luck, saying to myself at the same moment 'To Achieve Personal Greatness' before a couple of stretches and bends on the pavement to warm up. And then I'd be trotting up our street and round the corner onto the little patch of waste ground to do some star jumps and then properly off. When I was warmed up I'd be back down on to Elland Road in seconds, and well on my way from then on. Once I got into a comfortable breathing rhythm then I'd start with the 'song', in short breaths, in time with my paces. Like I was chanting but really quietly. It was more mumbling than anything, to drive me on up hills and keeping my brain from thinking it was all hurting too much. Daft stuff that wouldn't make sense to normal people because it didn't really make sense to me either. Little rhymes with players' names in. *Hunger of Younger, There like Hair, Good as Goodwin, High as Jack, Read it like Revie, Earn it like Eric, Make it like Madeley, A king like John.* And when I wanted to pick up the speed or make it more punishing, I'd change it around a bit, forcing the words out, sounding like a wild animal, growling, barking, grunting, reciting. *BETTER than Younger! BETTER than Hair! BETTER than Bremner!* and not caring by then if I looked rabid or like a maniac. It helped me, body and mind. To achieve personal greatness…

This one particular morning my route was Elland Road, past the Scratching Shed end of the stadium, the stretch of little shops and houses, the training pitches, more houses, the giant Greyhound Stadium stand, the workshops and factories and under the railway bridge. Advertising hoardings as big as the screen at the Rex. All the way along Elland Road until it rose into the hill up to Churwell, under another railway bridge while every time I'm looking out for the Morley Milestone, like it was an old friend. If ever I didn't finish the run, I decided to stop myself having breakfast to punish myself. So I made sure I always finished. I'd plod right round the New Inn, careful of any stray beer bottles at the back, and head back down Churwell Hill, back under the railway bridge and the great big billboard sign again. Water always trickled down the sides of that tunnel, even in summer, and moss permanently crept up the massive black bricks. It was as if it was mediaeval, that bridge. I'd pass the little beck at the bottom of the hill again, it usually whiffed of rotten chemicals or sewage. I never liked the look of that beck either, it reminded me of some or other fairy tale involving trolls or swamp monsters.

All the way back down I'd go, on to level ground. Past all the fields and Cottingley Cemetery again, past the 'Milky Way Ups and Downs' grassland near the Drysalters pub. All the factories and workshops again, the Greyhound Stadium, the shops and houses and the huge grey and black buildings dwarfing me but making me feel safe in some or other way too. And I honestly never saw one greyhound there in the whole of my life. Then by Turners the Boilermakers' row of buildings and into the open again and the great big United training pitches, approaching the stadium main gates again. And then, nearly always, I'd see this light-blue Ford Zephyr and its indicator blinking to turn right down through the gates. That usually meant it was eight o'clock, dead on near enough. Don Revie was a stickler for punctuality.

This time, right on cue, he was there, signalling to turn right, waiting till a couple of other cars passed the entrance gates. I slowed down to walking fast rate, sweating but not done in or anything. I got my breath back easy enough, walking brisk and sucking in the air the way I'd been taught, through my nostrils and with my mouth shut. Inflating the lungs and then breathing out the 'bad air' through my mouth.

Through the gates, just a few yards off now and Don Revie was getting out of his Zephyr, parked snug in between the white lines. He was dead well-dressed and his was the only motor there. Right down in the bottom corner at the back of the West Stand I saw Ces Burroughs, the boss groundsman, pushing a wooden cart alongside John Reynolds, his assistant. I always felt like calling Ces 'uncle' because he was always good to me, like I was one of his family. Even when he was telling me off or swearing like a thieving docker (even though he claimed to hardly ever swear) he meant only the best for me. John was a great bloke too, he'd do anything for you. Ces saw me and waved but they were both off sharpish before I could wave back. Out of view they'd gone, behind the Kop end, pushing the cart with the long rakes and hoes and shovels and spades pointing out of it. Don Revie had a shiny red-brown leather briefcase and he was smoothing down his shiny dark brown hair. His hairstyle was nearly like a Teddy boy's, side-parted but with a bit of a quiff at the front. Me, I had hair like a chimney sweep's brush, I looked like a tramp's neglected offspring, only muckier. I stood there watching, waiting, but he didn't see me, he was walking towards the little railings and fancy paved bit in front of the club reception doors.

Me being a bit shy plus my throat was dry, I croaked at first… 'Excuse me, Don… Mister Revie…' He looked a bit preoccupied so I coughed and then he did stop, and he looked at me. I bet he was thinking I was going to ask him for a shilling or some bread crusts or something. I couldn't have blamed him if he had.

'Yes?'

'Er I just wanted to… to congratulate you on being made new manager.'

'Right, thank you…'

'And to say I hope you do well for us…'

'That's nice of you, son…' and now he was looking at me odd like.

'…and to say sorry for being cheeky to you the other week.' And he'd just remembered who I was. He planted his briefcase on the ground. He marched over to me and before I knew it he was standing right above me, hovering like a domestic bird of prey or even a Triffid. There was me thinking I was going to get a whack for my troubles any second now, it didn't seem fair.

'Ah yes, the little so and so with a sprinter for a grandma…'

It felt like I was glowing red and I couldn't tell if he was joking or not so I answered 'I just wanted you to sign my autograph book and I'd been waiting ages and you told me to clear off.'

He thought for a second and then said, 'That's not exactly what happened now is it?' but his voice wasn't angry. In fact, he was smiling, miserable Don Revie was actually smiling. There and then, in that very second, I decided never to call him names ever again. Don Revie wasn't miserable at all, I'd been wrong. He was alright was Don Revie.

'What's your name?'

'Jimmy… er James. James O'Rourke.'

'Irish eh?'

'No.'

'Only asking lad, no need to get indignant.'

I wasn't even sure what indignant meant and I think he'd lost interest in talking to me. He says 'Apology accepted then, Jimmy' then picks his briefcase up and walks off, in to the reception through the glass doors and disappears through a door at the back. Leaving me on my own like a dunce, not knowing what to do, whether to stay or just bugger off. But then a few seconds later he comes back out, with a piece of paper in his hand.

'Here you go, add this to your collection.' It was a sheet of paper with the Leeds United Association Football Club owls coat of arms emblem on it and he's written *To Jimmy, Regards Don Revie* on it.

'Thank you!'

'That's alright, it's good to see you have learned some manners' and off he goes again.

'I'm good at football, Don!' I call.

He just smiled and carried on walking, like he'd heard it all before. He probably had, thinking about it. 'No I am, really!' If anyone heard me they'll have been thinking I was begging. 'And I've just run five mile!' And then they'd be thinking I was lying or that I'd lost my marbles.

He stopped again, turned to me - 'Have you really?'

I nodded - 'I do it nearly every morning.'

'What do your parents think about you doing that then?'

'I haven't got any parents, just my grandma.'

'Oh I see. How old are you?'

'I'm ten, nearly eleven. I play for my school, Cross Flatts Park, on the Park. Saturday mornings, ten o'clock a.m. kick off.' There was me chattering away like Tarzan's Cheeta while Don Revie's looking at me like I really was a speaking monkey. 'Well if you're that good, maybe we'll meet up again…' he said and then he was away, inside the reception and gone again, properly this time.

He didn't hear me shouting that I went to the same school as Paul Madeley had or that the teachers reckoned I could be as good as him. I walked back up, I had to get home and get ready for school. There was so much I forgot to tell him, like how dedicated I was and about Ces letting me into the ground on Sundays so's I could practice my dribbling and shooting against the wall in the car park with the goalposts painted on and Ces letting me in to matches so I could watch and learn from professionals. But then I thought it was a good job I didn't say half of that, I didn't want to get anyone into bother, least of all Ces. And then I bloody realised too that we were playing away that Saturday, not on Cross Flatts Park.

1 vi

Eamonn Andrews - 'Don, you turned to one man for advice. That man was then Britain's most famous manager.' Revie also contacted Bill Nicholson who was well on the way that season to winning Tottenham Hotspur the Double of the League Championship and the FA Cup.

The *This Is Your Life* music rises again - tonight, explains Andrews, Britain's most famous manager of 1961, after an important meeting in London, has managed to make a two hundred mile dash to attend this event. Great applause from the gathered audience greets Sir Matt Busby, former Manchester United manager, as he enters the stage.

*

Through the Pennines new Leeds manager Don Revie drove, the morning of 24th March, 1961. Meandering beneath low, grey grey clouds, twisting and grinding within Snake Pass, dwarfed by the moors, hillsides and fissures. Revie had lived and worked before in Manchester, he knew that the downpours of rain were not constant and that Manchester did have dry days and less-bitingly cold days. This was not one of those days however, it had thrown it down virtually all night and all morning. Fortunately, Revie's Ford Zephyr was reliable and resilient and it had carried him thousands of miles around the country without difficulty before. So reliable was this Z-car, he could have christened it Grenville Hair.

Matt Busby was a great success on and off the football field, as a player and then as a manager. One of the best, if not the best, bosses to grace the game, though his greatest ever achievement might actually be his recovery from the terrible injuries suffered in the deadly Munich air crash of 1958. Don Revie parked his trusty, standard-blue Ford yards away from the various Jaguars, Aston Martins, Mercedes, Humbers. Flash cars belonging to flash Manchester United personnel did not concern him, he was more interested in making a name for himself and succeeding as a boss rather than reaping the material rewards. He believed that preparation was everything - and he would be ready to take on the mighty tasks ahead. Even though he had been reassured by Harry Reynolds that he would have plenty of time to establish himself, Revie was not naïve - if it all went badly, too badly, he knew he would be out.

Some of the advice Busby gave Revie was to try and be brave and audacious, to instill in his players a family spirit, the ethic of teamwork on and off the pitch, and a hatred of losing. Revie demonstrated audacity soon after the meeting, by trying to persuade a certain Bobby Charlton to join his club. How impressed Busby would have been is anyone's guess. The day after his Old Trafford visit, Leeds' torturous season continued with a home 2-1 defeat to Sheffield United. Leeds' is an own goal at that, and less than fourteen thousand watched. Less than fourteen thousand spectators for Revie's home managerial debut. A pitiful, embarrassing attendance.

Before their next game, Revie commented that he would give anything to win his first points as Leeds manager. Not the wisest of remarks, considering illegal gambling and other improprieties in the game were rife at the time. That next game happened to be at Luton Town on Saturday April 1st - April Fools' Day. A Billy Bremner strike gained Leeds their first point under Revie in a 1-1 draw, to keep them midtable. More reasons for optimism arrived too with the official signing of South African winger Albert Johanneson.

Small stature, big talent, a quiet and gentle man, Johanneson brought potent outside-left creativity and pace to the squad. On the wing he would provide much-needed service to a gravely-lacking Leeds attack. The only element of glamour in a drab Leeds team more used to a pressing, hard running style of play, and used to not winning. Revie though, knew little of Johanneson's distressed Johannesburg childhood and turbulent background, or the violent bigotry he had met virtually every day of his life. Not entirely dissimilar aggression would occur on English fields of play too, in ugly efforts to unnerve and distract him or even put him *out* of the game. Terrible prejudice would be heard on the terraces of some football grounds, with peanuts and bananas thrown on to the pitch by spectators with, at best, a warped sense of humour. Revie wasn't aware either that Johanneson had spent much of his time avoiding gang violence on the streets of his home town Germiston, or trying to resist the temptation of exciting but dangerous pursuits and harmful substances. Although he would be immensely popular at Leeds, living away from the friends and family of his youth, Albert

Johanneson would suffer from loneliness, insecurity and a profound lack of self-belief - much of it brought on by the appalling treatment from opposing fans.

Just two days after the Luton game, it seemed to be the same old story for the team again. Despite two goals from Charlton, another defeat came at Scunthorpe United. With too few good or fit enough players to choose from already, Leeds were outfought by a physically fitter and faster side. Fortunately, results involving lower teams went Leeds' way and relegation looked virtually impossible. Not even a devoted pessimist - and there seemed to be plenty such devotees in that small arena of West Yorkshire - could expect matters to conspire so catastrophically against the team now.

1 vii

Up on my bedroom wall it went, written in big letters on the back of an old roll of wallpaper, covering a bit of the present pig-ugly pink roses decor.

Season 1960 - '61, football honours.

League Division One winners - Spurs, Runners up - Sheffield Wednesday.

League Division Two winners - Ipswich Town, Runners up - Sheffield United.

FA Cup winners - Spurs, Runners up - Leicester City.

League Cup winners - Aston Villa, Runners up - Rotherham.

European Cup winners - Benfica, Runners up - Barcelona.

European Cup Winners Cup winners - Fiorentina, Runners up - Rangers.

Inter-Cities Fairs Cup winners - Roma, Runners up - Birmingham.

Football Player of the Year - Danny Blanchflower, Spurs.

European Footballer of the Year - Omar Sivori, Juventus.

Sweet Bugger All winners - Leeds United.

Leeds Crowd average, home games - 13,440.

For us to have been relegated after Don Revie took over would have needed a major disaster to happen. Half the time though the team had looked like they were doing their best to achieve it. We scored over 70 goals but let in 83 - that was more generous than Viv

Nicholson spend, spend, spending in a pub. It worked out at nearly two goals a game - my own team Cross Flatts let in less than that and we were schoolboys. I'd made myself another chart too, a complete record of every official game I played in, the final scores and if, by some freak of nature, I scored in any. I've still got the charts somewhere, every year's, with not very many Jimmy O'Rourke goals on them.

Only a couple of teams in Division Two let in more goals than Leeds. It had got a bit better straight after Don Revie took over, and the players definitely worked harder. The fellas around me at home matches said that too, some of them went to away games as well, even though there weren't organized trips in those days. Whenever I got bored watching a match, which was all too often, I'd earwig them talking. I didn't have a clue who they were or what their names were but those blokes felt like old friends I saw them that often. I'd hunt them out on the terraces (not difficult that, very spacious times) just so I could listen to their banter. I'd hear how they were faring in life, how their wives and kids were, who was in work, who wasn't, who planned on voting for who, who was tight with the beer and didn't get his round in. And which one of them was guilty of dropping their guts and causing the frequent stenches. Those blokes were often more entertaining than the football, I mean it. Not that I had any right to complain, seeing as I hardly ever paid to watch the match, thanks to Ces or even thanks to my climbing abilities and the not-so-big wall behind the Kop.

My grandma was a Leeds supporter, on the quiet. Only a few women went to the match as far as I could tell, but it was her who took me to my first ever game, for my eighth birthday. It was all her fault, me being obsessed with Leeds United and with football. Obsessed was her word, not mine, and it wasn't intended as a compliment. We'd stood near the front of the Lowfields Road terrace, near the wall. In truth I wasn't that keen on *watching*, I preferred to be playing in our street. I'd been pretty bored up until some fella near us shouted 'Give the blooming ball to Gerry, you mugs!' or something similar. My grandma said she thought the man was drunk. You couldn't blame him. He was referring to Leeds' South African Gerry Francis who was playing on our side of the field, at outside-right to be exact. And he was right near us on the pitch, twenty foot away at the most. He'd been our first black player, and he was quite popular because he liked running at defenders and trying to get good crosses in for the forwards to score. I don't think he succeeded too often but at least he tried hard and Leeds folk always like a grafter. Anyhow, when Gerry heard the bloke shout, he looked over at the terrace, smiled and put his hand up to wave. And he grinned, right at us. He had a brilliant, bright white and cheeky smile and everyone around us laughed. And I was hooked.

Funnily enough, Gerry Francis had a hand in Revie's first signing, Albert Johanneson. Albert played his first game in April 1961 and it was still cold and I was still in my short trousers. Don promised the fans that Albert would excite us. He wasn't wrong, Albert was brilliant. In one of his best early matches, versus Swansea Town, he'd had made a sweet cross into the area for big Jack to head it into the net. It wasn't a cup final or anything (of course) but it was quite an important goal. Straight after, so pleased were the players with Albert that they all rushed over to congratulate him. But he didn't know what was happening and he looked scared to death at all these white men running at him! I once nicked in to the Rex to see that *The Defiant Ones* film, with Tony Curtis and Sidney Poitier in and set in America with all those freaks of nature in their robes and with pillowcases on their heads, so I knew all about skin colour prejudice and that. South Africa sounded even worse.

Albert wasn't like Gerry Francis, he was left-footed for one thing, and faster. Not that Gerry was a slouch. The supporters gave Albert nicknames, he'd only been here two minutes - *The Black Flash*, *AJ* and *Go-Go Jo-Jo*. There were stories some Leeds supporters threw bananas onto the Elland Road pitch for him and he and a few of the players would eat them before kick-off. I never saw it happen, that's the honest truth, and I wasn't sure whether it was meant to upset him or somehow to make him feel welcome. As far as I know, there weren't any Leeds fans who gave him the bird - not for the colour of his skin, at any rate - but, when he became more well-known and feared, at some away grounds there were supporters making monkey noises and giving him real abuse. *They* were calling *him* an animal.

As well as remembering loads of pointless things about Leeds, away from United there was plenty of personal stuff as well. For instance, it was on one of my morning runs that I first saw a sight to nearly make me puke - two dogs joined up at the tail-end, like something out of a Ray Harryhausen movie, except more real and definitely not entertaining. And in football, I could recall my first ever slide tackle as well, like it had happened yesterday. I was eight and it was at school in Games, we were playing a match on Cross Flatts Park. It had been raining all morning and there was a right *Wizard of Oz* gale blowing too. I played in lots of rotten conditions in my time – rain, snow, sleet, hail, thunder, lightning, *drought, disease, locusts* – but it was only ever the wind that really spoilt a game for me. Still, I loved hearing the wind blow through the Park trees - the elms, sycamores, beeches, birches - as it sounded dead eerie, with whistling, humming, roaring, *whooshing*. Those trees sounded like the sea and crowds and people talking and ghosts moaning, all rolled into one.

I must have slid at least six foot in our penalty area to get the ball off this lad who was shaping up to shoot. It was truly a lovely and fabulous feeling when I did it, no exaggeration. In soccer, some fellas love to score, some to dribble, some love to shoot from miles out and some love to take leave of their senses and go in goal. Me, I loved to tackle, always did, as far back as I remember. It often hurts but it's a good pain. I never tried to foul anyone, unless they had a go at me first, because I wasn't that sort of person. Maybe I would have fared better in life if I had've been. Anyway, on this particular occasion I won the ball like a train collecting a sack of mail, clean and so quick, but I followed through into him so hard that he actually did a somersault over my legs and landed on his back. He laid there, shocked and with his eyes wide open, and he started crying - I think it was more because of shock than pain - and I felt sort of high but low at the same time, like a prize fighter who's just knocked his opponent out but is feeling sorry for his victim as well.

The daft thing about that tackle is that it wasn't deliberate, I'd just slipped on the mud and ended torpedoing him. After that though, you couldn't stop me slide-tackling, even in the street.

Chapter 2: 1961/2 - The Scottish Jimmy Cagney

2 i

In the twenty-plus minutes of viewing time of *This Is Your Life*, Eamonn Andrews will tell the watching world about Don Revie's glorious achievements as a football player and later as a manager. There is though, nowhere near enough time to describe every significant event that occurred (good and bad), the influential people encountered (good and bad) and the important decisions made (yes, good and bad) which affected the life of Don Revie. And no word will be made of how bleak and stressful those early months of Revie's Leeds managerial reign were. Precious few notable or rousing achievements took place in those formative days, shining on the pitch glories to bask in were as rare as clean tenements and unbesmirched walls and buildings of the city of Leeds.

*

As a player, Revie had always put on his left football boot first, and as a manager - when not playing in the team - a new pre-match ritual was the insistence on walking at Les Cocker's left side as they made their way to the dugout, and never his right. And maybe, just maybe, it had worked - with 38 points, Leeds finished the 1960-'61 season fourteenth in Division Two, five points more than relegated Portsmouth and fourteen more than Lincoln. Revie bade good riddance to the whole sorry last campaign and began fastidiously planning for the next. His time leading the club had been short, so success or failure in the League table would not really have been of his making. The new 1961-'62 season however, would be different, everything would be his responsibility then. The support of the Leeds directors would enable him to spend a little more money as well as widen the scouting network. Investment in youth was crucial but with the club in debt for well over £100,000, Revie would need to wheel and deal and adhere strictly to the board's budget. A train crash occurred in the centre of Leeds that summer, Revie might have seen it as a premonition.

By July 1961, defender Jack Charlton was set on leaving Leeds United. Despite decent performances, Don Revie and the coaches' frustration with the player increased the longer he was at the club. Revie believed Charlton had the potential to become a fine central defender, *if* he followed their advice and if he did what he was told to do. But Jack Charlton never liked being ordered around, as if he always knew better than everyone else. Pay was Charlton's main gripes, and he wasn't the sort of person to keep his grievances to himself. He asked for a transfer and, almost in surrender, Revie decided to let him leave. For the right price. Charlton was confident his departure would be soon - Liverpool's Bill Shankly had enquired on his availability and Manchester United were keen too. Jack Charlton would relish the chance to play in the same team as brother Bobby, like they had when they were kids up in Ashington. Liverpool made an offer but it fell short of Leeds' asking price. Charlton felt Leeds were taking advantage of him, they were taking the piss. He calculated that to get the full match bonus the club had promised (nearly £15) each Elland Road match attendance would need to be over 31,000. Last season's average had been just 13,000, *thirteen* thousand. And when he learned that he would be paid the same wage as some of the younger first team squad players, he had had enough. Even though the club had paid for FA coaching lessons at Lilleshall for him, his relationship with the manager and coaches remained fraught.

Unfortunately for Charlton, Manchester United's official interest appeared to have waned, while people at Elland Road weren't even talking to him, he had bitten the hands that fed him too often, he'd caused too much upset. The appeal of Manchester United had been understandable - huge crowds, lots of money and generally better players, real class like Dennis Violett, Bill Foulkes, even little ankle-biting Nobby Stiles. And of course, Bobby. So, frustrated, Jack Charlton contacted Matt Busby, demanding to know what was happening. Busby admitted they had been monitoring another centre-half, a young lad who in fact had toured with the team. This apparent deceit was unacceptable to Charlton, and so he vowed to stay with Leeds and rebuild his bridges, if they'd still have him of course. Luckily, despite all the problems he'd caused over the years, Don Revie and Harry Reynolds accepted his apology and his promises that he would be no trouble to them again.

2 ii

Most people loved summer. I never did, I always hated it. There was never any football to watch and suddenly all the other kids wanted to play cricket as if football didn't matter any more. *'Foggy be Fred Trueman!'* or Illingworth or Cowdrey even though he wasn't from Yorkshire. Even the girls played, if the lads ever let them. They hardly ever did though which was how it should be, stick to skipping rope and whipping top - even my grandma said it. It was like some sort of law in St Anthony's School yard – cricket only when the cricket season's on, therefore no soccer in the summer. They even took the goal posts down on the Park, as if football didn't exist during the summer. It was stupid. I always thought of cricket as boring and not really a team game. More's the point, I wasn't very good at it, football was my business.

I was lucky because Ces and John let me play on the shale between the Fullerton pitches and the West Stand. No one ever seemed to take much notice of me running with the ball and whacking it at the wall to the side of the Elland Road gates with the goalposts painted on it. Not that there were many people there to watch me any road. I might have looked a bit odd, playing on my own, but it's how Bobby Charlton used to practise his shooting and why he was so bloody great at it. So most school holidays I was on my own, my only companion being a football as my grandma was out at work in the town centre. Ces and John were brilliant to me, letting me use the facilities and all that, and even my grandma seemed happy with the situation. Ces would let me borrow balls and even use the equipment in the gymnasium if no one else was around. Occasionally, if I was really lucky, John would have a kickabout with me and give me a bit of coaching. It was usually quiet at the ground in summer as that was when the playing and coaching staff had their holidays too. That is, *if* they took their holidays, I don't remember Don Revie ever being away very long. And course, if Ces ever wanted any help, like painting barriers and fences and that, I was ready and willing. I enjoyed it.

I didn't like the gymnasium much, all the bars and stuff were too high for me and the weights were miles too heavy, plus I didn't know how to use them properly. I was athletic and physically fit but still too skinny, there wasn't a lot of muscle on me. Ces used to pull my leg about it, reckoning I was like Norman Hunter - in the early days he was nicknamed 'Tarzan' because he was so thin. No wonder, his favourite food was salad sandwiches or something as daft - he really did look like he was in need of a good feed.

2 iii

As is customary in the business of football, the manager's preparation involves the buying and selling of players - negotiating, bartering, haggling - plus the making of tough, heart rending decisions. The most unpleasant task of football management arrives at the end of each football season - effectively, the ruining and curtailing of many young players' dreams. Scores of youngsters across the country learn that they will be leaving their club because, in the opinion of the coaching staff, they are not considered as good enough. The manager is normally the one blessed with breaking the news to the young dreamers - and just like any decent man, Don Revie detested this aspect of the job, even if it was the way of the football world. That summer, over a dozen young hopefuls were released, while the sales of two older, popular players were arranged too: John McCole and Gerry Francis. Francis's match performances were inconsistent; he would join York City. Although, Revie was looking to the future, searching for youth to invest in, getting rid of experienced players could prove risky and the sale of Scotsman McCole was a surprise as his scoring record was good. However, as likeable as McCole was, he hardly came close to fitting Revie's image of the ideal professional and so he went to Bradford City for £9,000.

September 1961, six months on from the beginning of Revie's tenure as Leeds manager, and his careful, detailed plans had barely begun to pay off. Six months on and the club, despite all the hard work, seemed in deeper trouble than when he began, on the pitch at least. Match results had been poor, so had the attendances and therefore so had the gate revenue. The city of Leeds, despite one of the biggest populations outside London, of around half a million, remained a rugby league stronghold and the Leeds RL team was much more successful than its football team. The people of Leeds - 'Loiners' - seemed unwilling to afford the indulgence of watching two sports, especially when one of the teams was in decline. And Leeds Rugby League had just won their first championship title.

Leeds United chairman Sam Bolton, responding to supporters' criticism, defended the manager, 'We shall back Mister Revie to the fullest extent, and his team, which is better than a lot of people think.' Privately however, Bolton admitted he was fast approaching the point of not being willing to take any more flak. Unrest at board level may not have represented the greatest news for Revie but much more to his dismay was finding out that the directors were looking to sell the Leeds player he regarded as the team's best asset. And without even telling the manager, they were planning to sell Billy Bremner! Everton were favourites to sign him, though Arsenal had been sniffing around too. In spite of Bremner's critics within the club and on the terraces who saw him as a hot-headed, complaining, conceited liability, there were wiser men who, like Revie, recognized the ginger Scot's great potential. The notion of selling Bremner horrified Revie and the fact that the directors appeared intent on doing it without his consent stank of disrespect and of undermining his authority as manager. He demanded a meeting with the board and told them that if Bremner was sold then they should start looking for a new manager too.

Angry, sad, frustrated, Revie retired from the meeting with the board's assurance that they would consider his comments. He met his sidekick Les Cocker nearby and told him that, seeing as they no longer had the support of the board, they should both resign their posts. But then hurried footsteps approached from behind, and with them the voice of Harry Reynolds, anxious to placate Revie and to make peace for the sake of the club.

*

On a filthy December night, 1961, a meeting is scheduled at the Queens Hotel. It is a grand building, with architecture and stylish interiors to be proud of, but like an inkblot stains a scroll, pollution taints this building - beautiful white stonework blackened, spoiled by smog and fumes inflicted by a busy city centre and surrounding industry. A few hundred yards easterly, the Corn Exchange, looking like a small-scale Royal Albert Hall, and the huge Parish Church nearby, endure the same blight. Age is not to blame, the blemishes are man-made. The Queens Hotel, overlooking City Square and its handsome statues of the Black Prince and various Leeds-related luminaries, surrounded by lamp-bearing nymphs, is host to Leeds United's Annual General Meeting. Important officials of Leeds United are present and important supporters of the club, too. Many of them men full of their own importance.

Don Revie was still the Leeds manager and Billy Bremner still a Leeds player, albeit a homesick and regularly complaining Leeds player. Revie had escaped with his threat to resign if Bremner left, and the good news now was that Harry Reynolds, Revie's main ally, was to succeed Sam Bolton as chairman. Alderman Percy Woodward would continue as vice chairman while wealthy local businessmen Manny Cussins and Albert Morris were officially made new directors. Canny men with money who had helped already by providing substantial interest-free loans to the club. John Bromley and Sidney Simon too were recruited on to the board, even more financial clout, and successful entrepreneur Bob Roberts returned after ill-health. There is a strong Jewish presence in the Elland Road boardroom, like there is in the whole of the city. Leeds, 'the Jerusalem of the North'.

The nickname was not meant as complimentary, and in the same vein, there were cynics in opposition to a Jewish presence in the Leeds boardroom as well. Harry Reynolds though, held no such prejudices - if a Leeds United director was trustworthy, loyal and dedicated to the club, then they were ideal partners. Even if one or two of them were attention-seeking 'peacocks' it did not bother him greatly, *he* was in charge, he would always have the final say. 'Without going into details, I can say that Don Revie has more of the 'sinews of war' – what we Yorkshiremen call brass – at his disposal than his predecessors had. How much more must remain our secret, the soccer market is as tricky a field of business to operate in as you will find. I have all possible confidence in Don Revie who has shown splendid balance and unsurpassable zeal in our recent weeks of adversity,' Reynolds declared. Certain other executive changes were declared, including the Earl of Harewood, a cousin of Her Majesty Queen Elizabeth no less, elected as the first president of the club. He had supported Leeds since childhood, followed them many times home and away.

*

Season 1961-62 saw much change for Leeds. The work atmosphere at Elland Road was healthier and more positive thanks to the Revie influence. He and Reynolds only wanted people at the club who enjoyed working there, from players to ground staff and laundry ladies, from coaches to administration and security staff. The Revie Revolution was happening, slowly and surely, though results were still far from satisfactory and the transfer market remained a source of frustration for the manager. Yes, he had been able to bring new players in – youngsters, as well as a few low priced and more experienced men – but the Leeds first team's quality still wasn't good enough. Sometimes switching solid, consistent players Willie Bell ('Hewn of Scottish granite') and Eric Smith into the back four alongside the more established defenders Grenville Hair and Freddie Goodwin helped reduce the Goals Against tally but the Goals For was still miserable. Leeds supporters - and maybe some of his team-mates too - considered striker Billy McAdams the guiltiest culprit, failing with straightforward goal scoring chances which looked harder to miss than score.

Revie told his chairman that he needed six new players if the team was to avoid relegation. Relegation to Division Three, for the first time in the club's history. Harry Reynolds offered a compromise - money enough to buy two possibly three medium-priced players. Revie always had a wants list but the lower his team sank, the slimmer the chances of those wishes being fulfilled became. One specific player was his priority - a big name player - a former international and a true, indefatigable leader. March 7th 1962 - Harry Reynolds drove to the north-west of England in the car his daughter Margaret called 'the tomato'. The orange Ford Consul had its black leather top fixed up all the way. Alongside Reynolds, in the passenger seat, sat Don Revie, with director Manny Cussins in the rear. Revie had, within the last week, announced his retirement as a player so he could commit more of his time to managing the club. Goalkeeper Tommy Younger had frequently told Revie that he should finish playing if he really wanted to manage the club well. Today's task was to convince a top Division One footballer to join lowly Leeds, it would surely be one of the hardest challenges in Revie's career. Even though the Leeds board had recently funded two signings in young forward Ian Lawson, £20,000 from Burnley, and safe, wily defender Cliff Mason from Sheffield United for £10,000, Revie knew that time was running out. The team remained in the depths of Division Two and the end of the season was not very far away. A major problem was the lack of a leader in his team. Revie had a player in mind who almost certainly could solve the problem...

The three men were en route to Liverpool, Merseyside, to the blue and more successful side of the city - Everton Football Club. Harry Reynolds had travelled all over the world, he knew the way to Goodison Park. Not that Leeds had played in Division One for a while and judging by the current League table, they were not likely to either. And Reynolds had forgotten the route and had had to ask for directions anyway. Everton boss Harry Catterick had given Leeds permission to speak to one of his players, a player he had controversially dropped from the first team recently. Les

Cocker had watched the player in an Everton FA Cup defeat at Burnley and since recommended him to Revie as he had been the best player on show. That player was Bobby Collins. At 31 years-old though, Catterick considered Collins as expendable, despite Collins always giving his all for the team and never giving in the fight. He had the reputation of possessing a heart like a lion, and his tackles certainly had *bite* in them. Jack Charlton called him an 'evil little man but what a player!' But 'Pocket Napoleon' Collins wanted to stay at Everton to fight for his place. Out of courtesy, he agreed to meet the Leeds contingent. He listened respectfully, quietly impressed by a chairman supporting his manager, somewhat of a rarity, but he simply did not want to move to Leeds United. With an accent more befitting Scottish gentry than a Wee Barra from working-class Glasgow, he thanked them for their interest but declined the invitation. The truth was, he didn't want to join a club at the bottom of the Second Division, and besides, he had everything he needed at Everton. Everything but a first team place and secure future, came the United response.

2 iv

Truly I was *The Long Distance Runner* - without *The Loneliness*. I'd just done my five mile Churwell Hill run. Out of breath I was, but not out of things to say, especially this particular morning. Scraping a bit of mud off my running shoes on the doorstep, I burst into the house. 'You'll never guess who we've bought!' I shouted, realising just at that very moment that my grandma was only four foot away to my right, in the scullery, having a smoke and cough. She was at the kitchen sink and because I made her jump so much she dropped her cigarette. I know it's not meant to be funny when you scare people out of their skins, but it is really and I had a battle on to stifle my laughs. She said something unholy that I probably wasn't meant to hear, and then asked, 'Go on then, who?'

I was dying to keep her guessing but had a feeling I'd get a clout if I wound her up any more. 'Bobby Collins - from Everton! Ces just told me – stood at the gates waiting for me he was. Can you believe it?'

'This isn't one of your little jokes is it?'

'No course not, I wouldn't, not if Ces has told me. It was the first thing Don Revie said to him when he turned up. Twenty-five thousand pounds. It's brilliant, isn't it?'

'How on earth can they afford it? Why on earth would he want to come to Leeds? Everton are doing well, they're a good team, it doesn't make sense.' She was asking questions and not waiting for me to answer, probably thinking I didn't really know, even though I'd just told her.

I carried on, 'Ces reckons they went to talk to Collins at Everton's ground and later on at his house. And they wouldn't take no for an answer. Didn't get back till after three o'clock this morning.'

She bought the Evening News later, specially, to get the facts about the signing. It wasn't that she thought I was telling lies, just that it was all too good to believe. Or so she said. Everyone said that Bobby was a brilliant player and just what we needed in the team, he'd tackle his grandma hard if it meant a chance of winning! We were having a rotten season, even grimmer than the last one, despite the team, I swear, being better under Don Revie. Buying Bobby Collins would give us new hope. And in Leeds city centre there was news of a flash new shopping and 'leisure' centre being built. Called the Merrion Centre, it would have its own ballroom, a cinema, bowling alley and hotel plus lots of other shops and offices and stuff. The city had that and the football team had Bobby, two massive developments, I was thinking.

The surprise was that the season had started well – two wins out of two and decent performances - but then we got trounced 5-0 at Liverpool. We were lucky it was only five. After that match, Don Revie said he hoped to do at Leeds what Bill Shankly was doing at Liverpool - it had taken Shankly about three years to build his team and now they were looking dead certs for promotion to Division One. Strange but we beat Liverpool 1-0 at Christmas though before Bobby Collins arrived we had more chance of being Accrington Stanley than being Liverpool. Accrington had just gone out of business and out of the League itself. Bobby Collins - £25,000 worked out at £390 per inch, so the paper said. 'The Scottish Jimmy Cagney' would be making his debut against Swansea Town, and it was a 'last gamble' by the Leeds United board to stave off the very real threat of relegation. He'd be wearing the number 8 shirt, recently vacated by Don Revie himself.

I couldn't concentrate even more in lessons now and I got a right bollocking again in Geography for day-dreaming - 'If you dreamt as much about capital cities and countries of the world as you do about football then you might actually get somewhere, O'Rourke,' the teacher had said, and I don't think he was trying to be witty either, the grumpy old goat. I was thinking about my running as well – I'd got quicker up that hill, as if Bobby Collins himself had put monkey glands or something in my blood stream! My grandma had even started asking me how I'd played in my matches for school, like she was interested all of a sudden, and she measured my height and marked it on the kitchen wall in pencil. I was just less than five foot tall, still a bit shorter than most lads in my school year but doing alright. Plus I was getting heavier, the tops of my legs were getting like tree trunks even though I had no fat on me. Trouble was I had calves like pipe-cleaners, I was worried I might grow up as skinny as Tarzan Norman. I say 'grow up' but he can't have been that much older than me.

Not sure that 'full' is the right word but there were a lot more people at the Leeds-Swansea Town match than normal for home games. It could only have been because of one thing: Bobby Collins. Even my grandma went, she paid us both in. She'd insisted I went with her and I couldn't exactly ask Ces to get us both in nor could I really see her getting over the wall into the Kop! It was a bit embarrassing at first, standing on the Kop with her but no one said anything untoward about us. The Kop end was something to see, it was massive, like one of the Wonders of the World for me. It was that high, stood on the back row you could chew the clouds! Not that you'd want to, they'd taste filthy I bet.

People were only interested in Bobby Collins. I wasn't much smaller than him but when he bounced onto that pitch, everyone was looking at him, and everyone knew then that Bobby Collins was one giant of a man, he had this sort of presence about him. I learned then from my grandma what an aura was, and Bobby definitely had one. It was funny the paper calling him the 'Scottish Jimmy Cagney' as well, because in a way it was dead right. When Cagney is on screen you can't take your eyes off him because something's always going to happen and you daren't look away in case you miss it. Exactly the same with Bobby Collins. As soon as the referee blew for kick-off, Bobby was everywhere on that pitch. Afterwards the papers called him the 'Pocket Puskas' what with him being the best player on the pitch and course, Leeds were in all white, like Puskas's team Real Madrid. Bobby hardly missed a tackle, never gave the ball away, played it simple with nothing fancy but always accurate passing. And he never ever stopped working. Fitter than a butcher's mongrel but with a sharper bite! And even though he wasn't the Leeds captain, it was Bobby doing all the ordering about and telling all the players what to do, where to position themselves. And he makes sure he looks after the younger Leeds players and Albert Johanneson - if the other team went in hard, Bobby would usually be first to dish it out back to them. My grandma mentioned how much harder opponents' tackling seemed to be on Albert Johanneson - when they could catch him - tackles that made you wince. Bobby always got them back anyway, and with double measures. Bobby always encouraged Albert, helping him, urging him on. None of the Leeds team ever disagreed or argued with Bobby, they just did what they were told. He was in midfield, right in the middle of everything, with four defenders behind him (plus the goalie, of course) and four attackers in front. And he was that fit he was involved in most of Leeds' defending plus *all* of the attacking.

'Side before self' I heard someone say.

Almost like it was meant to be, Bobby scored our first goal, beating a couple of defenders and then hitting a cracker from outside the area, high to the Swansea goalie's left. It was a 'trademark Collins shot', which curled and looped into the net. It was a trademark *beauty*, I know that much. Every single Leeds player on the field gathered round to congratulate him, it made hairs on the back of my neck stand on end, it really did. Even my grandma got a bit excited. And once we were in front it was obvious the only aim was to stop Swansea scoring. The players grafted like their lives depended on it, with the two wingers dropping back into midfield to help in defence. The two other latest Leeds signings did okay as well: Cliff Mason at left-back was solid and never looked in trouble while Ian Lawson looked sort of unfit and a bit slow but he ran hard. It was muddy though – there was more grass on our Cross Flatts Park pitch - and it's harder work running in mud.

Bobby had such a big effect that even at half-time I was thinking there was no way we'd get relegated now. The blokes I knew were talking at half time, saying that if you were in a war and there was one person you'd want by your side in the trenches it would be Bobby Collins. One of them said that whilst he was in agreement, he reckoned they'd need to get him a milk crate to stand on first. The second half came round and Swansea were much more up for a game, they went close three times but all our players tackled like demons and weren't afraid to get stuck in or get blood on their studs, as someone mentioned. And we even got a second goal to finish it, scored by Billy McAdams in a goal mouth 'scramble'. Someone commented that McAdams couldn't seem to hit a cow's backside with a banjo half the time, even though he played for Northern Ireland and had a good shot on him. He once got a hat-trick versus West Germany as well, the first ever Briton to do so. I wonder how many he missed though.

It said on the radio that due to Tommy Younger getting tonsillitis suddenly, Leeds didn't have a goalkeeper for the next game, at Southampton. Second-choice keeper Alan Humphreys was already injured and third-choice Terry Carling wouldn't have been able to get to the airport in time they said, so Leeds hired a private plane specially to fly Junior goalie Gary Sprake down on Saturday morning. They went from Manchester Airport, not Leeds/Bradford, I didn't understand why seeing as they did flights to New York from Yeadon by then, four times a week, said the advertisements. Gary Sprake would be making his Leeds debut and at sixteen would be the youngest ever player to play for us. My grandma said that tall, blond Gary Sprake was a very handsome young man and too pretty to be a goalkeeper, only ugly mugs should do it because it didn't matter if they got clobbered in the face, it wouldn't spoil their looks. This was football we were talking about, stuff like that didn't seem right, specially coming from your grandma. There couldn't be many worse ways of preparing for your first team debut than what Sprake had to go through, and to make matters worse he was suffering from air sickness as well. Before kick-off he was puking in a bucket, and he did that before every match since too I heard, like it was a tradition almost. Weird.

I'd have been happy if we'd drawn at Southampton but reports said we were there just to defend, not play entertaining football, plus it looked like we were 'playing uphill'. Southampton were near the top of the division and I bet Bobby Collins was a real joy to be near after they walloped us 4-1. Played off the park too, with Terry Paine their best player by miles. Just nine games left, we were still in the bottom two and still peering into Division Three.

Some time after, rumours surfaced about that match. My grandma just said not to take it seriously because there were always people every day, everywhere, up to no good, trying to make trouble for people for no just cause. 'Someone' said that Southampton's captain Tony Knabb got a telephone call the day before the game from a man claiming to be from Leeds United, offering to pay the Saints players to throw the match and let Leeds win. Ces was disgusted about it all, I remember he got dead angry about it, saying there were so many reasons how it was all a disgrace that someone could come out with such shit. Bearing in mind that Southampton hammered us, whoever supposedly tried to bribe them must have been offering washers and IOU's.

2 v

The script writers of the Don Revie *This Is Your Life* edition included the name of Bobby Collins not once, yet his 1962 arrival was one of the most significant transfers in British football and proved to be the turning point for Revie and Leeds. Collins was the catalyst for the upturn in the team's fortunes and had there been no Bobby Collins appearing for Leeds United, it is entirely plausible that there would have been no Don Revie appearing on *This Is Your Life* in 1974. When telling of the glories of Revie's managerial career too, the script writers, with so much material to use but too little time to use it all, were forced to miss out much more, not all of it positive. For a long time from the start the Revie's Leeds story was a grim one, and his first full season in charge was near disastrous.

*

Come Easter 1962, despite a reasonable run of unbeaten games, Leeds still laid perilously low in Division Two and they were scheduled to play, from 20th April to the 28th, four hugely important League matches which could decide the team's, the players' and the manager's future. Four crucial games in just nine days, three of them to be played within five days. Ludicrous. And two of them against the same team as well, Bury.

Bury were a tough, battling team. No 'prisoners' would be taken when they met the Peacocks, it was after all a dogfight of a division and *all* the games were tough, played on overused, weather-scarred and often quagmire pitches. Gruelling, painful, energy-sapping mêlées. No holding back from the players, no quarter asked and none ever given. In a season that had been arduous already, Revie told his players to start saying their prayers. Although they were quite low in the table, Bury looked safe from relegation, unlike Leeds.

2 vi

There's only about sixteen thousand in the whole world who can say the same as me - I saw Grenville Hair score a League goal! Someone reckoned he'd only ever scored once before, in the FA Cup. So if I ever had nippers I could tell them that I was 'one of the few', when Leeds beat Middlesbrough 2-0 on 7th April, 1962 and Grenville scored. Everyone was celebrating, clapping and that, even jumping up and down, while I was sort of just pretending due to the fat arsed lump in front of me blocking most of my view at the vital moment. Grenville never let the team down ever, I heard it said a thousand times. Either at left back or right back, he always looked fit and quick, even though he was in his thirties.

Two days after, we got a good 1-1 draw at Preston North End and moved up two places in the table and out of the relegation zone, for the first time in ages. It felt like a lead weight had been lifted from our necks, Ces said virtually the same and even John was more cheerful. I wouldn't have thought he could *be*. In the Preston game John Hawksby's left wing cross deflected into their net for our goal. A bit of luck going our way for once. He had his finest game ever for Leeds, the paper said. That didn't really say much but fair dos to him. The following week we earned another point in a decent 1-1 draw at Walsall. Albert Johanneson got the goal, he was the best attacker we had and could change a game all on his own. Having a player like that was brilliant because we weren't a 'pretty' side to watch most times, we played a pressing, hard-running style which some called 'kick and rush'. Exciting football wasn't a priority, and no one congratulates relegated teams for playing entertainingly anyway.

And then we beat Luton 2-1, both goals scored by Billy Bremner, and after that we got a great point in a 0-0 draw at Leyton Orient who were second top while we were second bottom again. It proved we could match anyone in Division Two when the players gave it their best. Billy Bremner was a strange player. Tons of skill, tons of energy and pace, but he seemed to spend more time trying to pick fights with opponents after they'd fouled him or been goading him – both happened aplenty - and then he'd get into bother with the referee as well. And soon he'd start getting the bird from some of the Leeds crowd, which was a bit rough seeing as he was only young. Slagging off your own players never helped no one but the other teams.

Every morning and night when I was out running, I seemed to have more energy in me the better Leeds were doing. Mr Hatfield told me to try and get my upper half stronger to make me harder to beat or push off in a game, so when I was running I started to box at the same time too, boxing thin air - like Paul Newman as Rocky Graziano in *Someone Up There Likes Me*. I bet I looked dead weird when I was doing the boxing but I wasn't fussed, it didn't matter me looking a bit different. Before I went to bed I'd do a hundred sit-ups as well as when I got up in the morning, my stomach was solid as a board.

1-1 away at Bury, great result, we couldn't really expect better than a point away from home. Jack Charlton, playing as centre-half, brilliantly headed in a 62nd minute Collins free kick after Bremner had been fouled again. Heavy rain before and during the match made it an ugly game to watch, though Albert played well and gave Bury's right-back a 'difficult' time while Noel Peyton worked hard for Leeds too and looked quite dangerous. He never scored enough goals, in my opinion, even though he made loads of chances. The match report wasn't all good - both teams looked like they wanted to kick each other all afternoon rather than play proper football. I didn't care, it was another well-won point. Years after, Bob Stokoe started coming out with some real bile about Don Revie trying to bribe him before the match. He said that Revie offered him five hundred quid if he told the Bury team to 'take it easy'. Stokoe said he reported the incident to his chairman and vice-chairman. Funny that no one else ever said anything about it, no one, not the Bury or Leeds directors or any of the players, only Bob Stokoe.

The day after Bury away was Derby County at home. And we played like a set of nervous cart-horses, it was infuriating. Luckily, Derby were just as bad and it ended up 0-0, one more point gained. Less than 12,000 bothered to turn up to watch, which I didn't understand, it was a huge game and the team needed our support more than ever. The next match was Stokoe's Bury, Tuesday, our third game in five days. And nearly ten thousand more people attended even when it had been miserable, cold and wet, all day. It had been miserable, cold and wet all season really. It was a dull game too, 'rough, tough and stormy' said the paper. Bury looked quicker and fitter than us but another draw and another decent point gained.

The bottom of Division Two, 24th April, 1962.

19 Leeds	Played 41, Points = 34
20 Swansea	Played 40, Points = 33
21 Bristol R.	Played 41, Points = 33
22 Brighton	Played 41, Points = 31

Away to Newcastle on the final Saturday, only if we lost and Bristol Rovers won really bloody well at Luton was there any chance of us getting relegated. It wouldn't happen, I was convinced of it, and by the looks of it, so was the team as they strolled to a fantastic 3 - 0 win, McAdams, Johanneson scoring as well as an own goal which I'm sure some clueless crank will have said we paid cash for. The team ended up nineteenth in Division Two, with Swansea just below us and Brighton and Bristol Rovers the bottom two - we had three more points than Bristol and a miles better goal average. It wasn't a case of thanking God for our being saved but more 'Thank Bobby'.

2 vii

As the summer of 1962 approached, a specific business transaction was ready to be completed. But the question for one Scottish family in Broughty Ferry on the east edge of Dundee was, who would be the buyers? More than thirty football clubs had tried to persuade the family's fifteen year-old 'Cannonball Kid' to sign for them. That kid was Peter Lorimer, a prodigious talent with a prolific goal-scoring record. For two years or so now, his family had been courted by talent scout John Quinn, in the employ of Leeds United, and they always looked forward to his Saturday morning visits, laden as he generally was with gifts and incentives. The father, Peter, a fisherman, would receive a crisp five pound note each time from Quinn, equivalent to nearly half his weekly wage, often spent in the local pub. Mother Janet looked forward to Quinn's visits because it meant a few pounds added to the house-keeping and more eggs, sherry, full-cream milk and steak for son Peter, to help broaden his impressively tall but typically lean fifteen year-old build. Son Peter looked forward to the visits because in addition to being well fed, he'd end up with ten bob in his pocket plus the thrill of being told he was one of the most promising footballers in the whole of Great Britain. He wasn't though always so keen on attending school half-pissed from that breakfast sherry. He'd visited Leeds' stadium a few times before and he liked what he'd seen. The training facilities were impressive, the general atmosphere was friendly and the welcomes always warm. The spirit of family right from the ground staff and laundry women up to the chairman greatly appealed to him, while young as well as older players greeted and treated him like he was already part of the close-knit group, almost as if he was their brother. Elland Road, Leeds, a home from home. Lorimer knew he would enjoy himself there, were he to sign. And of great appeal too was the fact that there were a fair few Scots already at the club. And one not very well-known matter boosted Leeds' hopes of signing him - the Lorimers were distant relatives of one Elsie Revie, wife of Don.

John Quinn had always shown Peter Lorimer respect and not treated him like just another 'possible' purchase. Unlike Glasgow Rangers and Manchester United who, in Lorimer's mind, showed little consideration for him or his family, despite big money being offered like the £5,000 in a briefcase from Manchester's Joe Armstrong. Such an amount was a drop in the ocean for a club the size of Manchester United but a huge amount for any working class family. And too high for a club like Leeds United, too. Quinn helped to make up for Leeds' lack of financial power with his persuasive and affable manner, and the young footballers and their families appreciated him. They believed his assurances that Don Revie would bring the lads up safely and responsibly and in healthy, respectable surroundings. And in addition to the club's excellent football coaching, they had a doctor (Dr Ian Adams), a padre (Reverend John Jackson of York) plus ex-headmaster Jeffrey Sanders to help the boys' development and academic needs. And the one and only Les Cocker gave the sex education talks. If there were *still* any doubts in the minds of the parents, the presence of the legendary Scotland international Bobby Collins would surely erase them.

Leeds did their best to entice Peter Lorimer with an £800 signing-on sweetener plus wages nearly as good as seasoned professionals already at the club. Janet Lorimer would have the last word on where her son's footballing future lay, to her, money was less important than his welfare and development. She liked and trusted Revie and believed Leeds would best take care of Peter.

Over the previous twelve months, Revie had made the long journey to Broughty Ferry on numerous occasions, calculating that he had driven more than 6,400 miles in total. On the night before Peter Lorimer was finishing school forever, Revie again set off in his trusty Ford, with chief scout Maurice Lindley keeping him company. Their departure for Scotland needed to be at that unreasonable time because they were scared they would miss out on signing the kid with a kick as hard as a mule and a shot like a bazooka if they were any later. Other clubs were prowling around, hoping to tempt the lad who scored goals for fun. Peter Lorimer belted in goals for his Stobbswell school, for Dundee Schoolboys and for Scotland Schoolboys no less. And Don Revie had witnessed what he described as one of the best goals he had ever seen, scored by Lorimer, at Ibrox, versus England Schoolboys. Information had reached Revie about other clubs' representatives intending to be at the Lorimer front door very early the next day, knocking loudly and talking persuasively.

Chapter 3: 1962/3 - King John's return

3 i

Clean Air by 1975 - thirteen years to go. I'd made a note of it, half in jest, half in seriousness. The older I got, the more I resented the fact that those pillocks in charge of our city had allowed people – poorer people of course - to live in unhealthy conditions in the first place. The poster on my wall wasn't exactly pretty reading either but Jesus it could have been a lot worse.

Season 1961 - '62 Honours.
League Division One winners - Ipswich Town, Runners up - Burnley.
League Division Two winners - Liverpool, Runners up - Leyton Orient.
FA Cup winners - Tottenham Hotspur, Runners up - Burnley.
League Cup winners - Norwich City, Runners up - Rochdale.
European Cup winners - Benfica, Runners up - Real Madrid.
European Cup Winners Cup winners - Atletico Madrid, Runners up - Fiorentina.
Inter-Cities Fairs Cup winners - Valencia, Runners up - Barcelona.
World Cup winners - Brazil, Runners-up - Czechoslovakia.
Football Player of the Year - Jimmy Adamson, Burnley.
European Footballer of the Year - Josef Masopust, Dukla Prague.
Leeds United crowd average, home games = 13,594.

It had been a busy summer over the road, some big news occurring before the start of the new season. If I hadn't seen it myself, I wouldn't have believed it: photographers taking snaps of him, his hands on his hips, dazzling white strip, sun tanned skin, brilliant white movie star smile and an orange football at his feet. I was only looking at the return of the King!

Big John Charles, back from Juventus, for more than £50,000. Fantastic news and it proved that Harry Reynolds and Don Revie were dead set on taking Leeds places. Charles' signing also meant that we had *two* new strikers because Jim Storrie, a Jock from Airdrie, signed in June for £16,000 as well. The Evening News called him 'Diamond Jim', a non-stop bustling Scot and another discovery by the United scouts in Scotland. He joined a month after we signed fifteen year-old 'prodigious talent' Peter Lorimer too. Lorimer was finally signed at three a.m. and he came back with Don and Maurice that same morning. It all sounded more like kidnap to me.

Around the same time another young player officially signed too, though Ces said he'd been with us a while in fact: speedy right-half Jimmy Greenhoff, born in Barnsley. When young players moved here as apprentices they were usually put up in houses in south Leeds, Beeston mainly, by families like the Leightons and Turners, just two names I'd heard. My grandma said that Jack Charlton lived in our street when I was a baby, before moving to a house on Beeston Hill near Cross Flatts Park. The players paid board and lodgings, so none of it was free, but I bet they had it nice and cosy. Maybe my grandma should have offered to be a landlady, to get a few more pennies in on top of her office job. I'd probably have benefited then as well.

The best news I heard, even better than Charlesy's return, hadn't even been mentioned and that was Paul Madeley signing professional forms for Leeds. He'd played well for the Juniors and Cyril Partridge reckoned he was going to become a right player, specially in defensive midfield. I was so pleased for him it nearly felt like it was me who'd signed. It all definitely helped to spur me on to try even harder - To Achieve Personal Greatness.

John Charles' coming back made the front page headlines, like it should have of course. He was supposedly even better at Juventus than when he was here in the fifties, he was a real hero over there. They didn't want him to leave but his wife Peggy was homesick and they wanted their sons to go to school here. We paid a lot of money for him so Juventus will have done alright out of it, I'm sure. Typical Italians some said, they couldn't be trusted, like in the war, and you could bet something shady was going on with the transfer money. I didn't know anything about any of that but it gave Ces a chance to tell me one of his favourite jokes - Italy's national flag is a white cross on a white background.

I believed Harry Reynolds when he said he had big ambitions for the club, as far as I could tell he always put his money where his mouth was. Some Leeds supporters were never happy though, slating him, calling him greedy and an idiot in letters to the Evening News. So there was me thinking 'Some bloody people' and all that, and ready to defend him, then the club only goes and doubles the price of season tickets. Suddenly some of the ranting seemed justified, we were in the Second Division after all. Not that any of this could excuse one graceless bastard for sending a funeral wreath with Harry Reynolds' name on to the club.

3 ii

Television airtime severely restricts the time allowed for guest appearances and the number of 'special mentions' of individuals who have contributed to the success of the *This Is Your Life* subject. As well as Bobby Collins, by the close of 1962, it was quite evident that other men would play major roles in crucially helping the managerial career of Don Revie. Men such as Les Cocker, Syd Owen, Maurice Lindley, Bob English and Cyril Partridge, as well as the talent scouts. And of course, most notably, Harry Reynolds, being the man responsible for persuading Revie to first venture into management.

*

Although Don Revie told the press differently, in August '62, he had high hopes for Leeds in the imminent new season. During pre-season he had worked tirelessly at improving the team. Out would go players who he regarded as good but not good enough overall or who he could get useful transfer fees for. Players like attackers Derek Mayers and Billy McAdams, wing-half Peter McConnell who had joined Leeds from school in the previous decade, and right-back Alf Jones. Revie spent more than most managers in the entire League, and throughout, chairman Harry Reynolds and the board had supported him, believing his decisions to be risk free. However, the club's purchase of John Charles was an expensive gamble; it nearly bankrupted the club.

Normal player signings saw transfer fees paid in instalments, making for easier, more sensible and safer business for the clubs involved. But the recruitment of John Charles was not a normal transfer - deals with Italian clubs generally involved 'cash on delivery' terms and the Leeds board did not have the £50,000-plus fee readily available. Therefore, urgent arrangements were needed for them to raise the funding. If they wanted King John back then they'd have to pay for it royally. One explanation for ticket price increases.

Revie told the local media that he was not one for building castles in the air and so would be happy with finishing in the top half of Division Two. Considering their scrape with relegation the previous season, it was a sensible remark to make but with his team containing such balance of youth and experience, pace and stamina, flair and grit; *rough and smooth*, the club's aspirations were undoubtedly higher. A team that hated losing and which contained fighters of the ilk of Goodwin, Charlton, Bremner, Bell and of course Collins, was going to be hard to beat and ought to be involved in the final promotion reckonings. Combined with the match-winning potential of men such as Charles, Albert Johanneson and Jim Storrie, going up as Second Division champions could not be dismissed as fantasy either.

And the new campaign started promisingly with a 1-0 win at Stoke and a decent team performance played in front of nearly 30,000, many of whom had travelled from Leeds to welcome Charles back. His 're-debut' had been reasonable if not outstanding. Importantly, his Elland Road homecoming appeared much less attractive to supporters due to the price increases. Only 14,119 attended on Wednesday 22nd August to witness a home 4-3 defeat to Rotherham, followed on the Saturday by a home win, 1-0, over Sunderland, the attendance 17,753. Rotherham did the double over Leeds the next Tuesday, 2-1, and then Leeds travelled the short distance to Huddersfield Town to pick up a 1-1 draw. Two wins, two defeats and a draw in their first five matches.

Respectable progress, except it was identical to the start of last season's lousy campaign, and the team displays this time around weren't much better. And come a midweek home defeat to Bob Stokoe's Bury, in front of an impressive but soon depressed crowd of 28,000, Revie's patience was worn thin. For the next match, at Swansea Town, changes to the team-sheet had to be made anyway: Jim Storrie, with a broken finger, and John Charles a back strain were late casualties and already out injured were captain Freddie Goodwin, forward Ian Lawson and left-half Willie Bell.

'Some of our senior players have not struck top form yet,' Revie said, as he dropped goalkeeper Tommy Younger and, perhaps most surprisingly, full-back Grenville Hair too, replacing them with youngsters. Making their first team debuts would be Norman Hunter and Paul Reaney in defence and Rod Johnson up front with Noel Peyton returning also. Mason at left-back would be captain. Brave, sweeping changes by the manager, seen as drastic by some. Courageous in another sense too, was allowing Jack Charlton to organize the defence 'his way', meaning that out went man-to-man marking and in came a zonal system of defending. He would organize the back four, and instruct the young lads where to go, when to mark, when to cover and how to pick up positions. The development delighted Charlton and would prove significant for his career He'll have felt relief too, at still being in the manager's plans after smashing a teacup too close to Revie's head at half-time in the Rotherham home game.

Meanwhile, 20 year-old Billy Bremner, despite being only slightly older than the new lads, had played many more first team matches and was much more experienced. He helped them develop as players, coaxing and encouraging them, almost like a watchful elder brother. He was however still unhappy at the club and persisted in 'bugging' Don Revie for a transfer as he wanted to be with girlfriend Vicky back home in Stirling.

Leeds were marginally lower than Swansea in the division and were expected to lose this game. With pleasant weather and a soft pitch though, the Leeds players, in all-blue, went out determined to show their true mettle and to enjoy theirselves. Swansea did have an early goal disallowed, Leeds grew in strength and confidence to outfight and outmanoeuvre the hosts. In goal, Gary Sprake, and in front of him Jack Charlton, played 'storybook' performances while Leeds' aggressive, hard-pressing style and impressive pace threatened the opposition with each attack. Collins, Bremner, Smith, Johanneson and Storrie dominated the play and early goals in each half by first Johnson and then Bremner gained an inspiring 2-0 win, their third this term. The next weekend, two goals from Johanneson brought a fine 2-0 home win against high-fliers Chelsea in front of over 27,000 spectators. Nine points out of a possible sixteen now, and the prospects seemed to be brightening, until a midweek 3-1 defeat, at Stokoe's Bury, starting a chain of five League games without a win.

*

September 1962, a Football League Commission investigated alleged bribery of Gillingham players in two matches the previous season, versus Wrexham. Wrexham won promotion to Division Three. The Commission declared that the allegations had not been proved.

*

During Leeds games and training matches in the 1950s, Jack Charlton often saw trails of human carnage left behind by the great John Charles; he scoffed at the Welshman's nickname 'Gentle Giant'. Charles would run with his arms and elbows high, powerful enough to pummel his way through and damage opponents' defences. Charles never deliberately hurt a player but it did not lessen the pain he often inflicted on the opposition. In 1962 however, after the heavier and slower John Charles was back to stretch on the (now white) shirt of Leeds United, there were precious few reminders of his glorious reputation.

With Charles in the side, opponents would designate two possibly even three defenders to mark him. So a main Leeds tactic was for the wingers - usually Johanneson and Bremner - to send crosses in to Charles in the penalty area for him to either try to go for goal or lay the ball off for a team-mate to have a go. Unfortunately, Leeds' game had become more direct and faster since Charles' earlier spell. *Too* direct, *too* fast. Despite good pay and a splendid new home in Wetherby, he was unhappy and frustrated, and troubled by lack of sleep and minor injuries. He wasn't able to train well as a result and it was apparent to those at the club that he had lost enthusiasm for the game. Les Cocker was annoyed at Charles' lack of fitness and perplexed as to why he had bothered coming back to England at all. Quite clearly, the player had lost the 'spark', physically and mentally, and he had other worries on his mind to contend with too: the family all missed Italian life and the views of the Alps, the good restaurants and fine foods, the sunnier climes and the beach excursions. Depressed, stressed and his marriage increasingly strained, by November John Charles had played eleven games and scored just three goals. Leeds failed to win the three games in which he'd scored.

Revie would not publicly criticise Charles, instead he tried to help and encourage him. But he was very unhappy with the situation, too – it just wasn't working out. In addition, as was pointed out by the Leeds board, when only fifteen thousand Leeds people out of a population of half a million were willing to pay a bit more cash to see a true great, it was time for an alternative plan. Fortunately, an Italian club had emerged with a possible solution to the problem. They contacted the Football League's Alan Hardaker and tabled a bid to Leeds to recruit John Charles' services. Harry Reynolds called a board meeting and after two hours announced that as John Charles and wife Peggy were unsettled, Leeds were selling him to AS Roma. At 6.59pm, November 2nd, 1962, the deal was sealed and Charles was on his way back to Italian soccer, for £70,000. He had been at Leeds United just 91 days.

Charles said, 'This is the first time my football has left me so long and I feel shattered. It was a mistake for me to come back.' He later added that leaving Juventus was his biggest ever misjudgement in the sport. He felt wracked with guilt for failing and disappointing so many Leeds people who cared so much for him. The Leeds board, also feeling embarrassed with the situation as they had profited nicely from it, offered refunds on season tickets and discounts on future home games. Harry Reynolds went to the extent of issuing an apology to the Leeds public for any offence the transfer had caused. For the personnel and supporters of Leeds United, and John Charles' friends and team-mates, it had been a frustrating time to see one of the world's finest players toiling. He was nowhere near the footballer they used to know, and he was unable to perform anywhere near as well as he had before. For all concerned the affair had been a crying shame but the only person to actually shed tears was John Charles himself.

3 iii

I wasn't Catholic so if I ever went to church as a kid it was St Mary's on Beeston Road (though I did go to Midnight Mass at St Anthony's one Christmas Eve when I was older, and drunk). I never had a clue what the difference was between religions, and I didn't really care either. Church and faith weren't topics of conversation in our house, mainly because my grandma wasn't interested. If I ever asked her about God and going to services and stuff, she'd just tell me to be quiet, and not in a very spiritual way either. Such grown-up stuff didn't concern me apparently, though I knew her attitude was due to my granddad dying in France in the war.

A young bloke called 'Passy', from a local church side, came to our house one evening, when I was thirteen, to ask me to play for Beeston St Anthony's. He was player-manager of the Sunday team which I thought was a bit odd, a church team playing on the Sabbath. For as long as I knew, St Anthony's was a good club and well-known in Leeds. They even had their own changing room and baths. My grandma had said it was up to me who I played for but when I was on the stairs I heard her asking Passy if I was old enough to look after myself in a men's league. He told her he'd seen me play and that I'd definitely be alright because I was quite quick and fit enough to look after myself. Just in case, he promised that the fellas in the team would always make sure I was alright. So I signed their forms and he said he'd make sure they paid my shilling registration fee and my subs each week. Training was on Tuesday nights and they went in the Peacock afterwards which was just about perfect for me, right next door near enough. I'd never been in a pub at that stage, it wouldn't be so long before you'd have trouble getting me out of them. I was chuffed to bits to be asked and couldn't wait to get going even though I was dead nervous with it - a *men's* team in an adult league, not just school now. If I ever got picked, of course.

Maybe I was being soft but I was upset when John Charles left, even though it was definitely the right thing to happen. Staying at Leeds wouldn't have helped him, he seemed miserable and that was from just watching him, I didn't need to ask Ces or John Reynolds for details. I'm sure John Reynolds would have known, him being Welsh and all. In September we lost Eric Smith as well, with a broken leg. Poor bloke. And it wasn't the first time he'd done it either. It was one of those horrible incidents which probably meant we'd never see him in a Leeds shirt again. Our season had looked dead promising at the start, now it was looking like it might just die off with hardly a whimper.

Once Charlesy had gone, Jim Storrie surprised plenty of people at how well he did, like he'd been given a new lease of life, and he scored a right rake of goals. And because he always ran his heart out, Leeds fans loved him. He never gave in, even when he'd been clattered by opposing defenders - plenty of the fans fell out with Charlesy for being just about the exact opposite. Daft thing was though, Diamond Jim missed more than he scored, and them that he did score were often harder chances than the ones he missed. We all loved to watch a grafter, and Jim Storrie chased everything, there was no such thing as a lost cause to him. You could be as gifted as King John but if your heart wasn't in it, you weren't any good for the team.

Storrie created loads of goals just by harrying defenders and goalkeepers. He tried to enjoy himself, having a laugh with players on both sides and taking the Mick out of opposing goalkeepers. He was one of the most popular Leeds players at the time, along with Bobby, Gary, Albert, and even Jack. Billy sort of split opinions, like Leeds supporters either loved him or loathed him. Like this season – he went off the boil and didn't seem to enjoy playing out wide, so he started slacking. He missed nearly half the games because he was either injured, dropped or even suspended. Even then he scored ten goals in the League. He'd played around a hundred games already, but his discipline let him down. You could hardly blame him when defenders kicked lumps out of him and tried to get him in to trouble with the referees.

We signed Don Weston from Rotherham with some of the Charles cash, a very nippy type who only went and scored a hat-trick on his debut. As the season went on Don Revie gave more young lads debuts too, though I couldn't really say how good or bad they were, they didn't seem to make much impact either way. It might sound mean but that always pleased me because I wanted to see Paul Madeley do well, not just *anyone*. There was Mike Addy, Barrie Wright and Tommy Henderson, a mate of Billy Bremner's, plus Jimmy Greenhoff late in the season. Even Peter Lorimer hadn't been any great shakes in his debut, against Southampton. Maybe it was too early to blood him, him being the youngest ever Leeds first teamer. And then he broke his leg in a Junior game soon after, rotten luck I wouldn't wish on my worst enemy. None of them made an impact like Sprake, Reaney and Hunter, or even Rod Johnson though he struggled a bit after a while. They all established themselves early on, and there was a great mix of youth with experience. Norman Hunter hadn't originally joined as a defender but it turned out that Jim Storrie advised Don Revie that he was very awkward to play against, despite being a beanpole. His tackling was hard and swift, and he was always getting his toe in there first before Storrie could bring the ball under control.

*

The whole British football world went haywire just after Christmas and right up to March 1963, with the lousy 'Big Freeze'. The year before's winter had been bad enough with gale force winds half the time and houses going all *Wizard of Oz* like, now it was freezing weather, proper blizzards and snowdrifts all over the place. It was bad enough up here but they had it worse down south, folk even died from the cold, and parts of the sea froze over. People even went ice skating on the River Thames. Our house was that perishing I half expected to wake up half dead some mornings. There were times when I had ice on my bedroom window, frozen snot (my own) on my face, sore throat and pounding head and I could see my breath, indoors. It just wasn't right.

Hardly a proper League game was played for three months. Even in our Sunday League we had to postpone loads of matches.

Half of our lot didn't mind, it meant they could have more ale on a Saturday night and not have to fret about Passy dropping them from the team in the morning. Me, I got really frustrated because I couldn't stand not playing so I'd go sprinting on icy grass in my studded boots or I'd kick the ball up in the air and practice trapping it, stuff like that, hour after hour till it got dark. People might not know that frozen or snow-covered grass is usually a lovely surface to play on, soft and crushy and therefore not as risky to the physical well-being.

Because of the weather I couldn't even use the facilities at Elland Road, as something was always going on there, players from all the squads plus all the staff knocking around. Ces said it would be best for me to lie low a bit in case anyone thought we were taking liberties. I kept away from Elland Road whilst the coaches had the players in for extra indoor training during the freeze, or injured players got treatment for injuries. Anyway, I must have passed it a million times before but I'd never taken any heed. There was a little factory just up the road from our Hoxtons street, in the side streets amongst all the houses and little shops and workyards behind the white New Peacock pub. Etched in stone in old-style letters over the big doorway of this one particular building was its name - Perseverance Works. From then on it was etched in my mind - Perseverance Works, along with To Achieve Personal Greatness, course.

When Walter Winterbottom left the England job, there were reports that the Football Association wanted Don Revie to replace him. Yes, our Don Revie. We weren't even top of Division Two at the time, it sounded like someone had made it up. Anyway, he said in the papers it was a ridiculous idea and that he was determined to stay at Leeds United and put them on the soccer map proper. I wonder what would have happened had they offered him the England job. Soon after, the Leeds board offered him a new, improved contract, proving that I hadn't been the only one wondering it.

I can't pretend that my grandma was always brilliant at encouraging me in life, but I know she wanted the best for me, especially when she found out I had potential to make it in football. While she didn't exactly go out of her way to support me - I suspected she was very shy at heart for one thing - plenty of the neighbours and people in Beeston did, whenever they saw me training with St Ant's or out running or kicking a ball about on my own. There was always someone giving me a wave or shouting 'Keep at it, lad!' in a good natured way. Folk in Beeston were great, it made me want to try harder and make more of myself, it really did. That season, Don did what he said he'd do – he put Leeds United on the soccer map. Unfortunately, we still missed out on promotion. Losing three games in a row late on in the season didn't help and so we ended up finishing fifth, a grand effort and a near miracle compared to last season. Still, when it boiled down to it, it was all pretty disappointing. Don't look back though, don't have regrets, some of the good advice I was brought up on. The club had good reason to be optimistic, I think they just had to stick at it and it would all turn out well. Even Eric Stanger, one of the newspaper reporters, said it about Revie's side – 'Their football, at times imaginative, fast and crowned by hard shooting was much better than much that has been seen even in the First Division this season. Leeds are blending in a harmony of purpose which comes from every player being prepared to put team needs before personal achievement.'

3 iv

On November 10th, 1962, Sheffield Wednesday and Aston Villa were reported to the FA due to a 'crowd disturbance'. Sheffield Wednesday were consequently fined for the trouble. Later that month, Huddersfield Town and Portsmouth were fined £50 by a League Management Committee for fielding less than their strongest teams in League Cup ties (versus Bradford City and Brighton respectively). In May 1963, in a 'friendly' match at Hampden Park, referee Jim Finney in the 79th minute abandoned the Scotland versus Austria game (Scotland led 4-1) after 'rough play' and two Austrian players having been sent off, one for spitting. The visitors were said to have spent most of the match trying to 'kick lumps out of' Denis Law.

Chapter 4: 1963/4 - PWTAPG

4 i

The Football Honours, season 1962 – '63, had that normal, bleak Leeds-less look about it
League Division One winners - Everton, Runners up - Tottenham Hotspur.
League Division Two winners - Stoke City, Runners up - Chelsea.
FA Cup winners - Manchester United, Runners up - Leicester City.
League Cup winners - Birmingham City, Runners up - Aston Villa.
European Cup winners - AC Milan, Runners up - Benfica.
European Cup Winners Cup winners - Tottenham, Runners up - Athletico Madrid.
Inter-Cities Fairs Cup winners - Valencia, Runners up - Dynamo Zagreb.
Football Player of the Year - Stanley Matthews.
European Footballer of the Year - Lev Yashin, Dynamo Moscow.
Leeds United crowd average, home games = 20,215.

But many of we supporters were optimistic about the team's chances. As a boy, nothing ever came around quickly enough - birthdays, Christmas, the new football season - and the wait and the pining for Leeds to win promotion back into Division One felt like torture, lifelong torture. It was like an obsession, nothing else was really important. Morning, afternoon and night, I couldn't get Leeds out of my head. The closest thing to it of course was my Sunday games for St Anthony's and that was bad enough, I used to get so 'up' for matches I could hardly sleep the night before.

4 ii

For the 1963–'64 season, soon after the Profumo scandal and the Great Train Robbery, and near to Martin Luther King's legendary 'I have a dream' speech, Leeds United's first match was against Rotherham United. Elland Road witnessed a deserved though difficult home win. Don Revie, desperate for a good start to the campaign, considered his team's performance as only satisfactory. Billy Bremner had moved into (the centre of) midfield at right-half after impressive pre-season friendly displays, including on tour against AS Roma as part of the John Charles transfer deal. In Bremner's place on the right flank came in Don Weston; he played well and had struck the only goal. Overall though, Revie worried that Weston was not the solution for Leeds' common failing - a lack of ammunition to the strikers from the right wing. Weston was quick and skilful but inconsistent. And so Leeds remained on the lookout for a replacement winger. The forward line too, could be improved, in terms of muscle and height. In the centre of midfield, Bobby Collins and Bremner looked an excellent combination, even though Revie's discovery was perhaps more by chance than planning.

Bremner enjoyed his football and received accolades for the quality of his play, but his name remained on the Available For Transfer list. It had been there a long time. He was a significant first team regular now, as well as being a significant first rate pain in the backside for Don Revie. Not that Revie took too seriously the player's dissatisfaction - for him to let his flame-haired protégé leave Leeds would need much more money and persuasion than had so far been offered. British clubs came in with enquiries and offers, Celtic and Hibernian the most recent, and Revie would apparently consider the offers and then casually reject them.

On 29th August 1963, a certain Leeds United man's own dream was a step closer to fulfilment - Don Revie's. The business deal was done, the documents signed and the handshakes made. In the local press, the resultant photograph prophetically showed Don Revie's smile as more satisfied and wider than the other officials' there. He has a look of not only a cat with the cream but one given a lifetime's supply of it. His eyes glint with pride, yet there is hint of incredulity too, as if he can't quite believe his luck. He has just signed a player he rates as potentially world class, for a bargain price of £33,000, from Busby's Manchester United. Busby was relieved to release the player, John Giles. He believed his club had done well out of the deal. He would in later years admit to the sale being one of his greatest regrets in football.

Soon after the deal had been finalised, in his office Don Revie was talking with his new player, a quiet, earnest young Dubliner known in his childhood as a 'house angel, street devil', dry-witted and full of pranks. Revie told him how he would feature in the team and how he wanted him to play, what his responsibilities would be. Giles was pleased to be appreciated and wanted. True, he was dropping down to a Division Two club but they were ambitious and the manager and chairman extremely persuasive, convinced that Leeds United were on the rise and that he, Giles, could play a crucial part in their quest for success. Early in his career, Giles had earned a reputation as a technically-gifted player with steady temperament and good fitness levels. But he suffered a badly broken leg, an injury which would easily end the playing careers of lesser men. It changed his attitude and approach to competitive football too, and toughened him up. He would always be on his guard during matches and be a much harder proposition for opponents. Not that he had been exactly a soft touch before. Professional football was a rough, tough game, with players at every club in the country bearing not only permanent battle scars but probably vindictive grudges too. In Giles' world, saying sorry was a weakness, sorry did not belong in the combat of sport and sorry did no one any good.

In his office, because he had been talking all the while, a newspaper-wrapped bundle Giles had placed on Revie's desk went unnoticed by the manager. He had been telling his new player, with great enthusiasm naturally, of his plans and vision for the club and the family atmosphere and healthy rivalry they were developing there. A family of players to which Giles would bring even more quality. Giles, who first played for Eire days before his nineteenth birthday - and scored a scorcher in a famous win over

World Cup finalists Sweden - was happy to listen. He actually had little choice as Revie was impressively in full flow. It was difficult not to be impressed by him, a man who inspired people, motivated them, made them feel wonderful about themselves; John Giles had never felt so important before.

And then Revie stopped speaking, abruptly, noticing the curious bundle on his desk. He stared at it. Puzzled, he then asked what it was. Football boots, advised Giles. Revie's facial expression changed, contradicting the confidence and composure of before; now his face was full of apprehension, even fear. Snatching up the package, he thrust it towards the player, with panic in his voice he said, 'Get them off quick, don't you know it's unlucky to put shoes on a table?' John Giles could have been forgiven for thinking he'd made a mistake in joining a club clearly run by a superstitious lunatic. His misgivings might have deepened too, when later learning that First Division Manchester City offered more money than Leeds for his signature.

4 iii

The 1963-'64 season was also the start of something big for me too, a 'storybook adventure' maybe, except that that made it sound like it was all a jolly lovely time, wrapped up with a nice sweet and cuddly ending. I wasn't fourteen yet but I was playing in the St Anthony's first team and there were club reps watching me so I heard - local teams' scouts as well as a couple of full time League clubs too. By nature, I was never a big-head or anything but I knew I was playing consistently well, in a very good team, we were always in the running for our league title and the local as well as West Riding district cups. It was easy for me to look good in that side, all the fellas could play a bit and even if the league was mostly made up of pub teams and Labour clubs, the standard was still high. Work hard, play hard was the St Ant's motto, which fitted in well with my own Perseverance Works To Achieve Personal Greatness, of course. Probably goes without needing to be said but the only scouts I wanted watching me were Leeds'. And so the first time I heard one of them *was,* I nearly soiled myself. Really. I don't know who it was doing the watching but I bet Ces or John had something to do with it all.

Each player in a team has a specific job to do. I played right-back but I always wanted to play in midfield, like Bobby Collins for Leeds. Passy played there though so I had no chance. My job first and foremost was to defend against whoever was on the left wing or midfield and then once I'd done my bit I could try and support our attack, combine with our right winger and sometimes swing in crosses myself for the forwards to pick off and notch a goal. It was just like how Leeds tried to do it. I watched every home game that season and the team looked like they knew promotion was coming, they all had this swagger about them while the all-white kit made them look bigger and stronger than everyone else. Maybe not like Real Madrid (yet) but the team was definitely on the up. It all just went dead steady with hardly any real tension at all, no nerves or panicking. I might have it wrong but I don't think we were ever out of the top four all season. Don Revie had opposing teams watched, usually by Syd Owen or Maurice Lindley, and he prepared a plan for each match which the Leeds players followed closely. And if ever Leeds did hit some sort of snag it would all be put right pronto, as if Don Revie and the coaches had expected and were ready for it. Anyone with a bit of football nous could see that Don Revie (or 'The Don' he was being called by now) had his players organized the way he wanted them. The Juniors, the Reserves and the first team all played the same system or pattern, so when one player had to drop out he'd be replaced by a similar player who knew exactly what he was supposed to do and was good enough to do it. It worked a treat nearly every single time.

In matches, once Leeds took the lead it was more important to not concede than to score more goals. That might not be very attractive to watch but it was still skill to be proud of, from the defenders and 'keeper. Seeing a defensive 'unit' working well and in harmony together is something special, it really is. Anyway, who gave a toss when it meant getting out of the division? Shankly, who'd took Liverpool up, always said that the Second Division was so tough that a team had to claw itself out to win promotion. The average Leeds home attendances went up to nearly thirty thousand per League game, too, so it was obvious the supporters were enjoying the 'clawing'. It was still quite rubbish a number when you look at how many people lived in Leeds but at least it had gone up and not down.

It was only my personal opinion but I reckoned once Leeds started doing well at last, something about Don Revie changed. Whenever he talked to the papers or on the radio about a match, it was like he was a different person now and he'd rehearsed what he was going to say. It was the same stock answers each time, almost as if he was reading from a manual or something. John told me that Revie was so focused on doing his job that he often walked straight by people without even seeming to know they were there. In the business of football, he'd bought brilliantly again, with Johnny Giles from Manchester United. Not the fastest wing man by any chalk but he was consistent and had the ability to swing in great crosses when it mattered, so that the forwards could get on the end of them and in on goal. And Leeds even got past the FA Cup third round which was little short of a miracle. We lost at Everton in the fourth round replay though but the good thing is we gave it a good go and Everton knew they'd been in a proper battle. We'd drawn 1-1 at home and over 48,000 turned up to watch, probably the biggest crowd I'd ever seen up to then.

By the looks of it, the good things at Leeds United were being noticed. We'd even had the Beatles appearing in Leeds again, at the Odeon as well as the old tram shed Queens Hall. When a club is taken notice of in football then it's a sure sign that a team is succeeding, even if you don't exactly welcome other clubs trying to disturb the balance. Maurice Lindley had turned down the Hull City manager's job while Syd Owen declined Tottenham Hotspur's offer to be their coach. There were some bad moments in that season too, none worse than for Freddie Goodwin - Leeds were playing at Cardiff in the Cup early 1964. John Charles had left Italy to join them for £25,000 about a year before and Freddie Goodwin was marking him. I'm glad I didn't see it because I'm squeamish, the radio reports about it were bad enough. After colliding with Charlesy, Goodwin had broken his leg in three places. Now I didn't like laughing at people's misfortunes but I must admit, my grandma made me chuckle about Freddie's injury. Well not the injury itself but my grandma's reaction when she heard about it. She said, 'Surely he must have been in one place, how could he have broken his leg in three separate places?'

Jim Storrie got injured quite badly too, nine games into the season, so in came Ian Lawson and he played really well which surprised a few Leeds supporters. Me included because before, I didn't think he was up to much. The coaches must have really put him through his paces. That's what having a strong squad and quality replacements to fill in for injured players was all about. Ian Lawson worked his clogs off and scored some important goals. Even though he wasn't 'the finished article' as a striker, Don Revie always said that Lawson had played 'heroically' well. Whenever he got a game, Don Weston received similar praise. In February, two-thirds through the season, Don was able to use Harry's cheque-book again, this time signing England centre-forward Alan Peacock from Middlesbrough for over £50,000, with £5,000 payable if Leeds won promotion. He was just what we needed, brilliant in the air and one of the bravest players around, a proven scorer not scared of putting his head in where it hurt. He'd missed a few games down the years with injuries though, so they reckoned it was likely he'd miss games every now and then for us too. With his slim face and immaculate greased back hair, to me he looked distinguished like an RAF pilot or something. Plenty of people said that buying him was a gamble. I didn't think it was anything like one, it was more a signal to the other clubs that Leeds meant real business.

As well as Freddie in the centre of defence, we lost Jack Charlton because of injury for nearly half the League games, too. Even now I don't think I ever saw a better header of a football than 'the Giraffe' Jack Charlton – ever, not even Peacock - so his being out could definitely have damaged our chances of promotion. But all Don Revie would do was shuffle the defence around so that Norman Hunter, Paul Reaney or Willie Bell played in different positions at the back even though none of them were great in the air. They had other great qualities to make up for it, and if the rest of the team could stop opponents crossing the ball into our area, there wasn't an aerial threat to worry about. As always too, when someone has bad luck, someone else often gets the good luck. Our Paul Madeley for one.

He made his debut, in defence, in January 1964 versus Man City and played a handful of games afterwards. Before the game, he got a telegram delivered, it was a Good Luck message, from Don and all the staff at Elland Road. How nice was that? Paul did alright in the match, Ces and John had been watching him closely, but Ces told me afterwards that the coaches still felt there was plenty of room for improvement.

With me, it seemed I was getting bigger and taller every day, and the taller I got the more my grandma got hacked off with it. It cost her more cash all the time in food and clothes than she cared for - I never blamed her for having a go at me, but I bet she never cut down on her smoking. Besides, she seemed to stop complaining if ever Ces brought steak or a tray of eggs and gold top milk or even the odd bottle of sherry to help build me up. I hated that milk, it was too thick and always used to clag up my throat. I hated mixed-up sherry and eggs too for that matter but I treated it like it was medicine and good for me.

4 iv

On March 4th at the FA Cup sixth round replay between Sunderland and Manchester United, over a hundred people were injured when crowds smashed the closed stadium gates. There were two deaths at the match, though the fatalities were unrelated to the crush. The official attendance at Roker Park was 46,727 but reports stated that over seventy thousand in fact had got into the ground. By March 11th 1964, the number of Football League players suspended in the season reached 32, out of 42 who had been sent off.

Chapter 5: 1964/5 - The Dirty tag

5 i

Don Revie - 'They have obeyed my orders perfectly on and off the field. We have not always played popular football and the players have been denied gaining the flattering headlines that they would have, because of their style. They have never grumbled once.'

He had arranged a special gathering in the Astoria Ballroom in the north of Leeds. A party in fact, to celebrate at long last, the team's promotion back in to the top tier of English football, as Division Two champions. Champions, worthy champions, despite their scores of critics, many of whom had never actually seen the team play. The promotion had been won two weeks before the season's end in a clinical 3-0 away win at Swansea Town. Harry Reynolds arranged for a congratulatory telegram to be sent to Sunderland AFC, on winning promotion with Leeds. Sunderland were reputedly the stronger, more exciting team of the two, but it was Leeds who took the championship trophy. After the match the emotional Reynolds joined in the celebrations in the players' dressing room. There and then the chairman embraced his manager and offered him an improved, extended contract. Whether Revie planned to accept it was another matter but that night was not the time to discuss it; he believed he deserved better, and he wanted the added security of a new five year deal, not just three which is what was being offered. That three-year extension would remain unsigned throughout the summer of 1964.

The players' celebratory meal on the coach journey back from Swansea's Vetch Field was fish and chips, wrapped in newspaper, and champagne drunk from any vessel available.

Champagne, incidentally, purchased after the game, from various Swansea public houses, because the superstitious Revie believed that buying it before the match would have been inviting bad luck.

5 ii

Well they did it, God bless them, they bloody well did it, and with the highest number of points ever as well. We were back, Leeds United were back, in the First Division where we belonged, and we'd won the West Riding Senior Cup. St Ant's were doing great too.

Season 1963 - '64 Football Honours list.

League Division One winners - Liverpool, Runners up - Manchester United.

League Division Two winners - Leeds United, Runners up - Sunderland.

FA Cup winners - West Ham United, Runners up - Preston North End.

League Cup winners - Leicester City, Runners up - Stoke City.

European Cup winners - Inter Milan, Runners up - Real Madrid.

European Cup Winners Cup winners - Sporting Lisbon, Runners up - MTK (Budapest).

Inter-Cities Fairs Cup winners - Real Zaragoza, Runners up - Valencia.

Football Player of the Year - Bobby Moore, West Ham United.

European Footballer of the Year - Denis Law, Manchester United.

Leeds crowd average, home games = 29,950.

1964 = 11 years' wait for Clean Air.

The club even brought a record out to celebrate going up, with no less than Ronnie Hilton singing *The Leeds United Calypso* and the b-side *Elland Road Baht'at* which means 'without hat' according to Ces and my grandma. It didn't make sense to me but anyway, the record came in a great sleeve with little photographs of the Leeds players' faces on the front. It didn't trouble the singles charts but I bet most people in Leeds who had a record player will have bought a copy. Maybe some who didn't have a record player either. Me, I always preferred the Beatles, as well as the Rolling Stones even though it seemed you were supposed to only like one of them.

Nearly all of my records were ex-jukebox ones, with the middles sawn out, that the Old Peacock landlord Aitch passed on to me. I thought the songs on the Leeds single were great, even if I was biased. Also in August that year, Schofield's department store in town on the Headrow had a *zoo* on the roof, a genuine little zoo, with a baby elephant and a baby polar bear on show amongst other things. I'd have suspected flying pigs were there too if I hadn't seen the photographs for myself.

Earlier in the year, Syd Owen had been sent out by Revie with specific remit to monitor a player who had been recommended to the club. Owen was to assess the player's suitability and to summarise his playing abilities as well as his temperament, attitude and intelligence. He returned with a summary however, consisting not of a few hastily-written notes but as a thick dossier containing detailed information that even the player himself might not have been aware of! The Leeds United dossiers were born, a first for British and possibly even world football, and a vital resource for years to come for the club.

The dossiers would be ready each Thursday morning and as well as the players being briefed by Revie and the coaches, they would be trained specifically to counteract those strengths and exploit the weaknesses, with practice matches against the Leeds Reserves team. The Reserve team would be instructed to copy the playing style of the first team's next 'official' opponents. Revie's use of dossiers, his acute attention to detail and the team's fervent 'professionalism' would provide his critics with ammunition for ridicule for years. But he was convinced that he and the club would have the last laugh.

*

Sunderland would do better than us in Division One, all the experts in the papers and football magazines said so. In fact, according to some of them, we'd go straight back down again too, while the bookmakers had us at 33 to 1 against winning the League Championship or the FA Cup. I never had one ha'penny to rub *itself*, never mind two together but if I had've, I'd have been tempted by those odds, Leeds had the best young manager around and alongside him the best coaching staff. The 1964-'65 season would be the time Don Revie and co proved what everyone involved with Leeds already knew. And what the Leeds coaches didn't know about football on the whole and opposing teams wasn't worth knowing. Syd Owen, Les Cocker and Maurice Lindley would travel all over the country to compile those great big dossiers on other teams' players. The club got slagged off big time for the dossiers but they worked a bloody treat which was probably why they weren't popular outside of Leeds, because they gave the team (fair) advantage before a football was kicked. Ces always reckoned that the club took the dossiers so seriously that when The Don was briefing the squad in the Players' Lounge, they had a doorman on guard each time.

Even at fourteen I thought I knew a fair bit about football - with playing for St Anthony's plus Ces and John to listen to most days, I'd have had to be thick as pig dirt not to pick up some tactical nous. John especially knew what he was talking about, I heard he'd been a great centre-half in his time until knee injuries screwed his chances up. I wrote a little dossier myself, on the Leeds players, just for fun, with a certain new name added on.

GARY SPRAKE – 19, the best young goalkeeper around, brave, agile, hard-working. Wales international but needs to communicate more with defence. Suspect temperament - retaliates when opponents go in hard on him, needs to stop punching them or will get sent off or chinned or both. Nervous prior to games, vomits before nearly every match. Likes pop music and golf.

PAUL REANEY – 19, born Fulham, bred Leeds, strong, fast, reliable, quick to tackle, never gives up. Started as central defender until The Don moved him, PR likes to attack down the right-wing but crossing could be better. Should play for England. Billy Bremner's nickname for Reaney, Sprake and Hunter is 'Snap, Crackle and Pop' as the three are just about inseparable.

WILLIE BELL – 26, Scottish. Very consistent, can play left-back or left-half or across defence. Fit but not the fastest, tough tackler, experienced, good leader. Sweetest left foot in the business.

BILLY BREMNER – 21, Scottish, can do just about anything but needs to stop arguing. Never gives up, could be as inspirational as Bobby. Likes DIY, golf, family drives, bacon and eggs breakfast, and salads. And smoking (in secret). Will play for Scotland, no doubt about it.

JACK CHARLTON – 29, born Ashington. Lynchpin, superb header of the football, good leader of back four. Useful in attack at

corners and free-kicks. Deserves to play for England. Likes hunting, fishing and smoking (also in secret) and letting Billy take the blame when caught.
NORMAN HUNTER – 20, born Eighton Banks. Ever-present last season, 'Tarzan' no more! Tackles like a demon, good striker of ball - left-footed but right-handed. Not very strong in the air. Started as a forward but The Don changed that - solid partnership with Charlton ever since. Norman should also play for England.
JOHNNY GILES – 24, born Dublin. Eire international, took time to settle but is a highly intelligent player, excellent crosser and passer of the ball, and penalty taker. Good with both feet so can play on right or left. Makes playing football look easy, can look after himself.
DON WESTON – 28, born Mansfield, good reserve right-winger or attacker, joint-top scorer last season but he needs to put himself about more and get stuck in more.
ALAN PEACOCK – 26, born Middlesbrough, not a good injury record but has scored crucial goals and set plenty more up. Walter Winterbottom said he was the finest header of the football he'd seen. Came to Leeds just at the right time, might be the main reason we won promotion.
BOBBY COLLINS - 33, born Glasgow. Brilliant leader, superb footballer, a perfect captain, incredible will-to-win. Tackles harder than anyone, brilliant passer and shooter. Should be playing for the Jocks' national team, whatever age he is.
TERRY COOPER – 20, born Brotherton. Left-footed, fast, keen tackler, great crosser.
JIM STORRIE – 24, Scottish, excellent work-rate and enthusiasm. If scored as many chances as he created, would be in Scotland team too. Last season ruined by injury, the team missed him and his goals. Nicknames 'Diamond Jim' or the 'Laughing Cavalier.'
ALBERT JOHANNESON – 24, South African. Excellent season, joint leading scorer, top goals-creator. Would be near unbeatable if had as much confidence as ability. Needs to toughen up, couldn't tackle my grandma and opponents try to foul him nearly as much as they do Billy.
IAN LAWSON - 25, born Ormston. Good worker, skilful, a good back-up forward and has a decent scoring record. Scored some important goals to help promotion.

JIMMY GREENHOFF – 19, born Barnsley. Quick, very promising right-sided forward.
PAUL MADELEY – 19, born Leeds. Looks useful anywhere in defensive role. Excellent worker, good with both feet. Should play for England, recently called up by the England Youth team.
PETER LORIMER – 17, born Broughty Ferry, Scotland. Right-sided forward or midfield player, the finest striker of a football ever. Youngest ever Leeds first teamer. Should play for Scotland.
JIMMY O'ROURKE - just gone 14, very promising. Not the fastest but easily makes up for it by being quick-minded, very fit and an excellent passer of the football as well as a good tackler. Potential captain of Leeds and then England if there's any justice in the world of football.

Football's an easy game to play - put more goals in your opponents' net than they put in yours and you win. That's the way it crumbles, soccer-wise! That said, it can be just as complicated as chess too. Each player has a job to do and he has his own specific skills or moves. And just like in chess, every single man involved can win the match. A good boss works out what his players' strengths and weaknesses are, and the best position to play them in. He makes sure they stick to his plan and do what he's told them to do, make the moves that they're supposed to make. A good footballer doesn't try stuff beyond his range, he doesn't drift out of position, he sticks to what he knows. A *great* footballer thinks along the same lines as his manager and leads the players during the games, he does the manager's planning and leading on the pitch for him. Bobby Collins was always that player for Leeds.

From the time Passy invited me to play for St Anthony's, I was in at right-back, and because we hardly lost a game, I didn't miss one game in the first couple of seasons. Dead lucky, that was me, I never lost sight of the fact. I learnt from the other three in our back four how to mark and defend properly and I hardly ever got blamed for any goals conceded. If I did, it was soon forgotten about, no one picked on me or had too much of a go at me. 'Learn from it' was usually the call if any of us slipped up, that's what team spirit is all about.

In the Peacock on a Sunday lunch after our matches, the lads would buy me a pint or two of beer or bitter-shandy to quench the thirst. My grandma never cottoned on to why I was always sleepy on Sunday afternoons when I got back, she thought it was probably because I'd had a strenuous game. Goalkeeper 'Town Hall' Roy (he had massive hands like a big clock) always bought beers for anyone who wanted one, he was dead generous. He had a few bob about him, him being a milkman, and Passy was a builder, working on some of the new 'high-rise apartments' just outside the town centre. There was a postman too - Grimmy who played on the right, near me - but the rest worked for places like Moorhouse's jam factory on Old Lane or the copperworks or at the Infirmary. Bandy-legs Mick, our left-back, was a porter there, as was our left-winger Julian 'Breeze'. Anyone asking Passy about what job he was working on would get the same sort of answer, that he was building the next blot on the landscape or the skyscraper slums of the future. Whenever I looked up at such creations in various parts of Leeds, I'd hark back to what he said and think yeah, he got it pretty bloody spot on.

Aitch (Harry Hogg) would put some grub on for us, usually bread and dripping and slices of black pudding but sometimes chips and stew as well, if we were really lucky. Best of all was when he gave us a Sunday afty lock-in, serving us after hours - or 'between hours' more like, before opening up for the evening. There was a jukebox, even a television on a stand attached to the wall, plus a fantastic pinball machine called 'Bongo' which two players could play against each other on. I didn't have a clue how to play it at first but Aitch taught me. I never ever beat him but I grew to really love pinball. Music was non-stop in the Peacock too but the jukebox saw none of my dough, mainly because I hardly ever had any. Aitch made sure that the Leeds songs were permanent choices on the jukebox. I couldn't fault him, he was a great bloke.

East End Park Working Men's Club in east Leeds had their own football ground. It had changing rooms for the players and officials, a tiny wooden 'dug out' for each team at opposite sides of the pitch and even a little concrete terrace for spectators to stand on. Their team was in a higher league than us so we never played them but their ground was used as a neutral venue for plenty of matches. They played in FA Cup Qualifying rounds each year they were that good, and the facilities and pitch were so good that the club hosted a youth international game in this year due to our Elland Road pitch being waterlogged. Ces wasn't happy.

I got to play on the East End Park pitch two months after that international match, in May 1964, as St Anthony's got to the final of the West Yorkshire District Cup. My first ever final. We were playing against West Yorkshire Amateurs FC though really, us being in the final hadn't been that big a deal - we'd only played four games to get there, all against lower league sides. The final was on a Tuesday night and they had the presentations and stuff at the Working Men's Club after the match. It was odd the other team being called 'Amateurs' - because it was a well-known fact that some of their players got paid for playing. We weren't expected to win or even come close as they were in a higher and better league than us but we were going to give it a bloody good go - *all or nothing*. The church hired a single-decker bus for us to travel in and it was proper swish. Inside on each seat was a new green kit for all of us with our team numbers on the shirts in white plus on the left leg of the shorts.

Passy always made notes on how Leeds played, formations and tactics and stuff. By that I mean that he tried to emulate Don Revie when he could, so the formation he used for us was nearly always the same as Leeds'. In front of the goalie, he would use the 4-2-4 formation for attacking, and as soon as we needed to defend it would automatically change to 4-4-2 so that there would be four in midfield instead of two. Our wingers, a.k.a. the wing-left and wing-right - would drop into our half and help me and Mick, the full-backs. It was Grimmy who always played in front of me and he was like a whippet when he got going, racing up and down the flank. He couldn't tackle a wet paper bag but then again he hardly ever needed to, good positional sense is half the battle of defending. He helped me loads of times and course, I returned the favour whenever I could, passing to him or just whacking the ball down the line for him to belt after, a bit like watching a dog chasing a stick but with less slavver and barking.

With Leeds, whenever the full-backs Willie Bell or Paul Reaney went attacking down the flanks, whoever was in front would drop back to cover the gap. Usually that was Albert Johanneson on the left and Johnny Giles on the right. The same sort of thing happened when Jack or Norman went up into the attack, usually at set-pieces, though Norman often supported the left midfield if Leeds were chasing a game and Bobby Collins would slot in near the halfway line to keep an eye on opposing forwards. A main beauty of the way Leeds played was that you could always rely on Bobby to run around like a lunatic, except he knew exactly what he was doing, every second of the game, so he was the furthest thing from a lunatic really.

The West Yorkshire District Cup was silver - in colour only - and nearly as big as me. It was definitely as wide as me. It doesn't hurt now to say that we were soundly beaten 3-0 but when it actually happened, I was near inconsolable. We tried our hardest and that's sometimes all you can ask, we could feel proud at a 'noble effort' as the local paper called it. I don't know if there were any club scouts there or if anyone noticed, but I thought I had an alright game, except for their third goal coming from a cross from my side of the pitch. Anyway, it was all handshakes and well dones at the end but I know none of those paid Amateurs bought us drinks in the Club after, the skinflints. I really liked that Working Men's Club, there were loads of people in, all ages, and it was a good atmosphere, really noisy with people talking and laughing and even singing. It had billiards tables and a dartboard too, and a television fixed on a wall in the corner. It was all so smoky though, like our front room on a windy day. After we got the medals, Passy had us all stand in a circle. Then he thanked us one by one, shaking our hands, telling us how proud he was to be player-manager of this fine team. And then he told us all to give ourselves a big round of applause. The other lot must have thought we were barmy but we didn't give a damn. Flushing hot, not from embarrassment but pride, I had a lump in my throat the size of a cue ball.

Those people who knew that it was always my ambition to play for Leeds backed me all the way with encouragement and advice. The best 'off the pitch' advice came from Ces, while John and Passy were always on the ball, so to speak, helping me with matters *on* it. Having said that, it was Ces who gave me *the* best ever football tip - it was a list that he wrote down for me that summer. 'Read these, learn them off by heart and you can't go wrong,' and then he gave me The Leeds United 10 Commandments. Moses can't have felt as special as I did.

1 Push back the opposition and play your football in the opposing two thirds of the field.

2 Failure is no crime provided you have spent your last breath trying to avoid defeat.

3 Expect to win every 50/50 ball in a tackle and mean to win every 60/40 ball.

4 Never be afraid of shooting in the box.

5 Never get caught in possession.

6 Always look for a team-mate to pass to before looking for an opponent to beat.

7 Every pass that leads to a goal rates equal merit with the goal itself.

8 In a tight situation don't pass the buck by passing the ball to a team-mate no better placed than yourself.

9 When you make a foolish mistake don't look for an excuse, look for a way to retrieve the situation.

10 When things are going badly for you, don't hide.

I copied them down, intending to learn them later. And then Ces had me peeing myself laughing with his own versions of the commandments which he said were aimed at *life* rather than footie: *1 - The best form of defence is attack, so get to them before the bastards get to you. 2 - Always try your hardest at whatever you do, even the shitty jobs. 3 - If you're in the right then every argument or fight is yours to win, so never give in. 4 - Never stop being ambitious, whatever your age. 5 - Never let an opponent get one over on you. 6 - If under pressure and support is offered, accept that support. 7 - Team work is often as important as the end result, sometimes more. 8 - Don't dump your problems on others unless they can help. 9 - When you cock up, don't bugger off, stay and try to put your mistakes right! 10 - When life's shit, face up to it, keep fighting!*

And when I got home there was a letter waiting for me, official-looking from LUFC, asking me to go see them one specific July morning to trial for them.

5 iii

Two of the main guests on Revie's *This Is Your Life* were to become, from the 1964-'65 season, his most prominent, intense rivals in football. These three managers would be embroiled in numerous battles for superiority over the years, the matches between their teams often regarded as fantastic, unparalleled footballing epics. There would be disagreements and even arguments between the men over the years but, in essence, they would fight the fiercest *and* healthiest of rivalries, holding one another in true high regard: Matt Busby and Bill Shankly.

*

Don Revie, prior to the start of the 1964-'65 season, 'We have eight players who have never played in Division One but if we get away to a good start, there should be some surprises.' There definitely were surprises headed Leeds' way, before the new season even started.

Manchester United's Denis Law was a great player - 'the Lawman' - I liked his style. It would have been brilliant had he played for Leeds. And just before the start of that season, some jokers plastered fake Evening Post billboard posters around town saying 'Leeds Sign Law for £200k!' I was honestly never fooled, only because I didn't see the posters. I wondered who'd done it and why, was it some devious ploy by the board or even The Don himself, to sell more season tickets? I mentioned my suspicions to Ces. He told me to shut up being so daft.

Don Revie instructed his players to 'expand' their game, to play a faster, more direct, more attacking style of football. Even the defenders, in particular the two full-backs, Willie Bell and Paul Reaney, would be required to defend as normal but then support the attack as secondary wingers whenever possible. Revie intended for his team to thrill the crowds as well as win the matches. Admirable intentions which might well have paid off along with helping Revie's and the players' popularity reach new heights, were it not for the Football Association's surprising actions on the eve of the new season.

The *FA News* was a newsletter produced by the Association and sent to every football club registered in the Football League. An article in the August 1964 edition was to permanently damage the reputation of Revie's Leeds. The crucial text read '*... the Disciplinary Committee considered the list of clubs whose players had been cautioned or suspended, censured or fined during the 1963-'64 season. Ipswich Town and Sheffield United had the best record and Leeds United the worst...*' It is unlikely the report was intended to harm anyone in particular or to create antipathy against one club, but that is undoubtedly what it achieved. Leeds were marked men and from then on the bad reputation preceded them.

The statistics were misleading, the condemnation harsh and unjust. In fact, the Leeds first team had by no means the worst disciplinary record of all first teams in the Football League. Don Revie, furious, felt compelled to protest, his argument based on fact, not on hypocritical outrage - 'We did not have a single first team player sent off last season and we had only one suspended, Billy Bremner, after a series of cautions, which is a lot more than many clubs can say. The majority of our offences were committed by junior, second team players or boys. For that I blame the tension which permeated the whole club in the long and hard drive for promotion in a very hot Second Division. It was a time of very great strain for us all, and the club spirit being as wholehearted as it is from top to bottom.' He was not trying to canonise his players, but he knew injustice when he saw it: that report was a glaring example. He was above 'mud slinging' and name calling, but there were teams across the country who had first team players sent off during that season, including Manchester United who not only saw Denis Law sent off in a match against Aston Villa but also suspended for 28-days. In protest, Leeds wrote to the FA: '...the Dirty Team tag, which was blown up by the Press, could prejudice not only the general public but the officials controlling the game, and to put it mildly, could have an effect on the subconscious approach of both referee and linesmen, to say nothing of the minds of spectators, especially some types who are watching football today. It could lead to some very unsavoury incidents.'

Everton were hosting Leeds in the League on Saturday November 7th. Goodison Park was described by Jack Charlton as the worst ground he ever played at, and the commonplace press reports telling of Everton fan-violence and vandalism supported the view. The match started off badly, Everton's Sandy Brown was sent off in the fourth minute for swinging a punch John Giles' way after a heavy challenge from the Leeds man. Gary Sprake was pelted with coins throughout the tie whilst the rest of the team had fruit, cushions, toilet rolls and other missiles aimed at them from the home fans. Albert Johanneson was frequently spat at by home fans too. A few minutes before half time, in what was thought by most spectators to be an accidental collision between Willie Bell and Derek Temple, both players ended up laid out on the turf. Bell was carried off the pitch by Les Cocker and Giles, while Temple had to be stretchered off. Both teams' trainers, as well as the referee Ken Stokes and one of his linesmen, were struck by more objects from the crowd. Referee Ken Stokes, 'like an exasperated school teacher', feared a pitch invasion and so decided to leave the pitch. The teams followed him minutes later. An announcement came over the stadium tannoy that the game would be restarted in five minutes but if objects continued to be thrown onto the pitch, it would be officially abandoned. It was a serious promise. The withdrawal of the teams was said to be the first such instance in English football history. Objects did continue to land on the pitch but the game was eventually played in full. Amidst the chaos and the rancour - and 'Dirty Leeds' chants from the crowd - the unwanted visitors forced a 1-0 win with a good Bell header after a precise free-kick from ex-Everton man Collins. Everton 'won' the fouls tally, 19 to 12.

After the match, Leeds made a swift getaway from the stadium, though their bus was hit by more missiles and a metal dustbin lid which smashed through the back window. Jack Charlton threw it back from whence it came. Mounted police were kept busy around the stadium and local area while the unfortunate referee and linesmen were holed up in their room for hours so as to avoid Everton fans looking for someone to blame and to punish for the loss.

Don Revie would bridle with indignation whenever a Leeds man was criticised, no matter how trivially, so his reaction to the Everton mêlée was rather predictable. Such over-protectiveness impressed few people outside of Leeds, and the media hardly seemed enamoured with him anyway. If the media is not on your side, the public finds it hard to be sympathetic too, even when you are in the right. 'After the incidents of this weekend I must defend my club and my players after all the bad things that had been said about them. I feel it started last season when we were in the Second Division when we were tagged as a hard, dirty side by the press. I am disgusted by these attacks on us and I ask that we be judged fairly and squarely on each match and not on this unfair tag that we have got ... we were wrongly labelled by the Press and then by the Football Association. The result has been that opposing teams have gone on to the field keyed up, expecting a hard match. I think the number of opposing players sent off in our matches proves it.'

League Division One table (top), up to 7th November, 1964

1 Man. Utd	Played 17	Points 26
2 Chelsea	Played 17	Points 25
3 Leeds Utd	Played 16	Points 22
4 Nottm. F.	Played 17	Points 22

Soon after the 'Battle of Goodison', the FA and the FL set up a special committee to investigate misbehaviour by players and spectators. That same month, the FA suspended Johnny Haynes for fourteen days for alleged misconduct during and after Fulham's League match with Sunderland a month before. In December, they sent a memorandum to all clubs warning players, managers, directors and spectators that any continuation of recent misconduct would result in tougher disciplinary measures. Days later, Denis Law, sent off in November at Blackpool for using bad language to the referee, was again suspended for 28 days and fined £50, and Sandy Brown was banned for two weeks and Everton fined £250 by the FA for their supporters' misbehaviour at the

Leeds match. And despite near hysterical press reaction to incidents during that match involving Revie's men, Leeds were not punished at all.

Jack Charlton was a regular in the Leeds first eleven now, and Don Revie perhaps imposed more influence on him than he realised. By way of superstitions. Charlton insisted he should always be the last Leeds player out on to the pitch - and the whole eleven would only change order if they lost a game - while he and Norman Hunter would only leave the dressing room when they had completed at least twenty consecutive headers between them. Whilst Leeds had established themselves as a team to be reckoned with, Elland Road had been a more unsettled camp than the team's performances suggested due to an invitation from Sunderland to Revie to become their manager. And to the dismay of Leeds fans and employees, the local press reported that he had accepted the Roker Park job. The same week, chairman Harry Reynolds had been involved in a car accident and was being treated in hospital for head and facial injuries. Revie visited him, as a friend would naturally do, but Reynolds was more concerned about his manager's intentions than his own welfare. Revie was overheard advising Reynolds that his grievances and leanings towards Sunderland were not based on money but more the lack of recognition and appreciation he received from the club board. From his hospital bed, Reynolds swiftly arranged for a media statement to be issued. 'It is not our policy to release vital first class assets. Only the best will do for United' and he promptly made an improved contract offer to Revie.

Revie however did not sign that new contract straight away, and in addition to Sunderland, Sheffield Wednesday were considering an approach for his services while Manchester City watched the situation closely too. As his management skills were increasingly coveted, all the better his bargaining position at Leeds became. Reynolds wanted to give Revie practically whatever he desired, but Revie intended serving the other directors a taste of their own medicine. He finally accepted the improved offer a few months later, stating that he would have been a hypocrite to leave, given the need, as he put it, for more loyalty in football. His procrastination though provided critics with more (perceived) evidence, that he was greedy.

*

Early in the new year of 1965, ten professional and former professional footballers were found guilty of conspiracy to defraud by fixing football matches. All were sent to prison. In Division One, the most consistent teams were Leeds, Chelsea and Manchester United. And Leeds and Manchester United were drawn to play each other in the FA Cup semi-final too, in late March. Revie's Leeds' first season in the top tier had seen them shake up the 'big boys' and establish themselves as strong contenders for honours. And with Chelsea faltering, their chances of a first League title win improved, it becoming effectively a two-horse race.

In the history of football, Yorkshire-Lancashire 'derby' games are frequently tough and hard-fought affairs, devoid of much goodwill. Possibly devoid of good play and good behaviour, too. Matt Busby was wary of the Leeds team's qualities but seemed of the view that they took professionalism and gamesmanship too far. He would perhaps acknowledge them as a better-organized side than his own, and that Revie might be a more 'modern thinking' manager, but nothing more; had he studied more closely his own club's disciplinary record and certain of his own players' behaviour, he might have felt more inclined to improve his opinion.

Sheffield Wednesday's Hillsborough, 27th March 1965, the FA Cup semi-final between Leeds and Manchester United. After the teams had met at Old Trafford late 1964, the football world should have known what to expect - it had been a bad-tempered match, with Leeds earning a hard-earned and gritty 1-0 win thanks to a Bobby Collins strike. In the tunnel before that kick off, that same Leeds player made his intentions for the night painfully clear. As the teams lined up to enter the arena, George Best felt a sharp twinge in his right calf. Someone had kicked him, and not gently. It was Bobby Collins giving him a 'dig', to intimidate him. 'And that's just for starters, Bestie,' he said. He didn't have the last word though. The man normally assigned to protect Best was hard-tackling midfielder Nobby Stiles, the short-sighted, false teeth wearing, soon to be England international. During the match he gained some revenge on behalf of Best by slamming Collins into a perimeter wall after a touch-line tussle for the ball. 'Every time you come down our right-hand side and kick George, you filthy bastard, I'm going to frigging well hit you like that, only harder!' Surprisingly perhaps, that match was not entirely without good humour - at one stage Billy Bremner had fouled Best and the referee had called Bremner over for a talking to. 'That tackle was late,' he said to the player. Bremner, arms out, innocence personified - 'I got there as quickly as I could.'

The FA Cup semi-final was ugly, mundane and hostile, played on a muddy pitch, officiated by a lenient referee. No goals, few scoring chances, many fouls, two bookings, a couple of injuries and no shortage of rancour. Reporters criticised the referee for being too soft with the players - especially Manchester United's - complaining that both sides had seemed more intent on kicking each other than the football itself. Stiles appeared to assault Albert Johanneson virtually all afternoon while Jack Charlton and Denis Law, and Billy Bremner and Pat Crerand, were embroiled in various confrontations, while Law was booked yet had his shirt practically ripped off his back during the match. A replay was needed, which Johanneson would miss due to injury.

Even though the Hillsborough tie contained 24 fouls committed by his own team (plus the two bookings) compared to 10 fouls by Leeds, Matt Busby's dryly bullish team-talk before the Wednesday night replay at Nottingham Forest's City Ground was something to be admired. His assistant Jimmy Murphy had handed him the Leeds team-sheet and Busby read it out, adding in his own remarks: 'Gary Sprake in goal - couldn't catch cold. On his day, a nasty piece of work. Don't let it be his day. Right-back Paul Reaney - dirty bastard, no skill. Left-half Terry Cooper - even dirtier bastard, likes going forward, let him. Right-half Johnny Giles - dirty little bastard and he hates us. Centre-half Jack Charlton - dirty big bastard, a clumsy lump. Norman Hunter - no self-control, play with him George, watch him get himself sent off... And left-half, wee Billy Bremner, a good Scottish boy.'

5 iv

I had to watch the Leeds-Man United replay on the Peacock's TV set which was miles better than ours, which looked like my grandma had bought before television had been invented. I'd been desperate to go to Sheffield and then the midweek replay in Nottingham, but my grandma wouldn't let me go to either game. It wasn't just about the cost, she didn't think it would be safe as there had been some trouble before, on and off the pitch at Hillsborough. I didn't moan but I was hardly chuffed about it all either - I mean, I wasn't even fifteen yet and I'd never even seen or smelled trouble at Leeds matches. My never having been away before didn't really help my cause either but she knew I was dead disappointed, she could see it in my face, so she promised to let me go to Wembley if we got there.

The Leeds team wasn't as fast or as fancy as theirs but football was a team game and it took more than a load of footballing Fred Astaires to win matches. I had a good feeling about the replay, I thought we'd beat them, especially if Paul Reaney could keep George Best shackled again. The FA Cup was always great for the underdogs and that's exactly what we were at the time, I don't think teams took us seriously enough. More fool them. Inside the pub it was standing room only, the seats and stools were all taken early on. There were hardly ever any football matches shown 'live' on television so this was a massive occasion. Well, a more massive occasion for Leeds. So I got crafty and asked this old couple from the Heaths, sitting on the comfy back-rest seats under the main window, if I could use the ledge behind them. As long as I didn't get over excited and kick him or his missus in the head then I'd be alright to, the chap said.

The print of my bottom cheeks could still be there in the dust on that ledge, the Peacock never saw much dusting or cleaning in its time. I had a perfect view through the tobacco fog though I got pins and needles in my legs and my backside. It was so crowded that the frosted windows were steamed up and condensation ran down the glass into the dust. My hands were filthy and I had a long damp patch down my right leg by the end of the night. Whenever I watched Leeds play, I was always totally biased, like I had white-tinted spectacles on. And tonight it was extreme, I felt sick with it and the nerves. The weather at Nottingham was a lot drier than Hillsborough so the pitch was in much better nick. I was a bit worried that that would suit Manchester, because they supposedly played a shorter, quicker passing game than us. Both teams were in the same colours as Saturday - us in the lovely all white and them in red shirts, white shorts and socks. Our players had black armbands on too, because the Leeds president Lord Harewood's mother, the Countess of Harewood, had died of a heart attack a couple of days before. I don't know if he attended the match, poor chap.

Most of the first half was Man United on the attack but our defence stood solid and Gary Sprake was his usual self. He had a flourishing reputation and on this night he definitely had to work hard for his pay, making good saves from Law, Herd, Best and Bobby Charlton. Our back *five* really did look like a wall, hard as brick to break through. Jack was winning everything in the air and probably everything on the ground too, *and* he hit the Reds' crossbar with a header. Alan Peacock went close a couple of times for us as well, twice just failing to connect with low crosses from Jim Storrie. The screen showed The Don and Les Cocker in the Leeds dugout. Les was that agitated he couldn't keep still or quiet while Don, I'll never forget the picture, with his legs crossed and him chewing his fingernails, looked scared stiff. They made me feel even more nervous, my stomach felt like it was doing somersaults. Half-time, 0-0. The chap from the Heaths tried to whisper up to me, 'It's closer than a stray dog's bollocks in winter!' but he didn't whisper quietly enough and I laughed even harder when his missus gave him a clout for being so crude.

The second half carried on much like the first - dead tight and cagey, like two boxers probing, sussing each other out, looking for the best point to attack. They were plugging away at each other all the time, looking for weaknesses in the opponent's defence and then trying to exploit it. But neither team looked like they had any real weaknesses, that was the problem. It looked like the game could go on forever, we were all on the edge of our seats, or window sills, it was that tense. And then, with about twenty minutes to go, the old chap tapped me on the leg to tell me something, above all the noise. 'Don Revie's done summat, look, look how he's told Johnny Giles to move into the middle and take Bremner's place. Jim Storrie's switched from inside-forward to Giles' place on the right wing so Bremner's playing up front now, in Jim's place. That'll confuse the Manchester defenders, you just watch kid.' And for those last twenty or so minutes, he was b right and all, we did most of the attacking now, as the final whistle got closer. We had five corners in a row in the last few minutes and even on the television you could hear the Man United fans whistling because they were so worried. The Reds managed to defend all those corners though so it stayed 0-0 and had been a great battle, real nerve-racking stuff. It looked like there'd be another half hour extra time and if it still stayed evens then there'd need to be another replay as well. But then Nobby Stiles gave away a free-kick for obstruction on John Giles in their half, just inside the centre circle.

There couldn't have been much more than a minute left, not that it stopped the Man United fans whistling, more of them by every second, trying to persuade the referee to blow his own whistle for full time. Meantime, we had that free-kick, in the middle of the pitch. Maybe the Man U crowd sensed something was going to happen, because their whistling got even louder as Giles got ready to take the kick. I couldn't hear the television commentator so I made my own up...

With number 7 on his back, John Giles sets himself to take the kick, the black armband at an angle, prominent above his left elbow. He's over forty yards away from the goal. He steps backwards, away from the ball, five, six, seven steps, eyes fixed on the opposition's penalty area. He's scanning, he's planning - scanning the scene and planning the attack. He's trying to secretly tell a team-mate where he intends hitting the ball. He takes a step and then a funny little skip towards the ball but then stops, like he's changed his mind, like there's been a breakdown in communication. And then it's back on again and Giles speeds to the ball - with a swift, sharp right-footed strike the ball launches into the air. A white dot floats across the top of the television screen, travelling through the floodlit night sky diagonally towards the Manchester penalty area, crowded with fourteen or fifteen men. It looks like Giles has over-hit the lob and it will just float over all the players' heads and harmlessly out for a goal-kick. Manchester United's goalkeeper, Dunne, seems to think the same, that it will bounce once and then out. All the nearby players seem to be of the same opinion too, reacting in slow-motion or not at all, just standing and watching the ball flying in the air in their direction. All except for one man, with a dark blue number 4 on the back of his white shirt. All except for a small, curly, sandy-haired man wearing the white of Leeds United - the white of an ordinary past but an extraordinary future. That one man keeps moving, keeps watching and keeps calculating. He tracks and anticipates the ball as it drops drops drops towards the six-yard box. He steals his way unseen through the crowded area. The football will be just too far in front for him to reach it, *just too far*, and will bounce safely out and into the jammed terrace of spectators. This small, curly, ginger-haired man though, is not ready to give up the cause. He never is. Instead, he 'gambles', because he has nothing to lose. One Manchester defender notices but he's too late, the ball is descending, approaching, homing in, too quickly for him. But possibly not for Billy Bremner. He is nearly there now, it is six five four feet off the ground. Three feet off the ground. Three, when Billy Bremner launches himself, amazingly, *backwards* somehow, twisting his body in mid-air, stretching, straining to meet the ball. With his back to the goal and his head facing upwards, his body near horizontal, mid-air, he connects to head the ball, firmly, with his left temple. Dunne moves but he is too late. The ball veers towards the goal and flies over the 'keeper's head and under the crossbar.

Amazed, disbelieving, to see the ball in the goalnet, Manchester United defenders wave their hands to protest that Bremner was offside, but no one, correctly, takes any notice of them. Blurs of white race by the Manchester players, chasing Bremner to congratulate and celebrate with their winning goal scorer. Although there are pockets of delighted Leeds fans scattered in the stand behind the goal, Bremner sprints towards the left corner where the closest Leeds crowd is. Nearly all of his team-mates follow him, and a couple of young supporters climb over the wall to join in the celebrations too. Further down the touchline, nearer the television cameraman, sheepskin coat clad Don Revie grabs sidekick Les Cocker in a tight embrace, lifting him up and twirling him round as if they're in a playground. They laugh and shout with triumphant glee, almost disbelieving - they have finally done it, they have beaten Matt Busby and Manchester United in the Cup. And now they are in the FA Cup final! I'm standing on the window ledge, fists clenched, arms up in the air, tears running down my face, and I'm dancing while the chap and his wife hug and laugh and get ready to catch me if I fall.

When the Leeds team got back into their changing room, there was even more good news waiting for Jack Charlton - he'd been picked for the next England team. The first person he wanted to tell was his brother Bobby, so off he ran, to Man United's changing room, to give him the good news. There, he was congratulated though hardly in the warmest of fashions, and then told to get out of the *losing semi-finalists'* dressing room, *definitely* not in the warmest of fashions. The day after, The Don was interviewed - 'My proudest moment in my career was when the whistle went last night and Leeds United were in the final. Manchester played some scintillating football also. I thought we were going to crack and we were certainly lucky not to go two down but we came through it and according to my instructions Jim Storrie switched to the right wing and Billy Bremner moved into the attack. It might not have come off but it did. What pleased me most was that Leeds kept their heads.'

Ces told me that after the match, our team bus had been 'ambushed' by Mancunian fans, with stones, bricks, bottles. No one was hurt though. The Leeds players stayed in a plush hotel in Grantham overnight - Bobby Collins said that the players had such a terrific night there and that he had to carry his room-mate to bed he was that drunk. It isn't certain who that player was but most bets seemed to be on Terry Cooper!

5 v

Prior to their first ever FA Cup final in May 1965, Leeds had the small matter of the League Championship title to settle too, a long arduous season entered its final week with Leeds and Manchester United still vying for first place. On the night of Monday 26th April, Leeds' last League game was away to already relegated Birmingham City. It had been a bad season for the city of Birmingham, as Aston Villa would accompany them in the drop to Division Two. Manchester United, with a game in hand and a superior goal average and just one point behind Leeds, were at home to Arsenal, while two nights later their final game was away to Aston Villa. So, if Leeds were to win their first ever title then they would have to beat Birmingham and hope Manchester United dropped points. Their chances of success were regarded as very slim.

Leeds' title winning hopes waned severely with defeats to Manchester United and Sheffield Wednesday in mid-April, and that Birmingham match saw their challenge all but extinguished with a 3-3 draw. Earning that one point had been some achievement in itself as they had been three goals down at one stage. Birmingham had been a man down early on, due to a shoulder injury to winger Jackson in the opening minutes, but the ten men were undeterred and fought like *they* were the ones chasing silverware. 1-0 at half time, within a few minutes of the second half they were 3-0 up.

Years later, this match would be central to more attempted match-fixing allegations against Don Revie. Allegations again, wholly unsubstantiated, while interesting reports from the match suggested that Revie had conceded defeat some time before the final whistle of the game, instructing his players to conserve their energies for the FA Cup final. With Arsenal losing 3-1 at Old Trafford, Leeds' draw meant they could only finish top if Aston Villa beat Manchester United by a phenomenal scoreline on the Wednesday night.

Top of Division One, with one game remaining:

1 Man. Utd. Played 41 Points = 61 Goal Average = 2.38

2 Leeds Utd. Played 42 Points = 61 Goal Average = 1.60

Revie knew miracles only happened in the Bible and so, shortly after their Monday matches had finished, he contacted Matt Busby to congratulate him and his team on being worthy League Champions. Leeds' 61 points was a record tally for runners-up.

After Leeds' hard slog of five League games in ten days, the Cup final was due on May 1st, just five days after the Birmingham match. The Leeds players might have benefited more had they been allowed to relax at home for a couple of days rather than spend all week at the team hotel in Selsdon Park near Croydon. Under normal circumstances, the players abided by whatever arrangements the club decreed, and whatever Revie said, it went, as if a law. But this week the players were unimpressed by the idea of spending so much time together. Even with Revie's close friend Herbert Warner on hand - a jeweller and the unofficial club court jester - to try and keep them entertained, there was unrest in the ranks. Even with the training in the daytime only gentle and the analysis of dossiers on the Liverpool team not too arduous, boredom set in. Bingo, dominoes, cards, carpet bowls, indoor golf, billiards and snooker and the like - and in-house gambling of course - could not keep them satisfied for long.

The day before the final, the squad exercised and were put through light running sessions and drills in the grounds of the hotel. Five-a-side matches were played too. Already notoriously competitive, during one such contest, Englishman Norman Hunter struck a volley which inadvertently smacked Scotsman Bobby Collins full in the face, causing his nose to bleed. After a brief pause to check he was okay, the game was restarted and everything seemed as normal. For a few seconds at least, until Hunter received the ball again and hadn't noticed Collins careering towards him, revenge on his mind. Fortunately, Jack Charlton did see and so shouted a warning to his compatriot of the impending peril. Collins launched himself at Hunter and hit him waist-high with both feet, the two players ending up on the ground, Collins on top aiming punches at his innocent prey. Charlton managed to drag him away but then realized he needed help too as the volatile Collins was wanting to fight him now. 'Come on Bobby, calm down, we've got a Cup final tomorrow!'

5 vi

Even the secretary of the St Anthony's team got a ticket. The secretary, for God's sake. Apparently, secretaries at possibly every local league team in England could get them if they applied to the FA. Normal people though had more chance of finding a pot of rocking horse manure at the end of a rainbow. Even Ces couldn't help.

My grandma said sorry to me even though it wasn't her fault. *She* wasn't to blame for me not being able to get a Cup Final ticket, and she'd have paid for one for me if she could have. But I didn't want her paying more than she could afford and I told her that, it wouldn't be right. I knew what would happen on the morning of the Cup final, so I stayed in bed and purposely missed running for a day - I didn't want to see what I was missing out on. Dead early, even from my bedroom I could hear all the coach and car engines at Elland Road with all the Leeds fans getting ready to travel down to Wembley. Sounded like military manoeuvres. Genuinely, I felt sick with jealousy, and I can't have been the only one, loads of real supporters will have had to miss out. It wasn't fair on us who followed the team through good and bad times, especially people like me who lived so close to the Leeds ground we had to put up with all sorts of commotions at home games. The papers said that tickets normally a couple of quid at the most were going for fifteen times that on the black market. Two quid was more than enough as it was. My grandma made us steak and kidney pie specially for dinner. She'd already shocked me by asking Aitch if we, *we,* would be alright watching the match in the Peacock. He only went and put a cardboard RESERVED sign on a couple of seats for us and all. Maybe I should have asked for one on my window ledge spot again.

Some of the stuff Ces found in the rubbish bins of the Leeds United offices was amazing. And just like any normal Yorkshireman, he hated seeing things go to waste. One morning he called me into the ground staff's room to show me papers he'd found, sheets of hand-written notes, about specific opposing teams. They were part of one the dossiers compiled by the Leeds coaches. I did my best to learn those notes so I could write them down when I got home. They were nothing like I would have imagined them to be - I expected more sort of 'scientific' language but those I saw were more like a bloke talking in the pub or something, just commonsense really. Having said that, commonsense being talked in a pub isn't that common at all, thinking about it.

Notes on Liverpool

Shankly's tactics try to cover deficiencies in his team which we should be able to exploit.

TOMMY LAWRENCE - Goalkeeper, Scottish, nicknamed the Flying Pig as quite stocky and likes to throw himself around his area. Quite short for a keeper at 5' 11'' so we need a man near to him at corners and for crosses whenever possible, in case he 'flaps' or drops a cross. Has a very good understanding with Ron Yeats at

C/H and the other defenders, he is very quick off his line if a through ball beats the flat back four line of defence. He is brave, safe and agile. The Liverpool defence play square with the two full-backs Lawler and Byrne keeping close to the wingers. Passes into the areas behind the full-backs could be productive.

CHRIS LAWLER - Right-back, nicknamed The Ghost as has a knack of collecting the ball in defence, passing it forward and then taking the return pass up front to score. He does not seem the fastest full-back and he doesn't seem too keen on 'overlapping' but when he does go forward, his positioning and passing is good. We need to keep him occupied and therefore stop him advancing. Plain, simple style, no frills or tricks, he has a good right foot. Gives the impression he is very relaxed but we should not be misled. Both Liverpool full-backs lack pace so our wingers must seek the ball behind them or take them by counter-attack.

GERRY BYRNE - Left-back, nicknamed The Crunch, believed to be the toughest player in the team. Loves to tackle, hard and usually fair, the ball or player might get by him, but not both at the same time. The full-backs don't normally look to attack but this lad has his moments of marauding runs. As said before, both their full-backs lack pace so we should be looking to attack them and keep them busy.

TOMMY SMITH - defender, not much information on this lad, quite new to the team. A good tackler, quite fast, good worker, not scared to get stuck in.

RON YEATS - Centre-half, Scottish, The Colossus - 6' 2". Captain. The Liverpool team depend a great deal on him. He sticks like glue to the C/F and clears his lines decisively at all times. Very good in the air and reasonably fast for a big man but is beatable by pace and quick passes on the ground. For their corner kicks he comes into the area, taking up a very wide position to enable himself to have room to adjust to the direction of the kick. When in attack, he moves around the area quite a bit, 'showing' for the ball.

WILLIE STEVENSON - Left midfield, Scottish, 'elegant' player, thin but stronger and fitter than he looks. A good range of passing ability and a decent scoring record. Should be easy enough to keep quiet though he works hard.

GEOFF STRONG - inside-forward or left-back. Versatile, left-footed, works very hard for the team. Unselfish, unspectacular utility player, his strength seems to lie in that he will run all day and follow orders. Is the likely replacement for the injured Gordon Milne in midfield.

IAN CALLAGHAN - Right-wing, good crosser of the ball - not the fastest but is tricky and has good ability to swing crosses in from most angles. One Liverpool wing half-back stays back while the other goes in attack (even if an opportunity arises to move into a position of attack himself). Callaghan often takes over the ball from a team-mate carrying the ball in his direction. He then proceeds to strike through the inside-right towards goal, but he has difficulty because he prefers to not use his left foot.

ROGER HUNT - Centre-forward, dangerous but also unselfish and a good provider. Runs well off the ball, pulling defenders away to make space for any team-mate advancing with ball. Quick, strong, skilful, powerful shot, good with both feet. Feeds off St John well, always tries to be the most advance placed player with St John behind him. Likes to turn quickly with ball at his feet and get a shot in on goal. We need a man on him at all times.

IAN ST JOHN - Centre-forward, Scottish, 'The Saint' - good goal-scorer and dangerous partnership w/Hunt. 5' 7" but very good in the air. He is the 'bludgeon' of the two strikers while Hunt is the 'rapier'. Hard-running, non-stop feisty battler, few moments of peace with him, needs watching closely at all times. Likes to play close behind Hunt and feed the ball into him with head or feet. Good skill on the ball, not easy to 'read'.

PETER THOMPSON - Left-winger, less direct than Callaghan but dangerous supplier for the forwards and can score spectacular goals too. Stays back if Callaghan goes forward, and vice-versa. Has speed and good ball control and usually takes on anybody in front of him. Sometimes too keen to take a player on when in fact it is easier to cross the ball in but if given too much space he will cause us problems. Needs to be closed down. Thompson, though on the left wing, tends to go inside or across the front of his full-back because he favours his right foot.

*

You could hardly hear the television commentator, the crowd was so noisy, it reached nearly deafening as everyone cheered the teams emerging out of the Wembley tunnel. We're all cheering in the pub as well, and it's one of those hairs sticking up on the back of my neck times again. Out the teams come, on to the pitch, side by side, Indian-file. It's a long walk. The Don leads Leeds out - he's in a sharp dark suit and tie and white shirt, looking dead respectable. *Respectful* too. The Leeds players look immaculate in the white shorts and socks (except for Bobby whose socks seem more cream coloured) and white tracksuit jackets which look fantastic. Bill Shankly and his lot are on the right. He's got a lighter coloured suit on and the Liverpool players are obviously in all-red with red tracksuit jackets on. Everyone knows Liverpool are red and if they didn't know we were white, they would do after today, all around the world. So it's all-white versus all-dark and with Bobby next to Ron Yeats, it's like David versus Goliath as well. I'm hoping this afternoon turns out just like that did.

Don Revie, walking in front, smiling at the camera and looking proud as a peacock. Then captain Bobby Collins, small, looking grim and tough, with his 'lucky' socks on, blond 'keeper Gary Sprake, tall and broad, like a warrior nearly. Dark, black-haired Paul Reaney, and slim and high Alan Peacock, lean Norman Hunter, all nearly as tall as Sprakey, Albert Johanneson and Johnny Giles both nearly as small as Bobby, gritty Willie Bell and Jim Storrie looking more like American squaddies to me, and then Billy Bremner bouncing an orange football on his head likes he's just got it for Christmas. At the back, as always, big, fair-haired Jack - serious, determined, cool. Every one of them looks deadly sombre as if they're walking into a gladiator arena. And suddenly I feel similar, because they *are* walking into a gladiator arena. I'm nervous as hell, I've gone cold and my hands are shaking a bit and so is the back of my neck which is weird and not a nice feeling.

Quite a while after the final, various info came out about both teams' and managers' preparations for it. Bill Shankly had ordered his players to enjoy the occasion as much as possible, make it a time to remember. Before kick-off, they had visits in their north-facing Wembley dressing room from two famous supporters. Jokes were told and songs were sung, to relax the players. Popular comedian Jimmy Tarbuck and famous crooner Frankie Vaughan led the pre-match entertainment. Vaughan had actually lived in Leeds when younger, the bloody traitor. I doubted there was ever a more relaxed Wembley dressing room in FA Cup final history than Liverpool's that day, regardless of the quality of the jokes or songs. Meanwhile, in the Leeds dressing room, our players weren't entertained but more or less re-briefed on tactics and formations. And as they sat and listened to Don Revie's instructions, it was claimed that Shankly stood outside the door, sneakily listening in. He then told his own team that Revie had those 'poor buggers of Leeds locked up' and that they were crapping themselves. Despite losing 4-2 at Elland Road nine months ago, Shankly's only worry was the threat posed by Leeds at set-pieces. So persuasive was Shankly, his players all *expected* to win the Cup that afternoon.

Wembley's pitch was huge, the grass was long and the conditions very damp, so Shankly told his players to not race after every ball or try and cover every blade of grass but to conserve their energies, let the football do the work and leave our lads to do all the stamina-sapping leg graft. And to cause a bit of confusion he named Tommy Smith at number 10, the shirt normally worn by an attacker. Smith would play in a defensive role as usual.

Bobby Collins had admitted before to team-mates that Wembley was a jinx ground for him and that he never played well there. And in the tunnel, before kick off, Shankly reportedly asked him how he was feeling and Collins answered that he felt 'awful.' Liverpool intended playing a simple game - short passes, keeping possession for as long as they could, keeping calm and playing tightly as a unit. It rained during the game too, and on the sideline both clubs' men sat huddled almost together on the rows of benches, vainly trying to keep dry. High in the main stand, Queen Elizabeth, wore red. That fact won't have escaped Don Revie's notice, it didn't take much to alarm his superstitious nature. Leeds chairman Harry Reynolds had the honour of sitting next to the Queen, and he was so nervous about the match that he had been granted special dispensation to smoke cigarettes while in her company. Her husband, Prince Philip, the Duke of Edinburgh, was on the pitch beforehand to meet the teams and the match officials. He commented on Collins' socks which were an odd yellowy colour compared to the rest of our lads' pristine white ones. Collins informed him that they were his lucky woollen socks, which he had worn all season, and which his manager insisted he wore today, too. Just before the match was to start, Billy Bremner rushed across to The Don to pass him his wedding ring, another Leeds superstition which he had almost forgotten.

I knew that before the big day, Revie had told the players, 'Don't make the occasion bigger than you' but it definitely didn't seem to register. It was our first ever FA Cup final appearance but Liverpool's third, and it turned out to be third time lucky for them, beating us 2-1, after extra time. It meant, in our first season back in Division One, we'd come second in the League and second in the FA Cup. Not bad for a team of vicious cloggers and no-hopers tipped to be relegated straight back down. Liverpool had been the better team in a poor match, they looked more composed, more confident and tighter organized than us. And their tactics definitely worked better than ours. For various reasons, we had players who just couldn't seem to turn it on. It was a crying shame, and I did actually have a few tears leaking from my eyes at the end of the match. Our performance had been so frustrating, half of the Leeds players looked scared. God forbid, they looked like they wanted to be somewhere else, anywhere else, like they had stage fright. Only Billy Bremner, Norman Hunter, Gary Sprake especially and Paul Reaney played anywhere near their usual standards. Albert Johanneson and Jim Storrie were the biggest disappointments for us, and Bobby Collins wasn't far behind them, much as I hated saying that. He wasn't injured or anything, I couldn't work out what was wrong with him, he just didn't seem right, he wasn't his normal self. And when he did get the ball, there was never much on to aim for - Albert and Jim were just about invisible.

Early on in the match, in a foul that didn't look much like one to me, he'd slammed his shoulder into Gerry Byrne. It was revealed later that Byrne's collar bone had been broken in the challenge. And he still played the rest of the match. That took real guts. Every now and then the television would show the rows of Leeds and Liverpool officials sitting on the benches at the side of the pitch. The Liverpool entourage looked brighter and livelier than ours, as if Don and the boys were too cold from the wet. Dr Ian

Adams was there for us too, dapper in his suit as always, he reminded me of George Martin. The doc should have give some of our players a shot up the behind to liven them up.

I don't believe Albert Johanneson was completely to blame for playing badly. It wasn't Diamond Jim's fault that *he* did either, he got injured quite early on and substitutes weren't allowed then, not even for injuries. Albert wasn't injured, at least not physically, I think it was more that he lost his nerve, he looked scared to death. People said he 'froze', overawed by the occasion, but I think there was more to it than that: whenever he got the ball, *stuff* happened, stuff that put him off playing his usual quick, tricky game. For all I know, he never fully recovered. I wasn't imagining it or exaggerating, right from the start, every time he got the ball, Liverpool fans booed, jeered, whistled him like he was a bloody child killer or something. But worse was their grunting, screeching and making monkey noises at him. Loads of the bastards were at it, the poor fella never got a moment's peace. The player selected to mark him, Chris Lawler, must have thought it was his birthday, he had that easy a game of it.

I wasn't even fifteen, and I was a white lad, so of course I didn't have a clue about what Albert must have felt and been thinking during the abuse. Or in fact, if she was there, how his wife Norma felt too, having to watch it, hear it, put up with it. But how disgustingly rotten it must have been, him being the only black fella on the pitch, not only having to put up with those lowlifes having a go at him, but knowing that there were one hundred thousand spectators there too, and probably millions of people around the world watching on television, witnessing it all. And the Queen was there too of course. Whenever he gets the ball there's this evil noise coming from hundreds of scummy Liverpudlians, how bloody rotten it all must have been for him. There were plenty of good, decent Liverpool fans who made it a right day, with all their banners and red and white scarves, singing non-stop and really backing their team, but their dreggy brethren spoiled it all.

In the football match itself, Roger Hunt took the lead, Billy Bremner equalised with a brilliant half-volley but then Ian St John scored in the second half of extra time with only nine minutes left. After we equalised we should have dropped back, soaked up the pressure and held out for a draw. It was clear that Liverpool had more energy than we did, I don't think anyone was surprised that they got a second goal. We should have got everybody behind the ball rather than look for a winner. Jim Storrie could hardly even walk! Billy was crying at the end. He just stood there on the pitch, swiping tears off his face while The Don consoled him. His goal deserved to win the game, any game, but it didn't and that was the point - the team had lost, rightly, and hard as it was to swallow, we all had to accept it. We all had to accept it and try and build on the experience. What they'd achieved that season was bloody amazing. I truly hoped they felt as proud as we fans felt about them. The players and the staff were heroes, each and every one of them.

5 vii

Soon after their astonishing so near, so far season ended, Don Revie dispensed with the services of forwards Ian Lawson and Tommy Henderson, to Crystal Palace and Bury respectively. Both had served him well, especially Lawson with 21 goals in 51 Leeds appearances, but Revie was looking to the future and believed he had better, more dynamic players in the Reserves, ready for promotion. And there was a player for another team who he was desperate to bring to Leeds, a small, cocky, ginger-haired nineteen year-old, with a curious high-pitched but inoffensive voice. Possessing good pace and agility, indomitable spirit, excellent stamina and quick-witted creativity, Alan Ball would be perfect for Leeds United.

Ball was not happy at Blackpool - they were a small club compared to most in Division One, and boardroom unrest was a feature there. He was of the opinion he was undervalued and that be deserved better pay for his efforts, so he asked for an improved contract. Revie knew how to make a player feel appreciated, and after secretly meeting Ball at a roadside café on Saddleworth Moor, clandestine arrangements were made to stir things up in Leeds' favour. Regular, generous cash gifts of £100 were unofficially handed over to Ball, usually at his home, by a mysterious man supposedly representing Leeds United. The cash was supposedly to keep Ball 'sweet' and to encourage him to prolong his dispute with Blackpool for as long as possible. The longer it went on, the better for all concerned Ball's departure would be and the easier it would be for Revie's Leeds to buy him.

Perturbed by his manager's keenness to bring in Ball, Leeds captain Bobby Collins considered his playing days at Elland Road under threat - 'If there is any transfer talk I would definitely not dismiss the idea of moving on,' he said, and why should he stay where he wasn't wanted? Revie must have been reminded of his own worrying situation at the club, less than five years before, and so he quickly tried to allay Collins' fears. He reassured him that he was very much a part of his plans, especially as Leeds were to venture into Europe for the first time in the new season.

Chapter 6: 1965/6 - Cruel breaks

6 i

It didn't look embarrassing any more, the **Football Honours List, season 1964 to '65**.
League Division One winners - Man United, Runners up - us, LEEDS UNITED.
FA Cup winners - Liverpool, Runners up - also LEEDS UNITED.
League Cup winners - Chelsea, Runners up - Leicester City.
European Cup winners - Inter Milan, Runners up - Benfica.
European Cup Winners Cup winners - West Ham Utd, Runners up - TSV 1860 Munich.
Inter-Cities Fairs Cup winners - Ferencvarós, Runners up - Juventus.
Football Player of the Year - BOBBY COLLINS, LEEDS UNITED.
European Footballer of the Year - Eusebio, Benfica.
Leeds' average home gate = 37,484, proof that folk had rediscovered the use of their legs.
Wait for Clean Air - 10 years.

We had won bugger all in reality but at least there was credit for the team's efforts, plus really good crowds and Bobby Collins getting the recognition he deserved. Actually, we did 'win' something, for finishing second in the League we qualified for the European competition, the Inter-Cities Fairs Cup. Even when it was always 'You get nowt for coming second' at Leeds, the council went and held a civic reception for the team a week after losing in the Cup final. A civic reception and big slaps on the back for coming second, twice, all seemed a bit too sugary to me.

Even if bad events in life make you want to just pack it all in, that's never the answer. There was a young Scottish lad, two years or so older than me, who had been playing for Leeds Juniors but not actually signed professionally, and he'd gone and torn his thigh muscle playing in a match. It's an injury which can finish a player's career. It even got worse but this lad never gave in, he just kept working at his recovery with the help of the Leeds staff. Eddie Gray was a great example to follow for anyone feeling sorry for themselves.

There's about twenty different lads in all sorts of football kit and a few men in clean, bright blue Leeds tracksuits. Coaches Cyril Partridge and Bob English are running it all, like it's an army sports day, telling us where to stand, what stretches and exercises to do while giving us a green bib or a yellow bib each. We're all gathered on the Fullerton Park training pitches with Cyril who's less his usual 'Nice Guy' self and Bob who isn't his 'Smiling' self either - this is all deadly serious business and woe betide any of us who aren't treating it properly. I've no worries on that count, I haven't slept well for days, I'm *totally* serious about it all.

My lack of sleep wasn't just because I was excited about today but also because I was woken up by some strange noises. At one stage I thought we had a ghost or something but then it turned out it was just a bird trapped down the chimney. My grandma didn't seem too concerned but I nearly browned my bed sheets with the fright at first. Probably a spug (a sparrow) and probably dead by now. Nothing to do with the spug but my grandma's cough was getting worse, I was sure of it, even in the summer. She'd always tell me she was fine and that I should worry about my own affairs.

There's red cones dotted all over the place, flags on all the pitch corners, net-bags with white leather footballs in as well as brown and orange ones, small-scale goalposts and big cloth soccer kit bags, and the huge grass-roller over at the side. Further in the distance, near the boiler-making factory side of Fullerton Park, a few of the Junior players are knocking footballs around. They practice free-kicks using wooden 'cut outs', whack long passes to each other across the field, try and outdo each other at whatever they do. Trapping the ball stone-dead, expertly, with either foot or on their chests, then they keep the ball up, juggle it with their feet and head and shoulders, like it's second nature. And I'm watching them as I stretch and warm up, thinking, *knowing,* that I can do just as well as them all, and better.

I lost count of the number of times I'd stood at the top of the little embankment, above the car park, watching the training and drills. When I first started coming down I was sometimes the only one. Loads of times in fact. Nowadays, because Leeds are doing well, there's hundreds there, especially in school holidays. Sort of makes me feel like an intruder at my own party. I'd peer through the tall wire fence as the first team squad was put through its paces by the tyrant coaches and as they'd kick lumps out of each other in England versus Scotland tournaments and stuff. And now I'm here, inside that fence, inside the heart of the club itself, about to set out on a quest to join my heroes as one of the next generation of Leeds players, I feel like D'Artagnan waiting to join the Musketeers.

I don't know any of the other lads who are here for the trial match. None of them seem right friendly but it's not like I'm full of warm welcome either. This is business after all, it's now or never, and it's time for me To Achieve Personal Greatness. I've been persevering for years and now's the time for the perseverance to work. I'm fixed on giving it my very best shot and nothing else. Nerves is just another obstacle, an unimportant obstacle. Nerves is small fry. If ever I'm nervous, scared even, I try to turn it into a positive, as if it's a challenge.

I don't care about trying to put any of the other lads off or getting one over them, it's what *I* do that counts, me, what I do right, not what anyone else does wrong. Being a good sport is my nature and I think it's a good quality, a strength. My feet will do the talking for me, I'll make sure of it. I'm not blind or stupid, the majority of young lads at football clubs never make it into the first team. But I'm different, I'm like Leeds United - I've had a dismal past but I've got a bright future. I deserve this chance, because I was a Leeds supporter through and through, and even if things went bad again, I'd still be there, backing them. Always. And, truthfully, I would shed blood for The Don and Leeds if I had to.

I'm a better player than all of the other lads here. Fitter. Cleverer. Harder. Even faster than most too. Them that are quicker than me, it's up to me to show I'm quicker *thinking*. It's time for me to prove what I already know and what most of Beeston knows, what I've worked my socks off for years for. This is the time to prove it to the important people, the ones that really matter. Nothing fancy, I just need to play my normal game - effective, efficient, essential. If I make a mistake then I admit it and I make up for it.

We've been split into two teams - Bob English reads them out and where each of us is going to be playing. He tells us not to worry if it's not our normal position as talent always shines through and versatility is a skill in itself. I've been picked for midfield, operating directly in front of our team's centre-halves, where I always want to play. Let's see if I can play like Passy, or even like the Pocket Puskas himself. But first they make us do a few more warm-up exercises and stretches, and then three laps around the pitch which has one set of goalposts overlooking the car park. As I run down the length of the pitch, I can't take my eyes off the fantastic LEEDS UNITED AFC lettering fixed on the bright blue wall-front as big as the Rex screen. And below the letters, the beautiful coat of arms, it makes my heart pound whenever I look at it. The golds and whites and blues, the owls and the lamb, the three stars. I don't know what it's made out of but it's precious to me, priceless, a real work of art.

Ten or so of the lads rolled up late on a Wallace Arnold coach from town so I supposed they'd got to Leeds by train. 'I bet that'll be the Welsh lot - the Taffs,' a big Scotch lad said, to no one in particular. He was huge, lean but muscly. I was glad he had a yellow bib on like me so we were in the same team - I wouldn't have fancied marking him. He was half right about the Welsh contingent, because there were three or four lads from London on the same bus. Half of them looked German to me anyway, they had bright blond hair. They were like *'Children of the Damned'* or something. I was raring to get started, I could have sprinted a marathon never mind those three laps, the adrenaline was pumping through me big time. It was the middle of July, I'd just turned fifteen and school was no more. Here I was, *here*, after years longing for the chance, on the threshold of something brilliant. My life was about to take off, my future was starting here.

This match would be Wales plus a couple of southerners versus us, a Great Britain Eleven. The pitch was quite stiff and there wasn't much grass on it. Dried mud was rutted in the centre circle and in both penalty areas but a plus point was that it wasn't sun-baked and it wasn't liable to cripple you if you landed badly. There's a bit of give in the surface and in the middle it's even quite gluey. My team kicked off, the two forwards commencing proceedings with the orange ball. One taps the ball inches into the opposing half and the other then passes it back to another team-mate, that's how it normally works. It's passed to me and I try to keep hold of it longer than the others, to try and show I'm not nervous but in fact confident and composed. I look up towards our attackers in the Wales half, as if I'm going to hit a long pass, but then I side-foot it short, horizontally to our right-back, a yard in front of him – place the ball in front so he can run onto it and not have to alter his stride. Short, simple, *effective* passing, that's all it needs. Bob English was refereeing. He might have been older and a bit round and small but there was no doubt about it, he was just as fit as any of us.

Some of our lads were nervous, like they were short of confidence and didn't want anything more than the briefest touch of the ball. Maybe that way they could 'hide' from making mistakes. Thing is, you can't afford to hide if you want to do well and to win. I couldn't blame any one of them for being edgy because my legs felt a bit shaky and more tired than normal, too, it surprised me. The advantage I had was knowing it was just my brain trying to play tricks, trying to fool my body that I was scared, trying to make out somehow that this game was different from a normal football match. So I kept active all the time, even if the play stopped, and I breathed in oxygen as deep as I could, to keep my heartbeat regular and to keep my lungs full. *And* I think my team-mates spotted it and took encouragement from me. I kept on fighting, against the other team as well as any stupid, negative thoughts that popped up in my head. I never gave in and if any one on our side did something good, I clapped them or shouted 'Well played' and the like. Our performance definitely improved as the first half went on, and that's when I began to notice a few more spectators on the touchline.

There was Maurice Lindley and Syd Owen, and Bobby Collins too. Bobby Collins! Ces was there of course, and a couple of the other ground staff. I didn't see John but he'll have been somewhere in the vicinity. I saw Passy too, which I thought was great of him. There was no Don Revie though. I knew he'd be given a detailed report about the game anyway, on which of us had performed well or not. I had a good feeling my name would be on the Recommended list, because I was playing alright, better than alright in fact. The Welsh lads were getting annoyed with how well our side was ticking. We were only 1-0 up at half time, and the goal was a fluky deflection off a defender's shoulder, but our display deserved more, I don't remember our 'keeper having a shot to save. The result wasn't important – even though no one likes losing unless they're simple – it's how we've played that mattered. I was lucky in that I never lost a tackle and that most of my passes were accurate and struck well. I even played a part in the goal – a headed clearance came out to me, I controlled it just inside their half, ran a few yards with it and then shaped to pass to my right but swerved and went left instead. Our man on the left wing crossed it in and it went in off one of their centre-halves. The other team were no mugs though, and I was thinking, I wouldn't want to cross them, some of them were right bruisers. Especially in midfield, directly opposite me, and both central defenders had faces only a mother could be proud of - if she were blind - perfect for fighting.

At half time we're given water in plastic cups to drink, plus segments of orange to chew and suck the juice out of. We're on this side of the pitch on the halfway line whilst the Welsh are opposite. We've got Cyril Partridge checking we're all okay and not injured, he's coaching us, encouraging us, telling us to keep focused and to carry on playing as we are. He tells our Geordie goalkeeper to make the penalty area 'his' and to keep shouting at his defenders to keep them alert. Bob English comes over to us and he also tells us that we're doing well and that we're dominating the game, especially in the midfield area. And he looks right at me and my midfield 'partner', a little ginger-haired lad called Billy, funnily enough. And he tells us two to keep on linking up and backing each other up. Fantastic! I am disappointed at one thing though - on the other side of the pitch, while we've got Cyril, and Bob for a few seconds, the other team have only got Bobby Collins talking to them. I'm jealous, I can't deny it, and seeing him all animated and clenched fists like, makes me greener than Glasgow Celtic.

The Welsh are playing better in the second half, putting us under pressure and giving us less time on the ball. Pressure like that can cause players to make mistakes because they're made to hurry and they have less time to consider their options for passing. When a defender's being chased and an easy pass to a team-mate isn't on, the safest option is to 'get rid' by just clouting the ball upfield or even out of play. We started losing possession too easily and hardly put any good moves together at all. It needed someone to try and calm things down and to take control, which is really what we in midfield are there for – help the defence to defend as well as link up with and supply the attacking players. And, as if giving me perfect chance to prove my point, we get a free kick on the edge of our area – and instead of a defender bashing the ball up the field, I call for it, a short pass off him. I receive it and turn to run a short distance with it before passing. That was my plan at least... I do collect the ball and I do turn with it, but then I trip and stumble slightly on the rutted mud. What happens next is dizzy – I keep on my feet and *just* keep control of the ball though it's gone a tiny bit further from me than I intended. At the same time, one of the blond Welsh lads comes tearing in to try and tackle me. Except he misses the ball and he misses me - and I've managed to toe-poke the ball between his legs, fooling him as well as making him look like a fool - I've flukily nutmegged him. I've shamed him, completely by accident. To add to his embarrassment, as I've sneaked the ball through him, there's a cheer from a couple of the spectators. I say sorry to the lad and he grunts back but when I look at him, he isn't even *nearly* smiling, his face is flushed and furious.

The match carries on and it's all a bit stale and ordinary, like everyone's just going through the motions. That's fine for me to do as my job is straightforward, but the attacking players need to play with pace and flair and find space to try everything they can to get in on goal. Neither side was doing anything like that, the match was just tailing off. Then, with only a few minutes left, we got another free kick on the edge of our area, and our 'keeper decides to take the kick and pass it short to me. Except I don't know anything about it as my back's turned away from him, I'm facing up the pitch. I'm completely unawares that he's passed the ball to me. Suddenly realising his error, he's then calling out to me and I stop and turn around to look at him. Once I'm alerted, I hurry towards the ball. And then I get the weird sense that the pass is not the only thing intended for me, something else is coming my way.

The Welsh lad from before has watched it all happen and he's smelled a chance of an attack. He wants the ball and he's got a few yards and seconds start on me. So while I'm rushing towards the ball, he's sprinting full pelt. I'm closer to the ball and I get to it first. I put my right foot on it in readiness to spot a team-mate to pass to. Then 'Man on!' my team-mate Billy shouts, as someone closes in on me, like a bird of prey diving in on its next victim. Billy's words vanish into an irrelevant past. For a second, my right foot is off the ground and on the ball, while my body weight is all on my left leg. And it's at this exact, precise, evil moment, the blond Welsh lad slams his self into me. The sole of his left foot lands on my left ankle while his right boot, studs first, pummels into my left leg just below my knee - like a wrecking ball on an old brick wall. The sick bastard has actually jumped *into* me. Everything whirls by dizzyingly, except the feeling I've been hit by a bolt of freezing lightning. My ankle has given way and I know there's disgusting pain there, outdone though by the horror inflicted higher up my leg. I thought I heard a snap like a dry twig as my leg bent unnaturally inwards and too far.

I'm on the ground, dead still, I'm woozy, trembling, I'm nauseous and I'm out of it, I'm yelping without knowing I'm doing it, I can't move my legs or even breathe without awful, pulverising stabbing screams searing through my legs and my body. Any movement just makes it worse, just being awake makes it worse. I know I fainted - I know I woke up with Bob English trying to treat my wounds and trying to calm me down while Cyril Partridge and Ces and even Passy were looking down at me. Someone put a blanket over me, it was turquoise. I couldn't stop shivering, in the summer sunshine.

Real men don't cry, real men don't let on they're hurt, real men don't faint, real men *black out*, real men grin and bear it, real men take it on the chin, real men take it in their bloody stride, real men get on with their lives. Real men don't bawl and wail like a baby. I wasn't a real man, no way, I begged and pleaded with them not to move my leg. But they did when they tried taking my left sock off, and I fainted again.

6 ii

Nothing was said on *This Is Your Life* about Revie's and Leeds' first foray into European competition, which began in late September, 1965, and how strong an impression they had made on English football in their debut Division One season. True, no trophies had been won and so the relevance for such a television programme was only slight, but European qualification was, nonetheless, a fine achievement. Playing in Europe would boost the club's coffers as well as the reputations of the manager and players, too. But amongst the many highlights and triumphs of that initial European foray, there would come cruel tragedy.

*

In the summer of 1965, with insight perhaps on a par to that of the notorious Beatles-rejecting Decca man, football experts casually wrote off Leeds United's chances of success for the forthcoming campaign. The team had done well so far but would undoubtedly be found out as a 'one season wonder', unable to repeat the success this time around. Indeed, until *Match of the Day* first reached the public's screens in August 1964, sceptics even suggested that the lack of television coverage before had given Leeds an advantage over other Division One sides, as hardly anyone in football had seen them play before. Their compiling of dossiers on opposing teams was never a popular strategy, as if in some mysterious way it was unethical or even cheating. Scant recognition of the team's qualities, came Leeds' way, while the FA-inflicted dirty reputation showed no signs of subsiding.

By the end of September, Leeds were joint top of Division One, with fourteen points won out of a possible twenty. A decent start with just two narrow defeats - at West Ham and Tottenham - and two draws with Sheffield United and Leicester City. Good hard-earned wins over Sunderland, Aston Villa (twice), Nottingham Forest, Blackburn Rovers and a revenge win over Spurs indicated that Leeds would be strong candidates again.

Before the start of each season, Don Revie would prioritise the various competitions Leeds were in. The 'lesser' games would give him the chance to utilise some of the younger or peripheral players at the club. Sensible management, though not in the eyes of the game's authorities. With the manager and coaches pushing the players hard, complacency would not be a danger in season 1965-'66. Alan Peacock for one, stormed back on to the scene, scoring six League goals by late September and playing so well that England manager Alf Ramsey recalled him to the national squad. Peacock graciously attributed the selection to the Leeds coaching staff who had pushed him so hard, while Revie beamed that he couldn't have been happier had he himself received the call-up. International call-ups would become a regular occurrence but Revie rarely welcomed them, they disrupted his plans far too often.

Young 'hotshot' Lorimer had recovered from a broken leg and returned to first team action in scorching form. Due to injuries to Bell and Johanneson, chances for first team action arrived for Paul Madeley at left-back and Terry Cooper on the left side of midfield. Occasionally, Rod Johnson would re-enter the scene, while young forward Jimmy Greenhoff appeared a number of times, proving himself as a versatile and capable prospect. Despite being selected, Cooper was frustrated at not being a first team regular, and so he put in a transfer request. Revie reluctantly placed him on the transfer list, describing him as 'a great club man'. There was no shortage of enquiries but Cooper eventually retracted his request after Revie reassured him that more chances would come his way and that he was very highly regarded. As the season wore on, other youngsters would play 'bit parts' too - Mick Bates, Terry Hibbitt, David Harvey, Nigel Davey, Rod Belfitt and Dennis Hawkins. The young Scot Edwin Gray had officially signed forms for the club too, and was a superstar in the making, according to Syd Owen. And it took a great deal to impress Syd Owen. Gray had it all, Owen said, and had been pursued by even more clubs than Peter Lorimer had before him. Along with Gray arrived his mate Jimmy Lumsden, a promising, fair-haired inside-right. Both were signed from school and it is rumoured that Revie needed more than just his powers of persuasion to convince Gray's headmaster that a career in football, at Leeds United, was the calling. Gray, like a few Scottish lads at Elland Road before him, had not heard of the city of Leeds before, thinking that it was situated in Wales.

In his apprentice days, Gray endured a terrible injury playing for the youth team against Sheffield Wednesday. A sharp pain in his left thigh turned out to be a muscle tear but thinking it was only a minor 'niggle', Gray also played in the next match a few days later and the injury worsened dramatically. Despite operations and intensive treatment, the muscle damage in Gray's thigh was never to properly repair. Injured football players are often at risk of leading very lonely existences in the long journeys of recuperation to recovery but Syd Owen and Les Cocker hardly let Gray out of their sights, with three sometimes four rigorous sessions of physiotherapy a day. Regrettably, calcification occurred in Gray's damaged thigh, in effect shortening the muscle and consequently affecting his pace and agility. He was as fast as the fastest Leeds player (Paul Madeley) over short, straight distances, but now, turning and changing pace or direction proved more difficult. He even had to be careful when striking the ball hard. His fancy footwork and delicate ball-skills might have suggested that he himself was a delicate soul too, but far from it, Gray suffered more pain throughout his career than any player could be reasonably expected to endure.

*

The Leeds United European debut came in the Inter-Cities Fairs Cup, first round. Ties were played over two legs, on home and away basis. Soon after the draw for round one had been made, Don Revie and Syd Owen travelled to Italy to analyse their opponents - Torino. The two spies returned carrying a hefty and detailed dossier. Revie discussed the merits of Torino with the English press - 'They are a hard, strong side and will be difficult to beat. Their defence is very tight and they have several cracking good players. They will be hard to open out.'

Leeds went into the first game, at Elland Road, on 29th September fresh from a sound home victory against lowly Blackburn Rovers. Leading 3-0 at half-time, the two points were practically United's already and so Revie told his players to go easy in the second half and conserve energy for the Torino tie. They followed his orders but during that second half, Revie was appalled to hear fans complaining and slow handclapping his team; they wanted more goals and were perhaps oblivious to why the team was playing at a more casual pace. For the first leg against Torino, he swapped around his players' shirt numbers in an attempt to confuse the visitors. The ruse was ineffective as Leeds began so well that the Italian goal was bombarded from all angles, thus numbers on shirts had mattered not. The Leeds midfield bossed the game throughout, with Giles and Bremner outstanding, and the defence snuffed out every Torino threat comfortably. The Peacocks played fluent, fast, attacking football - Torino's impressive goalkeeper Vieri seemed to be keeping his team in the match all on his own. However, the first ever Leeds goal in Europe came from a 'speculative' shot by Bremner on 25 minutes and an embarrassing error as Vieri fumbled the ball into his own net.

Alan Peacock, despite being marked by two defenders, headed the second Leeds goal soon after half-time. Although Leeds wore angelic, pure white, they looked anything but European football virgins, though in their haste to score a third, they allowed Torino to grab a breakaway goal with only a few minutes of the tie left; it might prove to be a crucial error. Italian teams were renowned for their ability to soak up pressure and then score vital goals against the run of play. Leeds held on to win 2-1 but thanks to that late goal, Torino were confident of going through to the next round. Their manager/coach Nereo Rocco complimented Leeds United and the Elland Road crowd as being magnificent and splendid, but his charm offensive fooled very few people.

The Stadio Communale, Turin, October 6th 1965, the night Brady and Hindley commit their last appalling crime, Torino, in maroon shirts, white shorts and socks, played host to the all-white Leeds United. They welcomed back Gigi Meroni 'the Italian George Best' to their line-up and were hoping to finish the tie quickly, believing an early goal would kill Leeds' spirit and make for a comparatively easy game. They had underestimated the strength and commitment of Revie's Leeds. Over two hundred Leeds supporters made their presence known from the Torino terraces, loudly backing their favourites and urging the team on, with renditions of 'Leeds Leeds Leeds' and 'Elland Road Baht'at'. A customarily passionate display came from the Leeds players as well, while no one at the club seemed to have listened to British accounts of unpleasant experiences in European competition, the hostile 'welcomes', the underhand tactics and the dubious refereeing, in addition to the alleged and frequent whiff of corruption. But so far these two Leeds-Torino matches had been played in the proper sporting spirit. Until that is, five minutes in to the second half when one Leeds man's life was to be changed forever.

Bobby Collins had collected the ball twenty or so yards outside the Torino penalty area. Opposing left-back Fabrizio Poletti intended to stop him. Over a short distance, Collins remained one of the fastest players around and it is possible Poletti misjudged that pace. Careering towards his target, as Collins nudged the ball forward a few yards, Poletti changed neither his speed nor angle of approach. He appeared now to be aiming for the *man,* not the ball. At full speed he thuds into Collins, his knee thrusting into the Scot's right thigh, excruciatingly, sickeningly, disgracefully. The Italian's body weight is focused, concentrated, speared into one small area of Collins' leg. It is grievous bodily harm barely disguised as a football tackle. Norman Hunter and Jack Charlton immediately realize the damage is serious - if Collins stays down then he is genuinely injured and in need of medical attention. Sitting in the main stand, tearful players' wives Vicky Bremner and May Bell seem to realise the severity of the situation too. But the referee ignores Collins' agonized scream, instead gesticulating that the player should be lifted off the pitch to allow play to continue. Heeding this, a couple of Torino players make to drag him over the nearest touchline. But the protective frame of Charlton strides in to stand over and shield the motionless Leeds captain, as if a bodyguard. He pushes Italian players away, threatens them and even punches them - not one of the bastards will get near his team-mate.

Billy Bremner, like his and Willie Bell's wife, also weeps but his tears are more of revulsion than grief. He spits out a promise to Poletti, to kill him. Poletti speaks little if any English but he needs no translation. The referee finally grasps the extent of Collins' injury and signals for a stretcher to be brought on. Les Cocker races from the Leeds dugout. He tries to comfort Collins but it's a lost cause, the injury is severe. Blanketed by his manager's raincoat, the stricken player is carried off by the shocked Cocker and Willie Bell. Every inch of the way, every single, slight movement, sends stabs of merciless pain through the Collins' body.

Needing no more encouragement other than 'Let's do it for Bobby!' the now ten men of Leeds defended and fought the contest as if their lives depended on it. Ending as a 0-0 stalemate, Leeds went through to the next round, winning 2-1 on aggregate. The Torino fans and the Italian press praised their superbly defiant performance while English newspapers somewhat tactlessly compared it to a World War Two triumph won on foreign soil. Regardless, Collins' injury caused it to be something of a hollow victory.

The Torino players visited Collins in the local hospital soon after, and Poletti - who in fact held a good reputation in Italy as a fair and honest player - showed sincere remorse. The violence was said to be out of character for the 22 year-old, though a week later Collins wryly noted that Poletti caused injury to another opponent in his very next game. Collins would receive the best treatment possible, with world-renowned surgeon Professor Re and his team helping to mend the splintered femur bone. A fifteen-inch pin was inserted in to the injured leg to pin the bone together. Surprisingly, the in-traction Scot was in good spirits, telling Don Revie he would be back playing soon. Two weeks later he returned to a hero's welcome at Yeadon Airport, greeted by a small, very appreciative crowd of fans. Revie moved quickly to 'repair' the team, switching Giles from the right flank to fill Collins' place in the centre, and buying a new player, the skilful winger Mike O'Grady from Huddersfield Town for £30,000. Signing on his 23rd birthday, he had played once for England, scoring twice against Northern Ireland.

*

The night Leeds faced Torino, Chelsea were in Italy too, playing Roma. Chelsea players were pelted throughout the match with missiles thrown by Italian supporters: rotten fruit, metal seats, lumps of concrete and chunks of ice. Chelsea players John Boyle and Eddie McCreadie were both knocked unconscious by missiles and John Hollins had a metal hook-like stanchion just miss him and stick in the ground. After the game, around sixty armed police guarded the players' gate against hundreds of Roma hooligans. As the Chelsea team coach exited, more stones and bottles thudded against it, smashing two windows but causing no more injuries. Worryingly, as if football crowd violence was continentally contagious, disturbances occurred at English grounds the following Saturday. At Old Trafford, club windows were stoned after the hosts beat Liverpool, while there were several arrests following Burnley's match with Blackburn, and trouble occurred at Huddersfield Town's game with Manchester City. On November 6th, Manchester United 'keeper Harry Gregg was sent off near the end of their match with Blackburn and later, the Rovers team bus was struck by various objects as it left Old Trafford. Disorder at Hillsborough with Sheffield Wednesday versus Liverpool saw nine fans arrested and, incredibly, in London, during the Brentford against Millwall Third Division match, a Millwall fan threw a hand-grenade on to the pitch. It wasn't 'live' but those who fled the scene won't have been aware of that fact. And Millwall won the match.

6 iii

In a matter of obscene seconds, my hopes had changed to fears, my dreams into tears. And my leg to mush. The pains were bad in the daytime, very bad, but there were things to help take my mind off them then, it was the nights that killed, the nights when I could only lie on my back like a sodding upturned tortoise. My leg hurt so much that I cried lots of times, and I cursed everything and everybody, I really didn't deserve any of the shitty luck that I'd been showered with. It sounds obvious saying it but when you're awake in the day and you've got a bad injury, you *know* that you've got a bad injury. With a broken leg and ankle, which is what I had, there's not exactly much chance of forgetting the pain, especially while a one ton pot weighs you down. But when you're *asleep*, you're not in the real world, you're in dream land and dream time. Lying there, having finally got to sleep, you move and fidget and twitch, and if you're anything like me, you sometimes even try to run and kick as well. The thigh-length plaster of Paris boot stops you moving properly, but not completely as you can still move the leg a fraction, broken bones or not. Agony doesn't need more than that fraction to introduce itself and knock the stuffing out of you.

I'd be lying on the settee cushions on the living-room floor and I'd wake up at the dead of night after moving in my sleep and with the small of my back aching like a dog. The tiniest move of my leg made me yelp and curse, and every time I did it, it felt like I was breaking the bones all over again, it really did. My crying out would wake my grandma up, even upstairs, and she'd chelp at me from her bedroom for disturbing her. I couldn't win, those nights made my life a misery. With throbbing, pulsing stabs piercing me all the while, good sleep was impossible. And because of the shocking state I was in, mixed with exhaustion in the blackness of the dead of night, clear thinking was a real rarity. With thoughts and suspicions racing inside my head faster than a pinball, I reckon I was closer to lunacy than I was to being normal. It's frightening what lack of sleep can do to your mind and how it can cause your breathing and heartbeat to be erratic. Not sure what was real and what was just imagined, I sometimes thought I'd have to have my leg amputated or that I'd be forever stuck there on the carpet in darkness. Or I'd be thinking I could walk again but only on stilts.

Because I'd not slept well in those nights, I'd often nod off in daytime to catch up on the lost sleep. Then I'd feel less tired the next night as a result, meaning I'd be more restless and wake up even more easily in the early hours again. It was a vicious circle, all thanks to that vicious blond Welsh bastard. I had to endure that filthy full-length pot for eight weeks while I had two wooden crutches to help me get around. Even they came at a price because they rubbed my armpits raw and caused infected sores under both arms. My grandma got me some cream from the chemist which did work but stunk something rancid. She felt terrible for me, I knew that, even if she wasn't ever great at expressing herself. She'd given me a hug when I got back from the Infirmary that first day, something that she'd never done before. Maybe I'd never deserved one before, thinking about it. That first day back from the hospital, I was pitiful, even more so when I lost my balance trying to get into the house and for a split second had to use my left leg to stand on. My left, *broken* leg. I shrieked, I really did, and then I started crying yet again, with my grandma standing there, tears in her eyes, not knowing what the hell to do.

Dead on quarter past seven in the morning she'd set off walking to work. She'd normally wake me up with a bowl of porridge - and her coughing of course - and leave me on my own for the rest of the day. But on that first morning she forgot, leaving the curtains shut and the porridge on the table and me lying on cushions on the floor like a corpse. I suppose it was lucky I didn't have much of an appetite because I could hardly get around the house without it being agony. 'Lucky' wasn't really what I was thinking at the time like. We did have an indoor toilet by then but I never tried getting to it, the staircase was too risky - narrow and winding, I could have easy done more damage to myself. If I needed a crap it'd be easier using the outside bog at the top of the street. I discovered how stupidly awkward and unpleasant it was trying to sit on the toilet when your leg's in plaster. I should have been thankful that I could use the kitchen sink to pee in but I didn't feel like counting my blessings, you don't when you're feeling lower than a woodlouse's tail. It was all pathetic self-pity but I really did feel an urge to try killing myself.

There was someone knocking on the door. It woke me up with a start, it was about eleven o'clock, and I was hot and I was worn out. Then another knock. It must have took me two minutes just to stand up but whoever was doing the knocking wasn't stopping or going away. Then they rapped on the window which caused me to shout that I was coming. Why they thought banging on the window would make any difference to banging on the door was beyond me. It was Ces, he'd come to see how I was coping. Or not coping more like. He had a bottle of sherry with him, a fancy card wishing me a speedy recovery and a letter in a white Leeds United envelope addressed to my grandma. First thing he did was go to the window and let some light in, then he re-opened the door like he was letting the bad atmosphere out.

The card was signed by the coaches as well as 'on behalf of' Don Revie, probably by his secretary Jean, I supposed - plus some of the ground staff and Bobby Collins and Nigel Davey who had seen what happened to me. One comic had written 'Life's not what it's cracked up to be!' but I couldn't make the signature out. Ces was here on a mission - he'd even been given permission by the club to do it - he was here to make me muster myself and pull myself together. After all, despite the frequent agony it caused, it wasn't a very serious injury, physios and coaches of football clubs had seen it all before many a time. To them, it's all quite trivial really, 'just' another injury easily mended. The club said I could go in for treatment and weight training whenever I liked, provided it was convenient for them. My leg would be in pot for weeks but that shouldn't stop me from exercising my upper body. I struggled to think of anything less appealing, I just wanted to rest and feel sorry for myself. Anyway, I had to just stew and let nature take its course in repairing my leg, knitting the bones back together and with luck, not letting the muscles waste away that much. Doctors said my ankle should heal quite quickly and easily; the fibula fracture was the main concern, it would take weeks longer.

Ces took me to the pub for dinner that first visit. The Peacock was about two hundred yards away - it took nearly twenty minutes to get there, I wasn't very adept with the crutches. Landlord Aitch stood behind the bar and started clapping me when I finally crutched my way in. I felt like roaring again, I really did, especially when I saw *him* wiping his eyes and blowing his nose all of a sudden. The big girl's blouse. They had it all worked out for me - they'd set out a little round table for me and put a stool and a cushion next to the seat for me to put my leg up. They'd picked the seat closest to the toilets, as well as near the pinball machine and the jukebox. The bog door was even propped open so as to make it easier for me to get in and out. I fell asleep in the Peacock loads of times in the daytime when Aitch closed for the afternoon, and there were times I had to dash to the toilet, only for my bladder to get there first.

*

If the Beatles can get MBE's awarded then Bobby Collins should have got more, for all he'd done for Leeds. At least he'd been capped again by Scotland before his injury, that will have made him proud as anything, I'm sure. It was October, my own season had been done for three months before, and my season watching Leeds hadn't been allowed to even start yet as my grandma said it wasn't safe for me to go to the matches while I was on crutches. Instead, I'd go to the Peacock most afternoons and get nice and cosy, courtesy of Aitch and any other generous souls who knew and felt sorry for the feckless invalid feeling sorry for himself that was me. On match days, plenty more fellas would be drinking there till about two o'clock, then Aitch would have to shut. He'd let me stay though and put the radio on so we could keep up to date with the football news. And obviously, we could usually hear how Leeds were doing just from the noise over the road - the cheers (and groans) from the crowd. It was nearly always cheers for Leeds, we hardly dropped points at home. There were always over 30,000 for League games - even midweek - and when Liverpool came here the crowd was over 49,000. That was Christmas week, and it was only a day after we'd beaten them 1-0 at Anfield. Peter Lorimer got that one but Liverpool got their revenge by beating us in the second match, same scoreline. Did anyone understand why the fixture planners scheduled two games in two days, especially involving the exact same two teams?

Two weeks after Christmas, Man United came and the crowd was only a couple of hundred short of 50,000. Harry and the board will have loved all that cash rolling in, no doubt about that. The Mancs got a 1-1 draw but they were never really in the title race this time around, even though they were the current holders. It was mostly us, Liverpool and Burnley in the running. The Saturday after, Leeds were at home again, to Stoke. And a week after that they were drawn to play Bury in the FA Cup at Elland Road as well. On its good days, the Elland Road pitch wasn't great but it was reasonable - it soaked up water too easily, as it didn't have any decent drainage, and often it turned in to a right mud heap. It was worse if there was frost or freezing fog because then the mud would freeze and the pitch be solid, with dangerous little frozen ridges all over the place. Jesus, if a player landed awkwardly on one of them, they knew about it. After the Man United game on the Wednesday, Ces and the ground staff, plus apprentices, were up against it to keep the pitch in good enough condition for the Stoke match. The weather stayed bad, which meant the pitch wouldn't improve, not by nature anyway as there was no sunshine, only freezing fog, sharp frosts and chill winds. The groundsmen would have their work cut out to keep the surface in good enough condition for the game to be on.

The day before it, Friday 14th January, had been a day I'd been looking forward to for ages. Six months in fact, as I was due to be freed completely from the pot on my left leg. Today would mean no more crutches, no more risking breaking more bones on cobbled streets or slippery pavement slabs. No more people looking at me like I was some sort of sideshow freak. So I had something to celebrate. And I had a sneaky sherry with my morning porridge and then another one to help me on my way. It was dead cold outside after all. I caught a bus to the Infirmary and waited for the nurses to improve my life. After they'd used some sort of scissors to cut off the half-pot which had replaced the full length one a few weeks before, I was surprised, shocked even, at how skinny my leg had got, especially below the knee. Suddenly I had the left leg of a concentration camp survivor, and I wasn't trying to be funny by saying that. Still, to build it up was a challenge and I was feeling at last, up for such a thing. No more feeling sorry for myself, no more being a lazy-arse layabout. Each day's aim would be to get better and stronger - To Achieve Personal Greatness. To Achieve Personal Greatness Again in fact. I'd been so close before. The doctor said I'd have to be careful but I could start training again, slowly and surely, just with long walks at first.

I'm sitting there, in the Peacock, and I've a pint of bitter and a morning paper to keep me company. I've just walked, dead carefully and slowly, with an NHS walking stick to support me, right from Leeds Infirmary all the way back to the pub. It took me over an hour and I wasn't bothered about it, even in the brass monkey cold, because I felt nearly normal again, sort of liberated. I'm wearing old tracksuit bottoms with elasticated waistband, wishing I'd took a pair of proper trousers with me. These must whiff a bit, I'd worn them for bloody ages. Without the pot I noticed straight away the cold draft around my emaciated leg, the support bandage on my shin not doing much at all to fend off winter. Aitch has kindly got the jukebox playing and I'm the first customer in there. Well, 'customer' is pushing it seeing as he's letting me drink for nothing. I always tell him I'll pay him back, once I've some cash to do it with. God only knows when that will be but he doesn't mind one bit, I think he likes me being around. I'm feeling a bit woozy, it's a nice feeling and I'm snug and happy and I've got some chips for dinner coming my way shortly, courtesy of the friendliest landlord in town He's got good taste in popular music has Aitch as well, and anything by the Beatles, Stones, Herman's Hermits and the Animals is alright by me. With a bit of luck, he might play me at pinball later, too. I'm drowsy, and for the first time in ages I feel like I've earned the right to have a dinner time nap.

I'm not asleep for long, maybe five minutes. The Righteous Brothers and their lost lovin' feeling drifts around and I hear a bit of talking at the bar too. Then someone plants a glass down on one of the tables a few feet away from me - I get the impression it's done *un*-quietly on purpose. So I force my eyes open to look, my eyelids feel like they're weighted down.

It's Ces - he's sitting nearby. He isn't looking at me though, he just sits there, dead still, faced forward to the bar. It probably sounds mad, but he doesn't look himself to me, he looks different. He definitely doesn't look too pleased with life, that's for sure, and he looks half asleep, like he's here but not really, like he hasn't slept for days. I know that feeling alright. He can't have missed me but he doesn't say a word. Aitch is just getting on with whatever he's doing at his side of the bar, minding his own. And maybe I should have minded mine too. Deciding to cheer Ces up, I stand, slowly, lifting myself up with hands flat on the cushioned seat, making sure that my left foot is planted firmly, flat and straight and no twisting, on the floor. I walk the few steps over to Ces, without using the walking stick. I reckon it's quite a feat. 'Afternoon Ces,' I say, waving my left leg at him. 'I'm potless at last!' He notices but doesn't look the slightest bit impressed - in fact he still looks grumpy as bollocks.

Then he mumbles, 'Are you pissed already?' There was no joking in his voice, no warmth or affection, it was more like he was royally narked at me but I couldn't work out why.

I plonked myself down next to him - 'Why, what's up?'

'Look at the state of you - you're nowt but a fat slob! Fifteen and you've got a beer gut!'

'Why are you getting at me, what have I done?'

'Lazy, time-wasting bloody idiot!'

And then, as I'm struggling to understand why he's saying what he's saying, and what I'm supposed to have done to deserve it, he stands up and he leaves the pub and I'm left there feeling like a grimy, *guilty* little bastard, with no idea why. Aitch says something along the lines of don't do anything hasty but I decide to cross the road and find out what I've done to upset Ces so much, because I'm *really* upset. *Don't do anything hasty* - how laughable a comment that was. I'm walking - with the aid of the NHS stick - slowly down near the stadium reception, to the ground staff's room and stores in the north-west corner. As I'm passing the reception, Bobby Collins comes walking out of the glass doors. He seems to be faring alright after that horrible injury, I'm pleased for him, and a bit envious. I stop for a second, standing there lamely with my stick at my side, looking at my hero, and I feel like crying and laughing at the same time. I'm standing, cringing, in the shadow of a small giant. I want to say something to him, to confide in him, because he'd know exactly how rotten I was feeling. He sees me and nods and says a standard 'Hello' but I notice - and I just know it isn't my imagination - that he's not impressed with me either. And Bobby Collins, the first ever Scot to win Footballer of the Year and my true all-time favourite player who I'd always looked up to and wanted to be like, studies me for a second more and then walks away, with the tiniest shake of his head and a not very pleasant expression on his face. He is disgusted with me, I'm like something he's just trodden in. It's bloody alright for him, he's got all the staff helping him get over a broken leg, he's even got Terry Yorath, one of the newer junior lads, doing all his carrying and stuff, like an assistant, like an army batman. What have I got? A bloody hospital walking stick, a grandma I hardly see and a two hundred yard trek to get fed properly, that's what. So I do what I think is the best option, I go home before any more uncalled for shit comes my way.

6 iv

Last season's losing finalists fell early in the next FA Cup. After impressively beating Bury 6-0 in the third round, the fourth round produced a much harder pairing for Leeds, at Chelsea, where they undeservedly went down 1-0. The Yorkshiremen outplayed the Londoners for long periods and their dominance had been so strong. But bad luck, the lack of a clinical finisher in attack and the presence of Peter Bonetti playing brilliantly in goal meant the hosts kept the visitors out. The Leeds attack had been seriously weakened by the loss of Alan Peacock in January with damaged knee ligaments.

The League was the most important competition in football, bringing with it the 'bread and butter' of regular revenue at the turnstiles. But most footballers often preferred cup ties as they had an edge over League games and were often more exciting. And knockout matches in general were by nature more dramatic too, with fates decided and heroes & villains made within a matter of minutes. The outcome of a League campaign normally stretched to nine months. The Football League Cup though was still young and a definite poor relation compared to the FA Cup, borne out by vastly inferior match attendances. It first appeared in the 1960-'61 season, won that year by Aston Villa, 3-2 over two legs against Rotherham United. On October 13th, Revie insisted his team selection for the League Cup third round tie at home to WBA had been entirely appropriate, even though his young Leeds side lost the match 4-2. And the crowd of just 13,455 demonstrated how highly the paying public rated the competition. Nevertheless, he was criticised for fielding a weakened team. It wouldn't be the last time.

*

Revie believed that to win the title *and* other trophies in the same season, using the same pool of eleven or twelve players, for what would probably involve more than sixty matches, was nigh on impossible. And this season there were times even Mother Nature seemed to be against them - Leeds had games in hand over their rivals for much of this season due to weather-postponed matches. Games in hand did not signify points of course, but they nearly always did signify fixture pile-ups and player-fatigue problems.

In the race for the Division One title, Leeds had occupied top spot for a short while early in the season but gradually fallen behind, due to losing points in surprising, disappointing draws and defeats or just by having matches postponed. In the Fairs Cup second round, they had been paired with SC Leipzig of East Germany. The first leg was away, behind the so-called Iron Curtain, in late November. It had snowed heavily but the tie had never been in doubt as the Leipzig ground staff had worked hard to flatten and pack the snow, paint blue pitch markings on it and provide orange rather than white footballs for the game.

In order to gain better grip on the icy surface, the Leeds players filed the studs on their boots down to the boot nails.

During the match, cut and bloodied SC Leipzig players complained to the referee, to no avail. Leeds carried their own provisions for their travels rather than trust the Eastern bloc hospitality, or any foreign hospitality for that matter. Revie would be criticised for being near paranoid on the club's travels overseas but the Leipzig tie was no ordinary tie, to be played in no ordinary country and in no ordinary political climate - it was after all, Russian territory they were visiting. He told his team to attack from the outset and to dominate the play in the hope of scoring early and then maybe sealing the match by half-time. Were that to happen it might cause the home supporters to turn against their own team, as they were prone to do, thus unnerving the Leipzig players. Tonight though, Revie's scheme faltered - Leeds, through Peter Lorimer and Billy Bremner, only managed to score in the last ten minutes of the match and even then Leipzig pulled a goal back to make it a tight 2-1 Leeds win. The return leg took place at Elland Road, on a cold December 1st night. Although Revie selected his strongest line-up, the 32,111 crowd were not much entertained, having to endure a dour 0-0 draw. At least Leeds advanced to the next round, where they were drawn against Spanish side Valencia, the first leg scheduled for Elland Road, February next year.

6 v

It takes a proper man to apologise and admit when he's in the wrong. Ces was one such man and I was chuffed that he was, I'd felt like one worthless waster after what had happened. He'd snapped at me because he'd been 'completely shagged out' as he put it, and in a 'bastard' of a mood, working through the night and morning on the Leeds pitch. There was only a few of them, trying to keep the surface from freezing as well as making the terraces safe enough for spectators for the Stoke match. No sleep, cold and working through the night. I couldn't really blame him for being annoyed, my mood would have been uglier than an Everton crowd if I'd been in the same boat. I think my not visiting him and John wound him up too, they'd wanted to see that I was getting myself better, and trying to keep reasonably fit. I'd just never felt like doing that, and that was the main problem, my mind.

My grandma had told me she wanted a little chat with me, 'adult to adult'. I must admit, I'd been expecting another bollocking, or at least a more than mild ticking off, but she was great, like she knew exactly what was going on in my head and how I was feeling. She would help me any way she could to recover from the injuries. And so, from late December, she'd get me up out of bed each morning again, seven or so o'clock, and pot free I'd go out for a brisk walk - running, even trotting, wasn't possible yet, my bones weren't anywhere near strong enough and I needed to build up my leg muscles as well. Regardless, running is risky on a winter's morning - if ice didn't get you then there was always chance in the dark that a dozy driver would. I'd even walk with my grandma to her work in town - well, half the way - turning back at the Commercial pub on the junction of Marshall Street, next to the Kays Catalogues buildings. There was something mysterious, even exciting, about walking into Leeds city centre first thing on a morning. It was even eerier when it was foggy.

I'd come back the way over Holbeck Moor, with the horrible yellow and cream high-rise flats - some of Passy's 'future slums' - towering above like King Kong and Godzilla but not as handsome. Without fail I'd get a bit spooked at St Matthew's Church in the dark, even though I was nearly sixteen. I'd walk the while past the Waggon and Horses pub, the various little shops, the rows and rows of cobbled streets, back-to-backs and terraced houses, some with squatty gardens, grimy workshops and yards, and more grotty 'Oliver Twist' houses and tenements. And of course, I'd pass Perseverance Works too, as the sky got lighter and the little floodlights of the stadium became more visible. I'd see a few people going to their various places of work, on buses or walking or in cars, and I'd ponder on the fact that I'd never done a proper day's work in my life. True, I'd trained hard but most of the kids I was at school with would be well into new jobs or apprenticeships. Printing, building, clerical, the copper-works, even in the forces or down one of the pits not too far away. Me, I'd set my stall out early on to be a professional football player, everyone knew that. It was on mornings like that when I really hoped those kids thought well of me. I'd try to not look at Perseverance Works as I passed it, as if it was a bloody vulture or something wanting to tear me apart, because all I'd got so far from persevering was agony. To Achieve Personal

Greatness Again wasn't going to be easy, and it would need more than just perseverance from me.

I'd missed a lot of Leeds games because I'd been laid up - or pissed up, as Ces would have put it - and so there were a load of arrivals and departures and debuts which had passed me by too. Don Weston joined Huddersfield for £3,500 while Mike O'Grady arrived here. Weston had done us proud in his time here, with a goal ratio of one in three. O'Grady had done excellently since joining, scoring a few, setting up a load and giving Leeds a fresh threat on the right-wing as Giles was moved in to Collins' place in central midfield. Everyone was saying it looked as if the position had been made for Giles, while gloomy sods were saying we'd seen the last of Collins in a Leeds shirt. Same with Albert as well maybe, due to rumours of 'drink problems'. In the League, after Christmas we were hardly in the frame to win it, Liverpool were coasting it. We'd been unlucky in the FA Cup, losing 1-0 away to Chelsea, and the League Cup finished early as well. So far I'd missed the debuts of Mick Bates, Eddie Gray, Dennis Hawkins, Nigel Davey, David Harvey in nets, Terry Hibbitt and of course O'Grady. There was a brilliant photograph of Bates in the paper, where his hair is so thick it's the same size as his face.

The League table, 29th January 1966 after we'd lost 2-0 at Sunderland.

1 Liverpool	Played 28	Points 41
2 Burnley	Played 27	Points 36
3 Man. Utd	Played 27	Points 34
4 LEEDS	Played 25	Points 33

It was obvious Liverpool were doing really well, but the fight for the Championship wasn't over by a long chalk. We were looking the likeliest to battle it out with them but I was never that confident, games in hand never equals points on the table.

Jimmy Greenhoff played well in a few games and eventually asked to be taken off the transfer list. 'Mr Versatile' as he was being called, Paul Madeley, had established himself in the first team and even scored his first goal, last September. The Leeds coaches had high hopes for all the new lads, none higher than Eddie Gray, though he was a bit of a skiver with the day to day chores, according to Ces. Billy Bremner nicknamed Gray and Peter Lorimer 'Pixie and Dixie', as they seemed to spend half their time together, and not working very hard said Ces.

6 vi

February 2nd, Elland Road - Valencia, twice winners and once losing finalists in the previous three years of the Inter-Cities Fairs Cup, wore all-red versus Leeds' all-white, and took an early lead thanks to hesitation between Norman Hunter and Paul Reaney which allowed Munoz a free run at goal and he coolly beat Sprake to make it 1-0. For Leeds, young centre-forward Rod Belfitt made his European debut. Leeds deservedly equalized in the 64th minute through a sweet strike from Lorimer feeding off of a cross from Giles. The match though, was remembered more not for the quality of play but its violence which, according to the Times, was very much the fault of Valencia players, with Leeds players simply giving as good as they got in response. It hit its peak, or nadir, late in the game when Jack Charlton went up front for a Leeds attack. He was first kicked and then punched by an opposing central-defender. Lorimer watched dumbfounded as Nito, the Valencia goalkeeper, spat at Charlton, too. Then realising he had made a big mistake, Nito fled the scene of the crime, looking for an escape route. Charlton pursued him. Dutch referee, Leo Horn, consequently instructed the teams to leave the pitch for a few minutes, so the players could calm down. In the dressing room, Horn advised Charlton he was being sent off for his indiscretions, while left-back Vidagany also was retired early. But the referee had been hoodwinked by the Valencia players: Vidagany was guilty only of having a stinker of a game, which is why his team-mates wanted him out of action. Once restarted, the aggression continued, mainly in Valencia fouls, but the result stayed the same, 1-1. As a result of the violence, the English FA decided to investigate Charlton's conduct. Despite the referee defending the Leeds man as the aggrieved victim, the FA found him guilty and fined him. Meanwhile, Spain's FA did nothing about the sent off Valencia players or the team's overall conduct. Revie was more angered at the Spanish authorities' blatant disregard for justice rather than Charlton's punishment by his own FA.

In Valencia, Leeds wore a seldom-seen change kit of blue shirts with yellow shorts and socks. Before the kick-off, as they warmed up on the pitch, Les Cocker jogged onto the pitch to John Giles, carrying a slip of paper in his hand and wearing a smile on his face. A broad smile at that, not the most common sight on match days. He had a telegram for Giles, it was from his pregnant wife Anne and it read 'We've had a little girl - Anna!' In the match, Gary Sprake was in fine form and made no mistakes after inconsequentially fumbling an early cross, while his outfield team-mates defended in number, soaking up wave after wave of Valencia attacks. The plan was to absorb the Valencia pressure and reply with counter-attacks. Charlton was playing like a true stalwart, leading by example, and the whole team fought magnificently throughout, in front of a partisan 45,000 crowd. In the 75th minute the visitors' resolve paid off as O'Grady, receiving a good pass from Madeley, ran on to the ball and beat the offside trap to then out-manoeuvre two challenges before striking a low, angled drive which eluded Nito inside his near post. 2-1 to Leeds on aggregate and another one of the favourites were out as a result. Next up for Leeds were highly-rated Ujpest Dozsa, from communist Hungary. Having already beaten FC Cologne and Everton, they were another side confident of beating the young debutantes.

Ujpest Dozsa's plan for away ties was to defend en masse and to score breakaway goals. If their opponents did manage to score, they had so much attacking flair within the team that hitting back quickly was probable rather than just possible. So far in the competition, they had lost by the odd goal in both their away ties but comfortably won their home ties by three or four goals. So being new to European tactics, Leeds would not represent much of a problem, plus Ujpest were one of the favourites to win the trophy. Their odds, however, began to lengthen due to early events in the first leg of the tie. To their annoyance, the game actually went ahead despite heavy rainfall and the pitch being a 'gluepot'. Such conditions hindered their normally quick, incisive passing and movement. Revie had had Ujpest watched three times and was well aware of their strengths; it was no exaggeration to say they were good enough to beat probably any side around. For the first leg, at Elland Road, he anticipated they would defend and hope to exploit any gaps at the back left by his side; he set out his instructions to his players accordingly. On the night, a crowd of 40,462 saw the blue shirts, yellow shorts and blue socks of Leeds lay siege to Ujpest's defence with quick and direct attacks. The Hungarians were surprised by such swift onslaught, and after only six minutes Leeds had scored their first goal, Terry Cooper netting from close range after a parried Willie Bell cross. Relentless pressure brought more home rewards and by half-time it was 4-0, with goals from Bell and Jim Storrie, both headers, and a Bremner tap-in. Ujpest, in all-white (with a purple diagonal on the shirts) scored a 'consolation' goal in the 74th minute but their quest for Inter-Cities glory looked gravely ill by the time of the return leg. Manager Sandor Balogh II went on to describe Leeds' Elland Road performance as 'simply fantastic'.

At the Szusza Ferenc Stadium near Budapest, the first half of the return match was a vintage display of continental attacking football, with Ujpest menacing Leeds' goal almost non-stop. It was however, met by a vintage display of English defending too. Even though Revie had cancelled training for the Leeds squad as his players were so tired - they made do with a brisk walk along the banks of the River Danube instead - United were more than a match for the hosts. Ujpest hit the post three times, and shot narrowly over a couple of times too, and when they were actually on target, Gary Sprake was again in superb form. He would be beaten just the once, shortly before half-time, Fazekas pouncing on a brilliant parry from the Welshman. The immense home pressure continued in the second half but to no avail, and late on, compounding their frustrations, wrong-footing two defenders by letting a pass from O'Grady go through his legs, Lorimer raced fifty yards before slotting the ball into the net. A highly impressive 5-2 aggregate win for the inexperienced Leeds, now through to the last four of their first ever European crusade.

In the Ujpest function room after the match, when it is customary for opponents to officially take refreshment together and exchange goodwill gifts, pleasantries and the like, rather more serious exchanges between the players took place. Insults and threats were made, resulting in scuffles and fisticuffs between both teams. Eyewitness accounts of Hungarian footballers fleeing down by the Danube would suggest that Leeds triumphed there too. Elsewhere, Chelsea narrowly won through 3-2 against 1860 Munich, and were now paired with Barcelona. Leeds' semi-final would be against a Spanish side too, the 1964 Fairs Cup winners, Real Zaragoza.

*

On January 15th, Everton manager Harry Catterick was kicked and knocked down by young men annoyed at their team losing the Blackpool-Everton match. They were *Everton* followers, Blackpool had won the match. In March, after four cautions, Billy Bremner was suspended for seven days and fined £100 by the FA Disciplinary Committee. On March 26th eleven people were injured when a wall collapsed at the Preston North End versus Manchester United FA Cup match. Liverpool's Ian St John (sent off at Fulham late February for striking an opponent) was warned on his future conduct and fined £100 by an FA Commission; Leeds' Jack Charlton received a £50 fine (plus £30 costs) for the Valencia sending off. On April 19th, over a hundred people needed treatment for injuries after bottles were thrown and fighting occurred before, during and after the Liverpool versus Celtic Cup Winners' Cup semi-final, second leg. And in *football* matters, preparing for their FA Cup semi-final against Manchester United, Everton rested a number of their first team players in the 4-1 defeat against Leeds on April 16th. They were fined £2000 for 'bending' the rules but won the semi-final 1-0 and later the final.

6 vii

Even though we beat Everton 4-1 on April 16th, we were definitely out of the title race as Liverpool beat Stoke while Burnley lost at Villa, meaning the Scousers couldn't be caught: deservedly League Champions 1965-'66. Having said that, what The Don and the lads had achieved so far was just as brilliant. And then there was little Burnley finishing second, near miracles were being worked there too. This season, the Inter-Cities Fairs Cup turned out to be our most realistic target. We'd done fantastically well and now were at the semi-final stage against Real Zaragoza, late April. The first game, away, Zaragoza won 1-0, by a penalty after Billy allegedly handled in the area. Allegedly. It seemed some dubious (French) refereeing had gone on as Johnny Giles was sent off too, for being punched! Zaragoza were meant to be a great attacking side so 0-1 wasn't so bad for us, plus Giles' suspension after the sending off didn't actually happen. Don Revie had planned an official appeal and asked UEFA for a private hearing, only to be refused because the match referee had since retired.

In the home leg, we started well and went close a few times early on, including a Willie Bell header hitting the post. Team captain was Jack Charlton and he seemed to be everywhere, and in the 23rd minute he headed on a Giles cross which Albert Johanneson trundled into the net to level the tie, 1-1 on aggregate. It looked like it wouldn't be long before we got the deciding goal, Zaragoza must have been looking forward to half-time, they were under so much pressure.

The second half though was different, the Spaniards looked much more composed and confident, and even though we had most of the possession still, we seemed to have lost impetus. Then, around the hour mark, Zaragoza scored with a cracking half-volley to make it 2-1 to them on aggregate. Revie pushed Charlton up into attack to try and get us back in to the lead again. It worked a treat within minutes - Albert pelted down the wing to reach the ball before it went out of play, and he passed it back down the touchline to Norman Hunter to cross in perfectly for Charlton to head home. 2-1 on the night, 2-2 on aggregate and it stayed that way. And not only had Jack set one up, scored one and won the man of the match award, he also won the toss of a red and white disc to decide where the replay would be played: Elland Road in two weeks' time.

As if the Elland Road pitch wasn't in a bad enough state as it was, even in May, The Don only went and got the fire brigade to flood it for the replay. I nearly couldn't believe what I was seeing - it was a lovely sunny day and Beeston was bone dry, yet there were firemen making a huge paddling pool of the pitch. Revie had seen the Zaragoza players training on Fullerton Park, he apparently was worried that they'd be too quick for us on a dry surface. There were quite a few Spanish internationals in their side, plus some Brazilians, too - their nickname 'Los Magnificos' wasn't for nothing

- so I suppose wetting the pitch made some sense. But the plan backfired, big time.

I seriously doubt anyone could have expected such a start: Zaragoza were three up inside the first quarter of an hour. Their second goal was a great strike but the other two were just poor defending. Jack pulled a late goal back, and we hit the post twice in the second half as well, but we were well beaten, that's the truth. It could have been worse, we could have been beaten by a team from Italy.

Chapter 7: 1966/7 - Farewell to the Pocket Puskas

7 i

It would have been an interesting series of questions for Eamonn Andrews to ask: without the influence of Don Revie, would Jack Charlton have developed into a world-class defender? Would coach and physio Les Cocker's reputation have flourished so much? And would now-renowned players like Norman Hunter, Paul Reaney and Gary Sprake (to name just three of the Leeds first team) have even made careers as professional footballers?

*

Up on my wall it went, **the 1965 - '66 honours list.**
League Champions - Liverpool, Runners up - us, Leeds, second time in a row.
FA Cup winners - Everton, Runners up - Sheffield Wednesday.
League Cup winners - WBA, Runners up - West Ham.
European Cup winners - Real Madrid, Runners up - Partizan Belgrade.
European Cup Winners Cup winners - Borussia Dortmund, Runners up - Liverpool.
Inter-Cities Fairs Cup winners - Barcelona, Runners up - Real Zaragoza.
Football Player of the Year - Bobby Charlton, Manchester United.
European Footballer of the Year - Bobby Charlton.
Average Leeds home gate = 35,773.
Clean Air in nine years.

7 ii

All over England kids would be playing football in the parks and playgrounds and streets, with jumpers for goalposts on the ground or chalk on the walls, and they'd nab the name of Geoff Hurst or Bobby Charlton or Roger Hunt, Alan Ball, Bobby Moore, Martin Peters, or even Jack Charlton, George Cohen, Ray Wilson, Nobby Stiles. The goalkeeper, of course, would always be Gordon Banks. But not in Leeds, not even after 1966. In Leeds, the kids would be Gary Sprake in goal or when playing out they were Paul Reaney or Willie Bell or Billy Bremner or Jackie Charlton or Norman Hunter or Eddie Gray or Peter Lorimer, or even Terry Cooper, Albert Johanneson, Paul Madeley, Jim Storrie, Alan Peacock, Jimmy Greenhoff or Mike O'Grady.

On July 30th 1966 there came that fantastic day for the nation - England beat West Germany 4-2 in the World Cup final. English and German players had shown remarkable levels of fitness and resilience to last the whole game, *plus* thirty minutes of extra time, as substitutions weren't part of the game then. Regardless of the controversy which justifiably raged over the legitimacy of Hurst's second and England's third goal, they deserved the victory thanks to the single-minded, highly professional manager and his superb squad of players and personnel.

One sure sign of a football club's successes is the recognition of its players by their individual countries. Goalkeeper Gary Sprake for example, was now just about a fixture in the Wales squad, and only 21 years old. Billy Bremner had recently been capped for Scotland and Willie Bell would get the call too. Bobby Collins had made a Scotland comeback during Leeds' momentous return to Division One, until his nasty injury, while teenagers Peter Lorimer and Eddie Gray were already well-known at Scotland Youth levels. If they continued playing well for Leeds then they surely would not have long to wait for their call-ups to the full squad. When he joined Leeds, John Giles was already a seasoned international and now a near-permanent cornerstone for the Eire team, and he wasn't even 26 years of age yet. In addition, there were English players at Leeds who enjoyed international successes, of varying degrees. Mike O'Grady, Alan Peacock, Norman Hunter and most notably of course, Jack Charlton, had already featured for England and young Paul Madeley, making a name for himself as the 'play anywhere Peacock', had appeared for the English Under-23 team. Hunter would be in the 1966 World Cup squad as deputy for captain Bobby Moore while Charlton would partner Moore throughout the whole tournament. And if apartheid had not prompted FIFA to suspend a South Africa national team, it is almost certain that Albert Johanneson would have represented his country many times. Certain other members of the Leeds squad would have to wait for their national chances, but considering that it had been only five years since Revie had taken charge, the progress of the club and the players was exceptional. In 1961, not one current international was playing for the club at the time.

The money men of Leeds United were reasonably satisfied too in 1966, as the club reported a profit and were completely debt free, apparently for the first time ever. There were rumblings of dissatisfaction from the supporters however, with the trophy cabinet still bare and with no big money transfers imminent. The Leeds public wanted to see new signings, most importantly a proven, high-scoring centre-forward. Don Revie though seemed prepared to wait for the players he wanted and who he considered as right for the club. He knew that if he bought a player who did not fit in well enough with the Leeds United 'way' or the family atmosphere, he believed all their hard work in building and developing the club could easily be ruined. Sunderland's former Glasgow Rangers 'maestro' Jim Baxter was a perfect example - a truly gifted player but one who Revie regarded as a risk, primarily due to his *active* social life.

Revie considered Jimmy Greenhoff and Rod Belfitt to be potentially the ideal striker partnership: Greenhoff a graceful, creative and quick 'blade', Belfitt a more physical, aggressive 'bludgeon' type who revelled in pressurising defenders. The main drawback was, at 20 and 21 years old respectively, both had very little experience. Once the 1966-'67 season commenced, supporter resentment intensified with each game. Injuries to Johanneson, O'Grady and Peacock severely limited the team's options in attack. A powerful target man was needed, and whilst Belfitt always battled valiantly, he was too lightweight to be the immediate solution. The season began badly for Leeds, with a 3-1 defeat at free-spending Tottenham Hotspur, on the day, livelier and more attack-minded. The week before, in a Hampden Park friendly against a Glasgow XI, Jack Charlton sustained a hamstring injury which would cause him to miss a third of Leeds' League programme, so he was out of the Spurs game, another big loss for the side. A forgettable result but the match at least provided the iconic image of Dave Mackay angrily gripping Billy Bremner by the shirt collar, in retaliation to a tackle from the Leeds number four.

Although Leeds were beaten soundly, the man of the match was returning captain Bobby Collins who showed skill and energy above most of the much younger players on show. Such a scintillating display made his absence (through injury) from the next game - a tight 2-1 win over West Bromwich Albion - all the more disappointing for the fans. Sadder still was the limited number of games he would feature in due to the ankle problem. A perfect midfield replacement was Giles, but a thigh injury was to cause him to miss a third of the season too.

*

The 1966 World Cup triumph boosted attendances in England but came at a cost: more trouble, on and off the fields of play. On November 18th, Malcolm Allison, the Manchester City assistant manager, was suspended from football for 28 days for using obscene language towards a referee. At the Southampton-Manchester United match, travelling supporters attacked a programme seller; it was the fourth reported attack of the season involving Manchester United fans. In December, Tottenham Hotspur expelled eight members of their own supporters club for disorderly conduct while Manchester United's Nobby Stiles was suspended for three weeks after three bookings so far; Stoke City's Maurice Setters was suspended for two matches after the same number of cautions. And on December 30th, Chelsea boss Tommy Docherty received a £100 fine for by the FA for insulting a referee.

*

Injuries to key players hindered any chances Leeds had of decent consistency. Up to the halfway stage of the season, they had drawn eight, lost five and won just ten of their League games. The good news though was that the league was proving to be a closely fought affair.

The League Division One table (top) 31st December, 1966.

1 Man. Utd	Played 24	Points 33
2 Liverpool	Played 23	Points 31
3 Nottm. F.	Played 24	Points 30
4 Stoke C.	Played 24	Points 29
5 Chelsea	Played 24	Points 28
6 Leeds Utd.	Played 23	Points 28

On the face of it, Leeds were capable of a serious challenge for the title, but a humiliating 5-0 defeat at Anfield in November cast serious doubts over their credentials, and an incredible 7-0 thrashing at Ron Greenwood's West Ham United two weeks before, had put paid to their League Cup hopes. Greenwood was allegedly less than gracious in victory to Revie, a poor attitude which he vowed to always remember, telling his team that they would never lose to 'that man' again.

*

January 14th, 1967, Leeds' Billy Bremner was sent off against Nottingham Forest and would receive a two-week suspension. The same day, after Plymouth had ended Millwall's unbeaten home run of 59 games, their coach was wrecked by angry supporters. February 4th, Stoke's Maurice Setters was sent off against West Bromwich Albion; February 7th, Fulham banned forty of their own supporters for being 'undesirable and unruly'; February 11th, Terry Venables of Tottenham Hotspur, and Fred Callaghan of Fulham, were sent off for fighting.

*

On Valentine's Day, 1967, Bobby Collins' romance with Leeds United finally ended as he left the club to join Bury. With Revie's fervent interest in signing Alan Ball, as well as the flourishing partnership of Giles and Bremner (Bremner was the new skipper, too) Collins knew his Leeds playing days were limited. And that was even after Ball signed for Everton the previous August. Bury came in for Collins and the 'Pocket Puskas' was allowed to leave on a free transfer. He went with the best wishes of everyone at Elland Road, and the eternal gratitude of manager Don Revie.

In comparison to recent years, the season had been an up and down time for Leeds, and with more downs to it than ups. However, with victories over DWS Amsterdam in the second round (including a Johanneson hat-trick), Valencia and then Bologna, ending with a May semi-final aggregate win over Kilmarnock - thanks mainly to a hat-trick from Belfitt - they had stealthily progressed to the Inter-Cities Fairs Cup final, to be played at the beginning of the next season due to fixture congestion. And, by finishing fourth in Division One, they had qualified for the same competition again, regardless of the result of the two-legged final.

7 iii

With me, beggars couldn't be choosers, a rubbish saying worn out more than the arse of Don Revie's lucky blue suit trousers but which summed up my own situation pretty well. My chances of playing football for Leeds weren't even a dream, they didn't exist. Once the pot and stuff had come off my leg, I soon discovered how badly I'd let myself go during those months in plaster, how unfit I'd got, and that was without me visiting Sheila's Café on Elland Road, which opened this year. It was all a bit of a shock, my belly had taken *Achieving Personal Greatness* a bit too literally while my lungs felt like they'd shrunk. And course, my left leg had lost strength in a big way. So I made some major changes to my life - I stopped drinking pints of beer through the day and only had sherry (with raw eggs) on a morning with my breakfast. And even though I wasn't running full pelt yet, just jogging, by July '66 I'd got myself quite a lot fitter, rebuilding muscles which seemed to have gone flabby - or just gone - and to help strengthen my ankle, I regularly hopped on my left leg. At first I'd been scared to even just stand on it. Whenever it was cold or damp, more often than not I'd get a throbbing chill in my leg where the fibia bone had been broken. The doctors said it was nothing to worry about - just in case though, I was told to drink more milk to increase my calcium content. Not just any old milk either, but full cream, handily available at the stadium. Mind you, I hated it, it was like drinking cold snot it was that thick.

Tuesday night was training night for St Anthony's - mainly shuttle running (which I also hated), a couple of laps round the Cross Flatts Park pitch and then a seven-a-side match. The first couple of times I just refereed rather than played in the game, but after a while I made my return. The lads wouldn't tackle hard in fear of hurting me, but I got back in to the swing of things quite soon. I planned to be back playing in the St Ant's eleven by spring 1967. By then I'd be seventeen or thereabouts, and would have missed nearly two full seasons, but you can't hurry recuperation from serious injury, no matter how desperate you are. Then, I hoped, I'd be fully fit again. Would I be confident enough, would I have the guts to tackle hard again, and to really give the ball a whack with my left foot? The closer the time got, the more the tummy butterflies were making their plans to visit.

In addition to Bobby Collins leaving Leeds, Jim Storrie had moved on by now, all sad news in my opinion, even though it was the business of football. I felt like I'd lost two friends, even though I hardly knew them. I'd never forget how much good they'd done for Leeds, especially Bobby. Without him we would have been a Division Three club by 1963, no doubt about that.

As substitute, I made my return early 1967 for St Anthony's against some Working Men's Club team from Swarcliffe. This being Leeds, I would have thought there'd be more Unemployed Working Men's Clubs about. Anyway, I only got on for the last twenty minutes and we were already winning 4-0 but it was so bloody good to be back. I'd been champing at the bit to get on so much that I'd forgotten to be nervous, though I'd not slept well the night before. When I first went on to the pitch, it was one of the proudest moments of my life, it really was, as the referee and all the players, both sets, applauded me as I ran on. I couldn't believe it, how generous was that? I felt as proud as a peacock but close to blubbing, too. And then I was rudely brought down to earth and back to my senses when their left winger gave me a whack on my left shin. 'Welcome back' he said, and I swore at him through my chuckling.

There were no twinges, no after-effects, nothing - my leg and my ankle felt as good as new. Still, I had a secret weapon - a homemade shin pad I'd created out of the mouldable pot the hospital put on my leg underneath the half-length pot. I'd heated it up again, shaped it round my leg and cut it down to size with scissors. And like pilots in the war made a record of their kills, I marked in ink on the pot each St Anthony's game I played. Meanwhile, I was often busy with work too. The ground staff at Elland Road consisted of the full and part-timers, led just about by Ces and John, plus loads of 'casuals' like me who helped out, especially when the weather was crap and when the games piled up so the pitch needed looking after more. A handful of us casuals were more like regulars, just not paid as much as the proper employees. I didn't mind that at all, I was grateful the club knew I existed and all that, as I felt part of a team, even if it wasn't one of the football teams just yet.

It was 3pm kick off but I knew before the kick-off whistle went that we'd lost the semi-final against those London ponces Chelsea. In fact, the Villa Park clock showed that my enlightenment took place at around 1.25pm on Saturday 29th April, 1967. Ces was with me to see it all, plus tons of Leeds and Chelsea fans milling around the place. 'That's our fucking goose cooked then, good and proper,' he said, on sight of a group of really big fellas in suits near the reception and officials' entrance, posturing like they owned the Villa Park stadium, like everyone was there to see *them* and not the FA Cup semi-final. Standing there, together - the match referee Ken Burns, posing for photographs - with twin brothers Reggie and Ronnie Kray. All shiny and black slicked-back hair, looking like they'd been dipped in Brylcreem, all *together*, like old bloody pals, plus other well-dressed, big blokes hanging around them, like guard dogs, watching and trying to menace anyone and everyone who went by. One thing was dead bloody sure, Ces said, that those two charmless Cockneys crooks were famous for a lot of things, but being football fans or Chelsea supporters wasn't among them.

To be chosen to officiate an FA Cup semi-final was quite an honour bestowed on a referee, it showed how highly the FA rated him. Ken Burns, from somewhere in the Midlands, had obviously done something right in his career to be so well-regarded. I don't know what that was though, he kept it a bloody secret from us in this game. Our chairman Harry Reynolds was pretty badly ill at the time, with arthritis I think, I'm not sure he was even at the game but if he had've been and he'd got wind of the crooked dealings it would have made him even poorlier.

Leeds didn't lose the match, they had it stolen. Even without Jack Charlton who had a broken toe and Albert Johanneson with a muscle strain, we were the better team but ended up getting cheated out of it. Leeds had supposedly been clear favourites to win the match. I don't know how they were so sure about it, especially as that big sod Tony Hateley played for Chelsea up front, and our best centre-half was out injured. With respect to Hateley, on the ground he couldn't trap a sack of spuds but he was excellent in the air. Chelsea played well, especially in the first half when they had a few good efforts on goal as well as scoring the one. Sprake made a truly great save from defender Eddie McCreadie and we were under a lot of pressure. Typical of Sprake though, he only went and kicked their player John Boyle in the head, knocking him out for a few seconds, early in the game. God alone knew what went through Sprake's head some times, we were lucky he stayed on the pitch because he'd definitely deserved sending off.

7 iv

Soon before the end of the first half at Villa Park, Chelsea's number 7, Charlie Cooke, received the ball on the left touchline and ran twenty yards with it into the Leeds half. It was more thanks to his quick-wittedness rather than his swift footwork which helped him elude Rod Belfitt, Billy Bremner and then Eddie Gray, to whip in a fine cross for centre-forward Tony Hateley. Hateley met the ball powerfully with a thrusting header before his marker Paul Madeley managed to challenge. Sprake in goal had no chance, 1-0 to Chelsea.

In the second half Leeds ran the game, having the majority of possession and efforts on goal. Those efforts on goal though had not much troubled goalkeeper Peter Bonetti until, with less than ten minutes of the ninety to go, the tempo of Leeds' advances increased dramatically. From the centre circle, Norman Hunter, stroked a thirty-yard pass to Greenhoff on the left wing. The blond number 9 controlled the ball and quickly lobbed it towards Chelsea's penalty area. Bremner, now in attack, jumped high for the ball to easily beat his marker, just outside the box, and flick the ball on. A few feet in advance of the red-headed captain is Leeds' young left-winger Terry Cooper. With great anticipation he watches the ball elude defenders' heads as it drops to him, just inside the penalty area. Trapping the ball expertly with his left foot, he takes less than a second before striking a sweet, low shot towards goal. Bonetti dives quickly to his left it but the velocity of the shot beats him and the ball lands in the corner of the net. But the linesman had raised his flag as soon as Cooper received the ball, in an offside position. It is by the narrowest of margins but nevertheless, it *is* a margin and the linesman is right, Cooper was offside.

A few minutes later, a foraying thirty-yard run from Hunter was abruptly stopped by a Tambling foul, one of many such infringements from Chelsea. Given the horrendous challenge by Sprake on Chelsea forward Doyle in the seventh minute, the Blues' aggression was hardly surprising. So Leeds have a free-kick thirty-five yards out. Number 7 John Giles has placed the ball on the turf and waits for the referee's permission to take the kick. So good a striker of the ball is Giles, Chelsea have formed a three-man defensive wall ten or so yards in front of him. Referee Burns is standing a few yards from the wall, almost parallel with it. Giles waits anxiously for the signal, and the Chelsea men in the wall twitch nervously. Belfitt's substitute, Peter Lorimer, 'the Cannonball Kid', probably an even better striker of the ball than Giles, stands a few yards square in-field to his team-mate. Lorimer wants the ball but Giles appears to ignore his pleas, nervously waving his left arm as if directing Leeds players in the penalty area. Giles looks at referee Burns. Referee Burns looks back at Giles and raises his whistle to his mouth. Giles takes the kick and it's a short pass to Lorimer - just as the whistle is being blown. Lorimer shoots, connecting so well that the ball rockets into Bonetti's top left corner of the net, despite a valiant attempt to stop it. It is feasible that Lorimer's missile was physically unstoppable, but tragically for Leeds, it *is* stopped from being the match's equalizer. To nearly everyone's great surprise, referee Burns decided the free kick should be re-taken. To the majority watching, Mr Burns appeared to wait until the ball had actually hit the Chelsea net before deciding to disallow the goal. Without doubt, to the neutral, and of course to everyone in the Leeds camp, the goal should have stood. Regardless, in such situations, the advantage should lie with the attacking team. But the referee ignored all Leeds' pleas and to add to the controversial and apparently unjust close of such an enthralling tie, the referee ended the match prematurely too, blowing the final whistle a full two minutes before it was due. The defeat left Revie and his young team with the chance of being the first ever British team to win a European trophy without actually winning a major domestic honour.

7 v

Referee Burns blew the final whistle and we were out of the FA Cup, beaten 1-0. Chelsea were off to Wembley and we were off back to sodding West Yorkshire with nothing but a moral victory, a bad taste in our mouths and our tails between our legs again. Even his final whistle was early, Ces had a watch on and there was a bloody great clock in Villa Park for all to see as well that Burns had made yet another 'mistake'. Not that that mattered one bit, with two Leeds goals disallowed in the last few minutes, we could have played for a month of Sundays and still not had a goal given. Bastards.

Anyway, we were lucky to have even reached the semi-final as we'd scraped by Sunderland and Man City in the two previous rounds. In the sixth round, City winger Mike 'Buzzer' Summerbee, had run the show, and in the fifth round it took three matches to beat Sunderland. We got the better of them in the end in the second replay at Hull's Boothferry Park. Sunderland had two men sent off and our decisive second goal was a dubious penalty, after Greenhoff had been pushed, possibly not a foul or even in the penalty area. Some Sunderland fans ran on to the pitch and one of them even punched Willie Bell. I don't know for sure but I would think Willie or one of the other players got the pillock back. Ces told me that if we'd drawn the match again and needed another replay, it would have had to be played on the same day as the Bologna game. I thought he was pulling my leg about it but he wasn't, he was deadly serious, saying that Don Revie had already picked the one team for Europe and the one to stay at home for the FA Cup. We'd drawn 1-1 at Sunderland and then at Elland Road, after extra time, in the replay. 57,892 were there, Wednesday 15th March 1967, and there were thousands locked out as well. At least, 57,892 was the *official* attendance but the crowd will have been bigger in reality, because every club in the land fiddled gate receipts to save on tax. The Beatles weren't the only ones who hated the taxman.

It was always exhilarating being in the mass of bodies on the terraces, swaying and singing with hundreds, thousands of your own supporters. Three or four years ago, if you'd swayed on the Leeds terrace then you'd have fallen over as there was no one else anywhere near you. Nowadays it was often bedlam wherever the fans stood - pushing, pulling, leaning, leaned on, tumbling, and *erupting* whenever Leeds scored. Exciting and sort of safely dangerous with it, if that makes any sense, but for the Sunderland game there had been too many people in the stadium. It had been pay on the night at the turnstiles rather than ticket admission, as the club reckoned they'd not had enough time to get replay tickets printed up. Whatever the reasons, those spectators in the corner part of the Lowfields Road terracing, were lucky to get out alive. I was okay, I was in the West Stand with the ground staff.

I wouldn't have believed there was any real risk to life until I saw the buckled barriers the day after. Thick, sturdy, metal barriers, bent out of shape like a bust staple in a comic book. Because so many people had been crammed in there like sardines in a tin. We were lucky no one was killed and the club was very lucky they weren't being blamed for it. When Jim Baxter signed for Sunderland, his cousin joined at the same time. The cousin had the most brilliant nickname of any football player I ever heard - George Kinnell, known to Sunderland supporters as 'Foo', George 'Foo' Kinnell!

After the FA Cup exit, we still had the Inter-Cities Fairs Cup to go for, and an outside chance (very outside chance) of the League title with five games left, so it wasn't completely grim. And in Europe we'd been drawn to play Kilmarnock in the semi-finals, a not too difficult tie, I thought.

Chapter 8: 1967/8 - Dreams come true - at last

8 i

Naturally, *This Is Your Life* focuses on the positive aspects of Don Revie's career, rather than the reported darker sides of his Leeds experiences. Nothing was said on the programme of the bad reputation the Leeds team had 'earned'. In the openly aggressive sport of professional football, the Leeds players most certainly were no angels, but there were plenty of other First Division players equally as tough, who also gave as good as they got and 'got their retaliation in first'. Every play or pantomime needs a villain, a 'baddie', and Revie's side was perfect, the nation's favourite - encouraged by the press, of course - in those particular roles.

*

May 3rd 1967, a Thursday, was Leeds United's first game since being controversially knocked out of the FA Cup semi-final stage by Chelsea. They were at home to Liverpool and a crowd of 36,547 watched as they won 2-1. Leeds fans had not been in good spirits though, due to the semi-final defeat, and referees could never be described as flavour of the month with them anyway. Numerous violent incidents occurred on the terraces during the match whilst the referee, Jack Taylor, was even attacked by a spectator on the pitch. The trouble reached such a level that Harry Reynolds stood armed with a microphone on the pitch and said that 'they' might want the ground closing but 'we don't'. Matters did calm down somewhat after but the Yorkshire Evening Post commented that Leeds 'has never seen worse conduct'.

On the final day of the 1966-'67 League season, Manchester United were crowned Division One champions with a 6-1 win at West Ham. Crowd trouble and rioting marred the day, with some spectators needing hospital treatment as a consequence of the violence.

*

In time for the new 1967-'68 season, Leeds had readied theirselves for fans trying to steal into Elland Road matches without paying. It was thought that the chaos at the Sunderland Cup replay had been caused by such gatecrashers, and on that occasion it was extremely fortunate there were no fatalities. Now, to improve spectator safety, admission prices had been increased and the damaged terracing rebuilt, plus corrugated sheeting added to the wall behind the Spion Kop to make it eight feet high and thus harder for illegal entry. And other changes had been made at the stadium too, mysterious changes.

Revie invited a well-known Blackpool fortune teller called Gypsy Rose Lee - not necessarily her real name - to help the Leeds cause. More odd behaviour from the notoriously superstitious manager, though it had not been an impulsive decision, he had discussed curses and the like in depth with Reverend John Jackson in the past. He was deadly serious, believing that the Elland Road ground had been cursed and that there were people genuinely capable of lifting such a bad luck. Revie, a Catholic, regarded superstitions as entirely relevant and often carried a small plastic figure of St John with him, as well as other lucky charms. Carrying such mementoes was to him no more bizarre than praying to God every night.

The rumour was that the site had been home for a community of gypsies early in the 20th century and that following a dispute with the council over land ownership, the gypsies were forced to leave. They put a curse on the land in response. Don Revie believed the story held credence and so, once there, Gypsy

Rose Lee demanded that every door within the stadium be locked and that only herself and Revie remained on site, everyone else had to leave. She proceeded to scatter a collection of seeds in each corner of the ground and also in the centre of the pitch. She also confided in Revie 'certain little secrets', all of which he considered as proof of the occult but which he would never publicly divulge.

More rituals had entered the world of the Leeds dressing room before each match's kick-off time. Revie would rub Cooper's back with Algipan, Bremner would have a lukewarm bath and Gray would ensure he was the first player changed into his kit. With Bremner, after his bath, the shorts were always the last part of his kit to go on, and he would borrow Norman Hunter's comb before leading the team out, carrying a ball thrown to him to catch each time. That particular custom had first begun with Hunter throwing a ball to Collins, a few seasons before. Hunter, after completing his specific game of head tennis with Charlton, would be the last player to comb his hair before going out to the pitch. And Reaney *needed* to kick a football against Revie's trouser leg at least once before every match.

Stemming from various incidents during his playing career, Revie believed he had valid reason for being so superstitious. Like in 1955, playing for Manchester City - the team had battled through to reach the FA Cup final for the first time in over twenty years, and they were strongly fancied to win it. However, bizarre problems arose involving their full-back Jimmy Meadows. The night before the game, in their hotel, he became extremely nervous and his night's sleep didn't last long though, as he woke himself and the other City players with his own screams. He had had nightmares about playing in the match and, because he was sweating so much, the club called the doctor in to examine him. There was nothing wrong with him, at least, not physically. In the match, Newcastle United took a first minute lead with the fastest ever goal scored in a FA Cup final, and not long afterwards, City were a man down - Meadows was carried off after seriously damaging his knee ligaments. With substitutes not in existence then, City's ten men were fighting a losing battle; Newcastle went on to win 3-1. Revie sympathised with Meadows but was convinced he had brought the misfortune on himself, as if his panicking had served as an invitation for bad luck to strike.

A few years before, just nineteen and playing for Leicester, Revie himself was seriously injured. After a collision with Spurs' left-half Ronnie Burgess, he suffered three fractures in his right ankle and had to spend days laid up in hospital, without medical staff even able to confirm how severe the injury actually was. Eventually doctors rated his chances of playing professional football again at a thousand-to-one probability. Revie though had developed the absolute belief that succeeding in football was his destiny, so retiring at nineteen could not happen, it simply was not meant to be. Helped by his manager Johnny Duncan, he was playing again in less than five months. And during those days of treatment and recuperation he met Johnny Duncan's niece, Elsie, for the first time. Don and Elsie got on so well together that Johnny Duncan soon became 'Uncle Jock' to Don and three years later Elsie became Mrs Revie.

In the year Don and Elsie married, 1949, his and Leicester's prospects looked very healthy. He had been called up by England for a summer tour and City had progressed impressively in the FA Cup. But again, the wheel of fortune had other grimmer turns in store. In a League match against West Ham on Easter Monday, a quite innocuous-looking knock to his nose caused him to withdraw from the match. Not only was it bloodier and more painful than first thought, it would threaten to have the most serious consequences of all. At first it seemed the injury had been treated successfully but in a game days later at Plymouth, the bloodflow returned and could not be stemmed. Nearly nine hours on, in hospital at last, a burst blood vessel was diagnosed with the doctors advising that had there been just one more hour's delay, Revie might well have died from loss of blood. He was forced to miss Leicester's FA Cup final against Wolves, too weak to even attend as a spectator, and the England tour was completely out of the question, of course. He would have to wait years for another chance.

It came when he was 27 when he received an invitation to join the England B team on tour. However, bad luck struck yet again - a groin injury ruled him out and he remained uncapped. Two years later, now with Manchester City, the team had made it to the 1956 FA Cup final. Team-mates and supporters knew that Revie had contributed crucially to their Cup run but due to a dispute with the club he was expected to be omitted from the final line-up. On the morning of the big game though, an amendment to the team-sheet had to be made: due to injury Billy Spurdle had to miss out, replaced by Don Revie. Another fine and influential Revie game followed, and City deservedly beat Birmingham 3-1. But even then came an unpleasant twist to the story - City's German goalkeeper Bert Trautmann, hurt late on in a heavy challenge with a Birmingham forward, was forced to play on for the last fifteen minutes with a painful neck injury which transpired to be a broken neck.

*

The football director was always a strange breed. Strange and rarely popular. Football supporters distrusted them and football players' opinions were rarely any more favourable. In his autobiography *The Clown Prince of Soccer* for instance, Len Shackleton included a chapter called 'The Average Director's Knowledge of Football' which consisted of just one page. An empty page at that. With even less affection, Tommy Docherty described the ideal board of directors as comprising 'three men - two dead and one dying.' Football fans were notorious too, for being fickle and forgetful, most directors knew this. At Leeds, just five years ago, the team teetered precariously over the chasm of Division Three, their safety confirmed only on the very last day of the season. Now, August 1967, three weeks in to the new campaign, Leeds are due to play in the two-legged Inter-Cities Fairs Cup final, yet supporters complained about high ticket prices.

Leeds would meet the highly-rated Yugoslavian team Dynamo Zagreb on August 30th and September 6th, with the new English season already three games old. It was their worst start for years, only one point out of a possible six earned and just one goal scored. Naturally, the situation was not helped by injuries to key players, but in certain minds the blame for the poor start lay solely at one man's door: Don Revie's, for not buying proven players, especially a top quality centre-forward. Nonetheless, the Leeds *defence* was giving most cause for concern.

For the very first time, Leeds conceded more than one goal in European competition, the first leg of the Inter-Cities Fairs Cup final, away at Dynamo Zagreb. Zagreb were renowned for their flair and ability to score goals aplenty, so a tough tie for the Peacocks had always been anticipated. The first leg result, 2-0 to Dynamo Zagreb, obviously wasn't a thrashing, but the worry was Leeds' inability to score. By now, the Away Goals rule had been introduced - if teams were level after the two legs, any goals scored by the away team would count as double - so had they managed to score, it could have proved crucial. Alas, one never looked likely, Zagreb had coped comfortably with all the Leeds attacks. Still, it had been the best Leeds performance of the season so far, all was not lost if they could build on the performance, especially as Dynamo Zagreb's weakpoint was, in theory, their defence.

*

Chairman Harry Reynolds had been suffering greatly from arthritis and his condition was not improving. Needing rest he decided to tender his resignation as chairman. The end of an era indeed, and without doubt, Don Revie and Leeds United would have been nowhere near as successful without Reynolds' influence. Chairmen rarely receive credit for their work at football clubs but this self-made Holbeck millionaire, a man who hated snobbery and who always stood firm for what he believed in, was probably the most important official to ever be associated with the club. His money and ambition combined with business acumen were integral in wrenching the club from near collapse to a thriving, highly respected organization. Without doubt, he enjoyed the trappings of his hard-earned wealth, with expensive cruises, a new Mercedes, rich meals at Sheeky's in London and the like, and playing polo and hunting, but he remained unwaveringly working class in attitude and manner, preferring beer to wine and fish and chips to caviar. Possibly the only serious professional disagreement between Reynolds and Don Revie was over the manager's pursuit of Blackpool FC's Alan Ball. Reynolds agreed all along that Ball was an excellent player but the board refused to match Everton's offer of £110,000 and were entirely against entering an auction for him. Revie, convinced Ball was the perfect player to complement Bremner and Giles in the Leeds midfield, was appalled to lose out on the player. But rumours circulated that Revie and Reynolds' dispute was irreconcilable - 'rumours' is all they were.

Albert Morris, a Leeds director since 1961, took over from Harry Reynolds. Although the choice of replacement was not surprising, with it came reports that Revie was unsettled. Negative rumours like manager unrest were of no benefit to anyone, and Revie knew that as well as damage being done to morale at the club and relationships within it, his own reputation could suffer. He acted quickly to scotch the gossip about his future in the job - 'I am very happy with United and I always have been,' he told the press. 'Since I became manager a family spirit has built up which I should hate to leave. I've had most of my players since they left school, and while we have won nothing yet we have been very close - and I want to see the job through. I grew up as a football manager under Harry Reynolds and I am positive the club spirit which he did so much to build will continue to be as strong as ever under Mister Morris and the other directors.' Nonetheless, ambitious Coventry City had hopes of luring him away, while Manchester United were on the look out for a successor to Matt Busby, who was supposedly planning retirement sooner rather than later. Regular conjecture from Italy linked various big clubs there with approaches for Revie's services, too. Also in the summer, Willie Bell was sold to Leicester City for £45,000. He had played 260 times for Leeds, the vast majority of the appearances for Revie, scoring 18 goals in that time. It was another sad departure as Bell had served the club well, always giving his all for the sake of the team and hardly ever having an 'off' day. Unfortunately for him, the emergence of Terry Cooper signified fewer opportunities for Bell to feature. Down the years, Revie would single out certain players for their professionalism, loyalty and commitment to his and the Leeds cause; Bell would almost always feature in that particular honours list. Revie held Grenville Hair in similar regard. Hair incidentally, was now in the management trade and doing well, in charge of Bradford City.

8 ii

In my thinking, the 1967-'68 season was always going to be hard because there wasn't enough quality in the Leeds squad to build on their achievements so far. It started badly with a draw at home to Sunderland and defeats away at Man United and Wolves, and then we sold one of my favourites, Willie Bell, to Leicester for £45,000. Worse was Harry Reynolds packing it all in. There was often talk of Harry wanting to retire but I never thought he'd actually do it, he was like a part of the furniture. No, he was more than that, he was a proper pillar of the football club. I remembered supporters taking the piss out of him - possibly me included - when he'd gone on to the pitch at half time to declare that Don Revie, the new manager, would take the club on to glory. Most people thought he'd lost his marbles. Thank God he was right, we had everything to thank Harry for, and I mean everything.

This season, bad signs were already there before a ball had been kicked - it looked like Johnny Giles might be out injured for a long time. We had last season's Inter-Cities Fairs Cup final to play though, both legs of it, against Dynamo Zagreb, on 30th August away and 6th September at home. In the first leg, we performed a lot better than we had in the three League games so far, though we didn't manage to score. 2-0 down, we had a so-called mountain to climb in the home leg, that was a definite. If we'd had Alan Peacock in the side, fit, it would have been different, but we didn't so there was no point me whining about it. Big Al only played six league games the season before and it wasn't much of a secret that his knees were just about done for. I never wanted to criticise The Don for his tactics and team selections and all that, but I had to say that I thought he made mistakes for the second leg against Dynamo Zagreb. We were 2-0 down after all, plus we were lacking height and heading power in attack, it was clear as day. No matter how hard Rod Belfitt and Jimmy Greenhoff tried - dead hard, as a matter of fact - neither of them was going to be as effective as Peacock who it turned out was fit to play but not picked. I couldn't fathom it - in the five matches before this one, we'd only scored five goals in total, it was embarrassing. I suppose beating Fulham 2 - 0 the previous Saturday in our first League win - with Belfitt getting both goals - must have given The Don a dilemma, but still.

Alan Peacock left Leeds not long after, to Plymouth Argyle for £10,000. He'd been criticised a fair bit and only played about sixty games for us in all, but he'd still managed a scoring rate of one goal in every two games nearly, plus he set up a load as well. His knees had had it, I think Revie sold him just so the player could get a few quid in his pocket. Nice gesture, though he'll have needed a chunk of it just to pay his bus fares! That win over Fulham was one of those silver linings with a cloud weighing it down - Billy Bremner had been sent off for arguing with the referee. And swearing at him, a lot. Reports said there was some 'crowd trouble' on the terraces as well, but I didn't see anything, though it's obvious the sending-off can't have gone down well with our fans. Billy got a 28-day ban by the League, which meant he'd miss seven matches. Seven matches, just for arguing with the referee and using colourful language. The Evening Post reckoned it made a total of 68 days' worth of suspensions in his career, plus he'd been fined £350 in all. An expensive bad habit, plus we were always a better side with him in so it was costly for the team as well.

Billy wasn't suspended for the Inter-Cities final though but with the team he picked, it looked like The Don showed too much respect for Zagreb. He picked Paul Reaney, not at right-back but on the right of midfield, which was just odd, full stop. Because of the away goals rule, if Zagreb scored one at our place then we'd need to score four. So you could see his point being defensive in his tactics but not *that* defensive. As it turned out, we didn't play badly but the problem was, neither did Zagreb. They defended really well and even though we bombarded their penalty area with crosses and long-range shots, there weren't any real chances to score. The sad fact is that the team was too predictable and the Zagreb defenders had quite an easy time of it all night. It ended up being a 0-0 draw and so we were losing finalists, again.

So the **Honours list for 1966 -'67** was complete.
League Division One winners - Man United, Runners up - Nottingham Forest.
FA Cup winners - Spurs, Runners up - Chelsea.
League Cup winners - Queens Park Rangers, Runners up - West Brom.
European Cup winners - Celtic, Runners up - Inter Milan.
European Cup Winners Cup winners - Bayern Munich, Runners up - Rangers.
Inter-Cities Fairs Cup winners - Dynamo Zagreb, Runners up - LEEDS UNITED.
Footballer of the Year - JACK CHARLTON, Leeds United.
European Footballer of the Year - Florian Albert, Ferencvaros.
Leeds' crowd average = 35,217.
Clean Air for Leeds - eight more years.

Celtic winning the European Cup was one hell of an achievement. I think most of the Scots at Leeds were Celtic fans and of course Bobby Collins used to be a Parkhead favourite. There was a good story about Celtic goalkeeper Ronnie Simpson. He was quite old but still a good goalie, proved by his playing in that European Cup final. Our Gary Sprake had a rag doll some lass made for him as a lucky mascot, it was always inside his goal-net, surrounded by his chomped chewing gum wrappers. Simpson had a cap that he put in the back of his net, to keep his false teeth in. For that final, it had some of his team-mates' in as well, they'd wanted to look their best when meeting the VIP's before the kick-off so had gone out onto the pitch with their falsies in for a change.

The Leeds performances and results began to improve almost straight away after the Fairs Cup defeat. There were close but still really good wins over Everton and Burnley and a draw away at Southampton. We beat Luton 3-1 in the League Cup second round as well, with Lorimer smacking in a hat-trick. He was proving himself as a real match-winner and was on a right scoring run, like we *didn't* need a target man after all. Course, we did, and late September, Don Revie finally did it, he bought a top striker.

There was never much happening at the club that Ces Burroughs didn't know about. Same with John Reynolds, the same with the full-time staff, the same with everyone just about, even the stray cats squatting under the stadium stands. *Everyone* knew what went on, everyone except me. Ever since I'd been one of the first to know about Bobby Collins signing, I'd be on at Ces to tell me about any more news or rumour. And when it was all quiet on the transfer front, I even half hoped he'd make something up just to keep me satisfied. So, when Leeds finally signed the new, record-breaking centre-forward, he'd teased me something rotten by saying 'I told you so' all the time. The problem was, he hadn't told me a bloody thing about us buying anyone. Then he revealed to me that Revie had been monitoring centre-forwards for a year, a whole year, and I'd not heard a sodding word about it.

There had been Francis Lee of Bolton, who had a great scoring ratio but wasn't anything special in the air which is what we most needed. Then there was Hull's Chris Chilton, who seemed perfect but they knocked us back, even after we'd offered Terry Cooper in part-exchange. We'd even enquired about Ray Crawford of Ipswich, but he was near thirty so too old. And there had been mention of Tony Hateley, before Chelsea bought him. In the end, we were paying Sheffield United £100,000 for Mick Jones, two weeks after the Zagreb game. Sheff United supporters were supposed to be furious about selling him, but money's always talked louder to certain clubs and directors. I could see the fans' point of view, what a time to sell your best player, less than two months into the season. Jones was only 22 but he'd already played for England twice, and the transfer fee was in fact £99,999, though no one seemed certain why it was a penny less than the full hundred thou.

Ces had cut his hours of work to part-time and then eventually just to casual hours, like me but for different reasons, obviously. He was knocking on in age while the amount of work was just getting more and more. So the club hired a new head groundsman while Ces would go in as and when they wanted him, and he was still treated like he was a part of the valuable furniture. The new bloke was Ray Hardy, and yet another proper nice bloke to join the club. He hadn't been there long when 'the Milk Tray man' started being advertised on television - even though Ray didn't wear all-black or go around leaving chocolates in strange women's bedrooms, he always reminded me of that fella in the ads.

8 iii

September 25th, 1967, a West Bromwich Albion fan was jailed for nine months and fined £50 after 'incidents' at their game against Nottingham Forest. On October 6th, Chelsea manager Tommy Docherty resigned following a 28-day ban imposed on him by the FA - for alleged incidents on a club tour in the Bahamas in May. Docherty was alleged to have insulted a referee in a game in Bermuda. The day after his resignation, Chelsea were humiliated at Elland Road, losing 7-0 to Leeds, for whom Billy Bremner was making his last appearance before serving his own 28-day ban. Strangely, Leeds had been fined too, ten guineas for wearing the same colour socks as Everton during a match at Goodison Park last season. Also on October 7th, Denis Law and Ian Ure were sent off for fighting in the Manchester United-Arsenal match; both players received six-week bans. At Millwall versus Aston Villa, referee Norman Burtenshaw was attacked on the pitch by a home supporter. November 21st, Division Three team Peterborough were punished for making illegal payments to players as 'sweeteners' for them to sign for the club - regardless of match results, Peterborough were to be demoted to Division Four at the end of the season.

*

Looking at his moderate scoring record for Sheffield United, Mick Jones' arrival at Leeds might not have appeared too significant, but for Revie it represented the final piece in his team jigsaw. He had waited months for Sheffield United to accept the bid for Jones' services. Even though the player had much to learn - he needed to improve his close-control, his shielding of the ball and keeping of possession - he was the high-quality striker Revie had yearned for. Whilst it took seven games before Jones scored his first League goal for Leeds (against Wolves, two days before Christmas) his early displays were widely praised, with one newspaper describing him as the finest centre-forward to play for Leeds since the great John Charles.

Leeds United had reported record profits for the second consecutive year but Revie certainly was not free to spend whatever amount of money he wanted, even though he had in his mind a constant 'wants' list of players. He was required, not forced, to release players too, to help balance the finances. And since their return to the top tier, the board of directors had drawn out ambitious plans for the club, primarily the improvement and expansion of the stadium and its facilities. Those plans though excluded Harry Reynolds' hopes of repositioning the Leeds pitch and building a direct railway link to the north-west of the stadium. He believed such development would enable easier access for more supporters and thus increased attendances and revenue. We would never know.

After a black August, Leeds seemed to have got their act together by the time of Jones' arrival. However, there were disappointments away in the League, to WBA, Manchester City, Liverpool (including a freakish own goal from Gary Sprake) and, also astonishingly, Sheffield United. Sheffield had been without their goalkeeper Hodgkinson for most of the game due to a dislocated finger injury, so winger Alan Woodward deputized in nets for eighty or so minutes. They kept Leeds out and went on to actually score and win the game 1-0.

By New Year's Day 1968 though, Leeds were sitting not exactly pretty but a relatively handsome third in Division One and in contention for all the trophies available to them, having racked up some memorable results along the way. In January, they slammed in ten goals without reply, in the games against Fulham and Southampton, and they could have scored more. They had hit a Fairs Cup record-breaking 9-0 away win at Spora Luxembourg (7-0 in the home leg) as well as defeating much better opposition, from Yugoslavia, Partizan Belgrade in the following round. There was that amazing 7-0 win against Chelsea in the League, too. In addition, with sound wins against Luton, a Bobby Collins-led Bury, and Sunderland and Stoke, Leeds had advanced to the semi-finals of the League Cup, the furthest they had ever reached in the competition. European qualification for the trophy winners, and the final being held at Wembley, now gave the competition much more appeal - Everton, Liverpool and Chelsea had previously chosen not to compete.

Division One League table (top), January 13th 1968.

1 Man. Utd	Played 25	Points 37
2 Leeds Utd.	Played 26	Points 35
3 Liverpool	Played 25	Points 34
4 Man. City	Played 25	Points 32.

Injuries and suspensions created opportunity for certain youngsters to prove their worth to the team. This season saw good performances from squad players such as Greenhoff, Belfitt, Hibbitt, Harvey and Bates. Even though he was barely twenty years of age, Mick Bates was proving himself a fine professional. His best position was in central midfield, which meant his chances would be very limited due to the quality of Bremner and Giles, but he never complained. From Armthorpe, near Doncaster (as was a lad called Kevin Keegan) Bates was proud just to be a part of such an outstanding squad of players. And the Leeds defence was arguably even more impressive than the midfield.

Such was the strength of the current back five of Sprake, Reaney, Charlton, Hunter and Cooper, when the line-up remained unchanged, high quality performances could usually be relied upon. Sometimes that defence had little work to do, like on January 6th, 1968, against a struggling Fulham side at Craven Cottage. Aside from injuries to O'Grady and Johanneson, they were at full strength again. Jones, Giles and Bremner were back and the gaps left by the two wing-men were more than ably filled by Greenhoff and Gray. An away win could hardly be classed as a major surprise but nonetheless, games in the capital were rarely easy for Leeds. Today though, was to prove different, and by the half hour mark, they were already leading 3-0, thanks to two goals from Greenhoff and a virtuoso effort from Jones. He headed his second soon after the restart and Greenhoff went on to grab his hat-trick soon after that. 5-0 to Leeds in a performance which manager Revie described as 'terrific' and the best in all his seven years as manager.

Frustratingly for Leeds fans, the team's form dropped. They met Hibernian in the Fairs Cup third round, second leg, and were blessed with good fortune, edging through 2-1 after being outplayed for much of the 1-1 leg at Hibernian. In the domestic cups, Leeds were scheduled to play Division Two Derby County in the two-legged League Cup semi-final as well as the FA Cup third round. All three ties were to be played within three weeks in January and February. Derby, managed by 31 year-old Brian Clough were struggling in Division Two and possible contenders for relegation. The similarities between the early managerial careers of Clough and Revie were strong. As a player, Clough had deserved better than just the two England appearances, his enforced retirement due to injury was cruel luck for a great talent. A record-breaking centre-forward, his career was effectively finished late in 1962 with knee ligaments damage after a heavy collision with the Bury goalkeeper. Bob Stokoe, playing for Bury that day, underestimated the severity of Clough's injured knee, accusing him of feigning injury. Clough returned to playing *two* years later but had lost pace and suppleness: he completed only a few more games more before retiring from the game. A bitter end to a short but outstanding career.

Before Leeds and Derby met, Clough was interviewed by the Yorkshire Post. After mentioning their forthcoming games and describing Leeds as 'such a good side with a top class manager' he added, 'They can teach my lads a lot - how hard they have to work, how much effort and dedication is required. In short, a complete picture of what we have to aim for in the future. Leeds must be the envy of nearly every club in the country with their spirit and running power and large pool of good players. People tend to underestimate their individual ability, but make no mistake about it - these lads can play.'

Clough and Revie were both Middlesbrough-born, yet they shared nothing like a good friendship. Before too long, whatever the extent of their relationship, it would markedly deteriorate. Four days before meeting Derby, Leeds swept aside Southampton 5-0 in the League, without Charlton, Bremner and Gray. Excellent teamwork combined with fine individual performances, notably from Bates and Hibbitt, made it somewhat of a canter. Giles and Madeley in midfield and Cooper at left-back (the position which looked 'made' for him) helped wrap up the points before half-time, against a poor Southampton side who had just sold Martin Chivers for a record £125,000 to Spurs.

Wednesday January 17th, League Cup semi-final, first leg, at Derby's Baseball Ground. While the Elland Road pitch was similar in quality to most British pitches - *low* quality - Derby's was commonly regarded as the worst in existence. Its main problem was that it held water and wouldn't let go of it. In the colder months, matches were played **in** the Baseball Ground pitch rather than on it. Leeds had scored ten goals without reply in their last two League games but anyone expecting an exciting goals-full semi-final was to be disappointed. Despite Derby's lowly position, Revie expected a tough affair and prepared his players accordingly - Derby would come at them from the kick-off, and Leeds needed to be ready for a torrid opening. They were, and they defended in number for much of the game, returning the pressure on the County defence only sporadically, by counter-attacking them.

His side played a classic 'away' performance, soaking up the pressure from their opponents and taking them on the break. Leeds-born Kevin Hector caused a few scares for Leeds but overall, the visitors coped well and their gritty display was rewarded with a penalty award after handball in the County penalty area. Giles rarely missed a spot-kick, and today was no exception. 1-0 to Leeds and the scoreline stayed that way. Watched by close to 32,000, the return leg at Elland Road would draw less than 30,000, whereas their FA Cup 3rd round tie attracted well over 39,000. Testament to the everlasting glamour of the FA Cup as well as proof of the League Cup needing an improved image.

8 iv

Five days before Christmas, I got a right surprise - I was playing for Hibernian against Leeds. It was in the Fairs Cup third round, home leg. Well it wasn't me of course, but a Jock player with my name, you'd have thought I'd have known about it. He played up front, 'the stockily built Jimmy O'Rourke, an instinctive goal scorer'. Stocky was a good description, his thighs were thicker than the whole of me and I wasn't exactly a beanpole, especially after my stretch of being an 'instinctive beer and egg and chip plate eater'.

Despite the decent reputation that Jimmy O'Rourke had, he didn't have a good game this night, Hibs' best player by a mile was Peter Cormack in midfield. He ran the show, even with Billy Bremner playing directly opposite him. Every attacking move seemed to come through Cormack. Neither side played particularly well and it was all a bit boring after a bright start. It was bloody freezing as well and the pitch was rock hard - there's not much the ground staff can do to improve it. If a pitch is frozen solid, you can't even fork it to give it more… give. There's not much good to be said about playing on frozen mud, it looks ugly, it feels ugly and by Christ if you land on it heavily, it hurts ugly as well.

The Leeds colours were yet another variation tonight, we'd played in some odd strips in our time, I wished they'd stick to all white, that *was* Leeds United. This time it was more like England's kit - white shirts and socks but dark blue shorts. Hibs played in their normal green tops with white sleeves, like the Arsenal kit gone wrong. Eddie Gray scored early on for us, after his first effort had been saved. That was about the sum total of excitement to it. Sprake nearly gave another stupid goal away while Lorimer had one disallowed for offside. Sprake had been holding the ball in his hands and was set to drop-kick it forward, as he often did, so he bounced it on the deck but too close to their striker Colin Stein. Stein stuck his foot out and prodded the ball into the net. The referee even awarded a goal at first but then noticed the linesman waving his flag, thank the gods.

Different people get different levels of tension when they watch football. Some get animated and can't keep still, like they're playing in the match themself, while others just seem to hunch up and freeze, they're so nervous. Having seen both men a million times, I can vouch that Les Cocker definitely fit the first description best and Don Revie the second. The Don looks like he's waiting for surgery, while Les looks like he's got big, vicious ants in his pants. I was never too bad watching, but I was bad *listening* to games on the radio. The really close matches were the worst, they frequently felt like torture, regardless of what competition. We'd beaten Luxembourg team Spora 9-0 away earlier on in the Fairs Cup, so that wasn't exactly edge of your seat stuff, but with tight matches I often felt ill with nerves. And if we ever lost, it was a good job we never had a pet cat, that's all I can say - I'd have been up in court for animal cruelty. Normally, I'd listen to the Leeds away games on the radiogram (what my grandma called it) while she'd try to watch television and pretend not to be interested in the game. 'Turn it down, James,' she'd say, when all the time it was her television making the most noise.

I'd usually lie on the floor, never able to get comfy, restless like a flea-bitten dog. I'd rest my head close to the radiogram speaker with its wire mesh covering, and try and visualise wherever it was Leeds were playing. No chance of that with European games, they were in different worlds apparently. There was hardly ever any relaxing when a game was on the radio. For me, Leeds matches outshone St Anthony's. Supporting Leeds never stopped me from playing well for St Anthony's but when it came to being motivated, I was always more nervous about the next Leeds match than I was for the next St Ant's one. It might have been the fact that no one seemed too fussed anymore about me returning to playing. I'd just turned fifteen when I played in that trial match, now I was approaching eighteen so in the eyes of the Leeds scouts maybe I was too old. Not really fair but maybe that was it: I mean, this was my second season back, St Ant's had won the league last term and were vying for it this time around, plus we reached two cup semi-finals. And after a shaky start, I was back to my old self plus I still trained once sometimes twice a day. I'd not lost any skill but I had lost plenty of fitness when I'd slobbed around in pot.

I was at ours on the night of the second leg of the Hibernian tie, it promised to be edgy. Hibs were no mugs and were keen as green mustard to beat us. Anyway, to help me picture it in my mind better, I had the first leg's match programme with me. Not that there were ever many photographs of the players to help you visualise, but at least there were black and white photos of both squads. The advertisements were often more interesting. It was always *'The Chairman and Directors of the football club are proud to host such a fine team as INSERT TEAM NAME in this INSERT COMPETITION NAME. We sincerely hope our visitors enjoy their stay in our fair city'* blah blah blah, as if anyone believed any of it or thought it important. They'd have short articles about the opposing players and manager and club history and how well the team was doing and stuff. All nice as pie credit and respect to the opposition, before the players kicked ten bags of stuffing out of each other on the pitch.

Don Revie on the radio before the game at Easter Road, being asked about our chances after the first leg 1-0 lead. '…we are not out yet' he said. 'It is bound to be difficult now but all matches are hard for Leeds these days, so that is nothing new to the players. If we get one goal up there, Hibernian have to score three to beat us.' I was surprised at his negative attitude and couldn't work out what he meant by 'We're not out yet', making Hibernian sound like world beaters and that we were favourites to be eliminated. Unless it was a canny Revie ruse of course... but then the game, in somewhere called Leith, Edinburgh, kicked off.

The radio said it was another freezing cold night and the pitch hard as rock. The bad conditions affected football all over Great Britain and most matches were called off. This meant that lucky Leeds and Hibernian fans were treated to extended coverage as I think there was only one other game still being played - Plymouth Argyle v Norwich City in Division Two. Not much comparison really. Hibernian levelled the tie in only the fourth minute with a well-taken goal by Stein. So you could definitely say it wasn't looking too promising, the only thing I had positive in my mind was that we'd only ever once conceded more than one goal away in Europe, and that was in the final last season. The trouble was, it all looked like it would go from bad to worse too, as the radio commentator said Hibernian looked easily the likelier to score again. We were under the cosh, as he put it, though defending valiantly too. Times like that, the match programme was a welcome distraction.

Get all your meat requirements at FRED DRING BUTCHERS in Leeds Kirkgate Market.

Hibernian nearly scored with a deflected shot, from Stein again. I don't know if it was deliberate but the advert next to the butcher's was for a nightclub - *A spectacular night of entertainment to be had at the BRADFORD LYCEUM, BINGO, CABARET & SOCIAL CLUB.*

Hibs had four corners in a row within two minutes. Ten Leeds men defending. Cormack hit a shot from outside the area, just over Sprake's crossbar.

WALLACE ARNOLD - excursions to all Leeds United away matches. It didn't sound like many had travelled up tonight, if the noise from the stadium was anything to go by. It sounded like Mick Jones was on a lonely journey as well, playing in attack on his own.

At least I could relax a bit whenever 'Jonah' got the ball, because he held it up so well, fending off his markers, waiting for the other Leeds players to catch him up and support him in attack. The trouble was, he wasn't receiving the ball anywhere near enough.
JACOMELLI - the perfect rendezvous after the match.
JOWETT & SOWRY LTD PRINTERS, for personal and commercial stationery.
MAN FANG CHINESE RESTAURANT.
THE WHEEL LICENSED GRILL BAR (LANDS LANE).

Thank God for that, the referee's blown his whistle for half time, Hibernian one up and it's 1-1 on aggregate. We need to buck our ideas up or else we're going out. Waiting for the second half, I made a pot of tea for me and my grandma. She'd started having a teaspoon of honey in hers, reckoning it was supposed to be good for your chest and throat. I'd not noticed any improvement, her coughing still sounded like a tied-up nag on Holbeck Moor in the tipping-down snow for a week. The windows would rattle on a morning with my grandma clearing her chest and blowing her nose.

It was torture, not being at a Leeds game and having to listen to the radio, especially in cup matches where any time we'd concede a goal I'd feel a bit more sick in my stomach and I'd start to shake like I was cold or something. I'd probably done Hibernian a disservice, underestimating them - I read about them beating Napoli and Porto to get to this stage of the Fairs Cup and you never got pushover teams from places like Italy and Portugal, it just didn't happen. Hibs must have played really well to knock both those out of the competition.
BRADY BROS. (ROOFING) LTD, Brown Lane, Holbeck, Leeds.
Step up with JOHNSTONE'S PAINTS LTD.
FINCH BATTERIES.
LEEDS SHAVER CENTRE.
If it's Barrels and Drums, then it's E PEASE & SON LTD, Ravell Cooperage.
FRANK FLETCHER MOTOR CYCLES LTD.
RELIANT Sales and Service, D G CHEESEMAN, YORK STREET, LEEDS 9.
See the world and join the ROYAL NAVY. And miss your football team, and get seasick or drowned or torpedoed while you're at it. No thanks, admiral.

Come work for the NATIONAL COAL BOARD (vacancies in Castleford). Aye but there's no vacancies around here is there? And they're closing the Middleton Broom Colliery, just up the road in Belle Isle. Anyway, I'd rather be in the Navy.
Get a career with BRITANNIA METALS. Breathe in even worse muck than down the pit.

We were better in the second half, it was like The Don had given the players a bollocking, told them to pull their socks up, figuratively speaking. They were not so lacklustre now, even though Hibs were still causing us a few problems. At least we were pressing them as well. I was feeling more confident and relaxed. But then the commentator suddenly gets all agitated and it's all gone wrong - Hibs have scored! And then the stupid Mr Magoo commentator apologises as Colin Stein hadn't scored at all, he'd hit the side-netting.
JOHN COLLIER - the window to watch. Unless you're this commentator because he'd be looking in the wrong shop. *GRIFFIN HOTEL - luxurious rooms at affordable prices. BRITISH RAIL - to and from the match. EL TORO COFFEE BAR. BENTLEY's YORKSHIRE BREWERIES - there's no better beer than BYB.* Yes there is, Double Diamond for one.
THE ANCIENT ORDER OF FORESTERS FRIENDLY SOCIETY - which is just another insurance company, nothing to get excited about.

Not much seemed to happen in the game after the imaginary goal. There was plenty of effort from both sides but not much action in either penalty area or by way of shots on goal. Our defence was winning just about everything, and Terry Cooper especially was playing well at left-back, linking up well with Eddie Gray in attack too. The Don had said that if ever Leeds played on snow, Eddie Gray never left footprints he was so fleet of foot - maybe it had started snowing up there. The radio said Eddie was beginning to put in some good balls for Jones and Greenhoff to feed on but we hadn't properly tested their goalkeeper yet.

If the scoreline stayed the same until full-time then there'd have to be thirty minutes extra time. Every year Leeds seemed to have fixture pile-ups near the end of the season, thirty minutes more in a midweek game was definitely something we could do without, especially as the pitch was hard as bone. The harder a pitch, the more chance of injuries, from broken bones or torn muscles or just plain cramp. And then with five minutes of normal time left, their goalie Wilson was penalised by the referee. No one seemed to know why, and obviously the bloke on the radio was all confused again. We were then informed that the referee had given Leeds an indirect free kick in the Hibernian penalty area due to the goalkeeper committing the crime of… taking more than four steps whilst holding the ball. It was a new-ish rule, to stop goalkeepers' time-wasting tactics. Sounded harsh to me, Hibs were at home and going for the winner.

There was a queue of Leeds players wanting to take the kick - John Giles, Peter Lorimer, Jimmy Greenhoff, even Mick Jones. Hibs had formed a defensive wall ten yards in front. It had to be Lorimer taking it, he had such a brilliant shot on him that there was always chance the ball would end up in the net with an opponent attached to it. The referee blew his whistle, Lorimer ran at the ball, about to whack it and if not provide the killer goal then at least to inflict major damage on one or two Hibs players in the wall. But he was pretending, he changed his mind and just jogged away from the ball. Then Greenhoff did the same, exactly the same. And straight after him, Jones did exactly the same too. It was like a Marx Brothers routine, and the commentator wasn't the only one out of breath because of it. The players in the wall will have suffered the most though, because they'd be all flinchy and jittery for a long time after.

In fact it was Giles who took the free kick. He walked up to the ball and casually chipped it over the Hibs wall to where Jack Charlton simply nipped in to meet it, jumping unmarked and heading it down and past the defenceless goalkeeper into the net. Get in there, the equalizer and winner on aggregate, we were in the quarter-finals now, no way could Hibs come back as they needed to score two goals to win, in less than four minutes. No chance.

8 v

Don Revie - 'None of my players is for sale, I want to repeat that in the most emphatic way. My staff have not spent those thousands of hours searching for capable young footballers and grooming them in order to strengthen teams of other clubs. We want such players to win something for Leeds United and not for other clubs.'

Newspaper gossip frequently claimed players were to be sold; this rankled with Revie and he even went as far as to say he was considering asking the Football League to officially investigate. Sunderland allegedly wanted Eddie Gray and Spurs and Arsenal were after Paul Madeley, yet no official enquiries had been made whatsoever.

With the match-winning qualities of Gray, a young player capable of scoring and creating sublime goals, it was obvious why other clubs would want to buy him. But match winners do not exist solely in the attack of a team, great sides have such champions throughout their squad. Madeley's gift was his versatility, he could play in any outfield position and do a good job there, a very good job. A good striker of the ball with either foot meant he had the ability to play in any of the back four positions, left or right. Many fans believed that while he was a class act in defence, in central midfield he was a *world class* act.

On another extremely cold Saturday afternoon in late-January, on another heavy-going, debilitating, muscle-wearing mudheap of a pitch, Leeds edged past Derby in the FA Cup third round 2-0. Second half goals from Charlton and Lorimer, in front of nearly 40,000 at the Baseball Ground, settled part two of the Peacocks-Rams trilogy. Part three, the Elland Road leg of the League Cup semi-final, was scheduled for the first Wednesday in February, kick-off 7-30pm.

1-0 down from the first leg, Clough's all-red men entered the pitch with instruction to attack from the first whistle. He had decided that if his team was going out of the competition then they might as well do it with a fight. And by twelve minutes it seemed to be working, Hector levelling the aggregate score with a flicked header past Sprake in goal. However, their lead didn't last long, for less than two minutes in fact. Lorimer, fouled on the edge of the Derby penalty area, stepped up to take the free-kick, naturally causing great concern in the minds of Derby players in the wall, worried about their personal well-being. Lorimer though did not shoot but he cleverly chipped the ball over the wall instead, straight to the advancing Madeley who headed it across the goal to Belfitt. Playing in place of the League Cup-tied Mick Jones, Belfitt controlled the ball neatly before shooting sharply home to equalise, the ball going in off the right post with goalkeeper Matthews stationary. 1-1 on the night, 2-1 to Leeds overall.

Derby were not discouraged, they tried to keep attacking and pressing the Leeds defence. Their battle became even more difficult just before half-time however, with Eddie Gray striking a second for Leeds. Fed by Johnny Giles, he gracefully dribbled the ball past three defenders before striking a low, angled shot from the edge of the area. Matthews stretched and made contact but not enough to stop the ball entering the net. To the Derby players and supporters, conceding again will have felt unfair, as they had been the more adventurous team after all, but teams chasing a result and perhaps focusing too much on attack, often leave theirselves vulnerable at the back. 2-1 at half-time, 3-1 on aggregate, 45 minutes left to decide who would be going to Wembley.

In the second half, Leeds controlled the game, due partly to Derby's desperation to keep in the tie. Saving a Giles penalty, Matthews certainly helped them do that but Belfitt went on to notch his second goal with a cool finish to make it 3-1 to Leeds. Very late on, Derby's Stewart made it 3-2 but it was too little too late: Leeds winning 4-2 on aggregate and into their second Wembley final in three years. They would play Arsenal, 6-3 victors over Huddersfield.

Three days later, mid-table West Ham were the Elland Road visitors, in the League. It would be Leeds' 44th game of the season, and it was only early February, the season not even six months old. Revie had warned his players that at this stage, their fitness was nearly as important as match results: injuries and fatigue could lose matches. And so, with around ten minutes of this match to go, with them leading 2-1, the players were more intent on keeping possession of the ball rather than trying to score a third. They were conserving their energies, not pointlessly 'busting a gut'. In other words, they were time-wasting, but Revie was incensed to hear boos, whistles and slow hand-claps from home fans. It had been an exciting game, with Leeds the much better team, so after the match, he snapped back at the dissenters

- 'We had provided far more than our fair share of entertaining football in the previous seventy-five minutes - in fact that was one of our best performances of the season! It was our third match in seven days, all of them being played on heavy pitches, so naturally the lads were feeling the effects a bit. When you're involved in so many important matches, no team can afford to do a lot of unnecessary tearing about. Any team would do the same as Leeds in this situation - if they had the skill.' And he was right, even the press agreed. Leeds' final match before the League Cup Final was the FA Cup fourth round tie at home to Nottingham Forest. They would then have the rare luxury of a two week break whereas their fellow finalists Arsenal would not, they would be playing Manchester United in the League.

8 vi

Why don't you go to the doctor's? I'd ask her, whenever her coughing and breathing sounded bad, which happened to be most of the time. *Because there's no need* my grandma would reply. Her coughing on mornings was as reliable as an alarm clock and it made me want to work that much harder when I went out running, as if the cold air could at least help to cleanse my lungs, if not hers. I just assumed she had a 'smoker's cough', and she never seemed worried by it. She never listened to me anyway. If she'd just have a good snook up and spit out on a morning, then I was sure she'd be alright. But she was a woman and women didn't do that sort of thing. Quite right and all, I suppose. Smoke from our coalfire nearly always made my throat sore and my chest hot. I'd get a nasty dry, burning feeling in my lungs which would make me wheezy and whistly as I breathed; maybe it was that to blame.

The February night we beat Derby in the League Cup semi-final second leg, was dead cold with frost and freezing fog. The weather might have affected the crowd as well, I don't know - less than 30,000 attended. Possibly ninety minutes away from Wembley, that crowd was rubbish. I always liked fog, it made things deathly quiet and mysterious, especially on a night. Not like London 'pea soupers' of course, they had an annoying and bad habit of killing people. Okay, so we were in 1968 but our street when it was foggy, with its cobbles and street lamps, definitely had a look of

Jack the Ripper London about it. After the match and after helping mend the pitch as best we could - about forty of us daft penguins - flattening it with the massive roller, replacing divots and then finishing off by covering the whole surface with straw to help protect it from more cold-damage. We had West Ham in the League on the Saturday and then Nottingham Forest the week after in the FA Cup, so the pitch was in for more hammer. Plus there was a Reserve match next Wednesday as well, for God's sake.

For as long as I remembered, Ces and John more so - and Ray Hardy now - had always got frustrated about the pitch being overused in winter. I mean, the Reserves could easily have used the Fullerton pitches, there was no rule to say that they couldn't, but the attitude of The Don and the coaches seemed to be that the quality of the playing surface wasn't particularly important. Normally, The Don could wrap Ces and John around his little finger but not where this was concerned, they'd keep on at him about it.

It was well-known that Don Revie had this *way* with people. Just a few words or a smile from him could make your day, it really could. I saw him a few times over the years, on dead cold days (and nights) come out on to the pitch to talk the groundsmen and ground staff tending the turf, and giving us glasses of whisky and brandy to help keep warm. He'd come out to see us tonight as well after the Derby game, just to say thank you for dragging all the pain in the arse straw back onto the field. Of course, he was in a good mood seeing as we were off to Wembley again, I'm not sure he'd have done it had we lost. I stood close to the players' tunnel when he'd walked out so he couldn't really have missed me. Even though he'd only said 'Hello Jim, how's the leg?' I couldn't describe how much it meant to me. Truly, I felt like a VIP. And maybe that was the point, if Don Revie knew and liked you, then you really were a very important person. He didn't dish out any booze this time though!

Ces sent us all off home at about half-ten and said to me that he'd see me in the morning. I always looked forward to Thursdays as it was pay day for everyone at Elland Road, including the players. I was never that interested in how much they got paid or what cars they drove because it would get me thinking too hard at what I was missing out on, but I did hear comment that some of them were getting up to a hundred quid a week, including bonuses. That's not to say that I thought they didn't deserve it, because they definitely did. I went home and went for a pee, my grandma had already gone to bed. It was quite late so I didn't think anything of it. I had a couple of nips of sherry to warm me up and then made myself a slice of unbuttered toast and a mug of tea and read the Derby match programme. A couple of sherries later to celebrate Wembley and the riveting read that the programme wasn't, I fell asleep on the settee. The fire had gone out and it was probably the cold that woke me up. Going up the stairs to my bedroom, I could hear a strange scraping noise coming from my grandma's room. It was her snoring.

I slept in, not by much but enough to miss my run. I thought my grandma must have forgotten to wake me up but as I was going down the stairs I *just* heard her voice, saying my name. I put my head round her bedroom door - she was still in bed and the room smelt musty and wasn't warm. 'You alright, grandma?' She didn't look alright, I could see that much even in the gloom. I pulled the curtains open, noticing a red and white handkerchief on her bed. 'I can't seem to get out of bed,' she said. 'No energy or anything, I've been coughing so much.' I looked at the handkerchief again and realised it was actually white, the red was caused by blood, 'Have you had a nosebleed or summat?' 'No, I must have coughed some blood up, that's all.' *That's all.*

I always prided myself on being able to show grace under pressure when on the football pitch, like Mr Madeley himself. But this wasn't on a football pitch, course. My grandma kept me calm enough I suppose, in spite of the crap she'd said about it not being anything to worry about. She told me to run over to Clarkson the chemist's on Cemetery Road and get whatever their strongest cough medicine was. I was no doctor of course, but I knew coughing up blood was more than just a bad cough. So I rushed downstairs, took a couple of pennies from her purse and then ran outside, down our street and along Elland Road, not to a chemist shop as none would have been open at that time anyway, but to the telephone kiosk opposite the stadium gates. I'd never used a telephone in my life before, and it felt like I took longer working out how to make a call than it did for the ambulance to turn up.

*

When I eventually got to work and explained to Ces what had happened (before he had chance to bollock me for being a bit late) he actually said, 'Well done' and that I'd done the right thing calling the ambulance. They wouldn't let me go with her to the hospital, which seemed a bit off to me, but there was nothing I could do about it. I didn't see them examine her but when they carried her out of the house they'd put a mask over her mouth to feed her with oxygen from a little air tank.

It turned out that it wasn't smoker's cough, it wasn't a bad cold and it wasn't influenza or bronchitis or emphysema or some never-heard-of-before disease. No, it was none of them. No, *somehow, somewhere,* my grandma had caught tuberculosis - TB - and the doctors said it wasn't even that serious. I'd hate to see what *serious* TB looked like then. They kept her in for two nights until she came home the Saturday morning. It was while I was visiting her that I realised how much I hated hospitals - I'm not sure if it was a natural hatred or something I'd learned, sort of. All the pain and suffering in there, the smell of the place, the bleakness.

She wasn't exactly right as rain straight away but she was in much better nick than I expected. I never let on to her but those two nights when she was in the Infirmary were the loneliest and most miserable I ever had in my whole life, even though I knew the neighbours were looking out for me. It was even worse than when I had my leg and ankle broken. Admittedly, I was feeling sorry for myself but the honest truth is I was feeling sorrier for my grandma, I couldn't help thinking what a shittily unfair life she'd had. She'd had to cope with the death of my granddad in World War Two, and as a widow she'd had to bring up her son on her own. And then, when he'd grown up she'd had to cope while his wife, my mum, died when I was born. And then, when the spineless bastard ran off because he was scared of the responsibility of being a widower and young father, my grandma was then lumped with having to bring me up on her own. And now she was ill, where was the fairness in that? If God had a fair answer to that then he was keeping it a big secret.

TB did used to be a major killer, even here in Blighty, right up to the early 1960's, I found that much out. They used to call it Consumption in the old days. Michael Caine even had it in *Alfie*. Scientists and doctors had developed a cure, here at least - my grandma had these yellow tablets to take, one at a time, four times a day, before food. And she had strict instruction to look after herself better, eat regularly and get as much fresh air as possible, because she'd been overdoing it and was run-down. I don't think there was any criticism of me in that but, just in case, I started helping more around the house. She insisted on going back to work, less than a week after. And she walked there. She had to go for routine check-ups at the Leeds Chest Clinic once a month for a while but the tablets should work without any problems, the doctors said, and she should be fully recovered within six months. Great news, but even better was that I didn't need to fret about missing the League Cup Final now. I'd be making my own sarnies though, I didn't want any germs.

8 vii

The date, Saturday 2nd March 1968, Wembley Stadium, London. The occasion, the Football League Cup Final, Leeds United v Arsenal. The attendance - 97,887.
Leeds United (white shirts, white shorts, white socks):
1 Sprake, 2 Reaney, 3 Cooper, 4 Bremner (captain), 5 Charlton, 6 Hunter, 7 Greenhoff, 8 Lorimer, 9 Madeley, 10 Giles, 11 Gray, 12 Belfitt.
Arsenal (red shirts/white sleeves, white shorts, white & blue ringed socks):
1 Furnell, 2 Storey, 3 McNab, 4 McLintock (captain), 5 Simpson, 6 Ure, 7 Radford, 8 Jenkins, 9 Graham, 10 Sammels, 11 Armstrong, 12 Neill.
Referee: L.J. Hamer (Horwich).

The Football League Cup is regarded as a poor relation to the League Championship, the FA Cup and the European trophies, even with Wembley Stadium as the final's host. The Leeds-Arsenal match was expected to be a hard fought, close run and tense match - but it was not expected to be a negative and dour display. The continually rough and unattractive play produced by both teams upset many people, and the lack of excitement throughout provided only meagre fare for the spectators. It was generally low-calibre entertainment with precious few enjoyable moments, while both teams' shooting caused much more work for the Wembley ball-boys than either goalkeeper.

The Guardian's Eric Todd described it as a 'poor do' (as Yorkshiremen would put it, he said) and many spectators suggested it was the worst final ever played at Wembley, with the players more interested in battering each other than scoring goals. Since promotion to the First Division in 1964, Leeds had finished as losers in two major finals and runners-up for the League title twice. They were the classic chokers of football, said the cynics, guilty of losing their nerve at the most crucial stages. And so, Don Revie pondered ways of motivating his players so they could avoid another failure and emerge, at last, as trophy winners. He even considered showing them the club's trophy cabinet, in all its glory - gloriously clean and gloriously empty of major silverware - to coldly show that all their hard work and endeavour so far had won them nothing of note apart from the Division Two title and a West Riding Trophy which, frankly, did not really matter. He decided against the ploy though, worrying that it might actually do more harm than good to their confidence, especially if Arsenal were to beat them.

In the week prior to the match, it seemed Leeds were already up against it, with the 'architect' Giles suffering from a heavy cold, Greenhoff not fully fit and Jones cup tied. Revie had tried to learn from his mistakes during the 1965 FA Cup final preparations, he knew that he should relax more and that the players should not see how anxious he himself was. But he was no actor, concealing his emotions and anxieties never came easy to him. Rarely enjoying a sound night's sleep at the best of times, the week up to the League Cup final caused even more sleep deprivation for the Leeds manager.

The big day arrived. That morning, a coach carrying Leeds supporters to Wembley was near wrecked after being attacked by missile-throwing Arsenal followers. And in the match itself, the Arsenal team was accused of 'unpardonable behaviour' too, blamed for a number of skirmishes on the pitch. Leeds were far from innocents though. Referee Hamer was criticised for not taking a firmer stance with the culprits but in his defence, the final is a major event, with royals and television cameras in attendance, so he could be forgiven for wanting to control the game calmly and civilly, as well as expecting both teams to act correspondingly as well as show suitable sporting respect for each other.

Arsenal were to gain far more possession of the ball than Leeds but achieve very little of attacking note with it. Billy Bremner, the Leeds captain, leader and all-round superhero - a fantastic 4 on his back supporting the image - began the game like a greyhound tearing out of the traps. With white socks rolled down round his ankles, and no pads only pearly white shins, the copper-topped spark of Leeds United - 'ten stones of barbed wire' - dare not even consider defeat this afternoon. And with around fifteen minutes gone in the game, he forges ahead down the Leeds right flank. He links up with Hunter on Arsenal's left, close to their penalty area. Hunter ventures forth with the orange ball at his feet towards the touch-ball line, hoping to make a cross to a team-mate in the danger zone. His route however, is blocked by Arsenal's Jenkins so Hunter knocks the ball against his opponent's shin to earn United a corner kick. Left-footed Eddie Gray will take it, probably using the old Leeds ploy of aiming his cross for Jack Charlton standing on the line just inside the near goalpost.

The tall frame of Charlton does indeed occupy a place on the goal-line inside the post nearest to Gray. George Graham and goalkeeper Jim Furnell are behind him, wary of the lofty Leeds defender's imposing presence. And, like a film director frames a camera shot using his hands and fingers, Charlton signals to Gray where exactly to deliver the ball, *exactly*. He wants the ball inches above where his head is. It is a well-used, well-known Leeds tactic, which no one away from Elland Road seems to appreciate, probably because most opposing teams have failed to cope with it. Some claim that the scheme is unsporting or even illegal. It is not - it might offend the purists but it is entirely lawful and part of the game, and frequently effective. Gray sends the corner kick in. It is not his best, missing as it does Charlton's head by inches. Goalkeeper Jim Furnell however, attempts to jump higher than his opponent and reach the ball but succeeds only in thudding in to the tree trunk that is Charlton's back. And as he does that, Leeds' number 9 Madeley outwits his marker Ian Ure to race in from the edge of the area and leap prodigiously for the ball. But mid-air,

Madeley's left elbow collides with the side of Furnell's skull and the goalkeeper ends up in a heap on the floor, crying foul. Fortunately for the Gunners, Graham is there as defensive cover to calmly head the ball off the goal-line.

Madeley's assault on Furnell was not deliberate but it *was* a foul. A foul however, missed by the referee. The penalty box remains a throng of players, all watching the descent of the ball. Four Arsenal men stand guard on the goal-line, while Furnell lies virtually incapacitated on the ground. Ten yards away from the goal, the ball slowly drops within the vicinity of the penalty spot. Each man watches closely, none more so than the man nearest, Terry Cooper, Leeds' left-back. Lining himself up to volley the descending ball, as it reaches knee-height, he strikes it with a clean, sharp connection. Anticipating the shot, the four Arsenal defenders all rush out bravely to try and block Cooper's rocket. All to no avail, the pace of the shot takes it millimetres over and past them, flashing towards the goal. And into the net. Seventeen minutes in, Leeds United 1, Arsenal 0. Eerily, for three consecutive nights running up to the final, Cooper had dreamt that he would score at Wembley, and the winning goal at that.

Like over-excited schoolboys on the sound of the last bell on the last day of term, the Leeds players reel away to celebrate. Ecstatic, they jump for joy, they run to congratulate Cooper and they hug each other, dancing, saluting the thirty thousand or so Leeds followers. And all the while the referee ignores heated protestations from hard-done-to Arsenal players.

Once they had taken the lead, manager Revie instructed his players accordingly and amended the configuration of the team, switching Madeley from his makeshift centre-forward position to that of auxiliary defender, operating in the midfield just in front of Hunter and Charlton, while Greenhoff became the lone Leeds attacker. These tactics of containment explained criticism of Revie and the team's 'spoiling' strategy, but really, understrength Leeds were simply playing to what strengths they had. It was not particularly attractive to watch but after their disappointments in the recent past, Revie could hardly be blamed for ordering the team to 'shut up shop'.

Midway through the second half, Bremner chases a long pass into the Arsenal penalty area but Furnell gets there first, easily. Bremner slows but continues running and sticks out a foot as if trying to knock the ball out of Furnell's hands. It is quite obviously a fair if pointless attempt to nick the ball, Bremner connecting with neither the ball nor the man. In aggressive remonstrations with the Leeds captain, the Arsenal players' reactions were undeniably 'over the top'.

Late in the game, it is the Arsenal captain's turn to be involved in controversy, in the match's main commotion. Arsenal win a corner, the resulting kick long and high, finding a red shirt on the far side of the Leeds penalty area. The ball is headed back in to the goal area where, under no pressure, Gary Sprake is able to leap high and easily catch it. Safe in his hands, the ball is unquestionably his, but the Gunners' number 4, captain Frank McLintock, appears to disagree as he too jumps, a split second later, to hit Sprake in the back stoutly with his shoulder. It is not a particularly serious or harmful foul but it did floor goalkeeper Sprake. And to exacerbate the situation, as Sprake lies there still clutching the ball, Ian Ure, bigger than Jack Charlton, rushes in and with feet a blazing. Apparently trying to dislodge the ball from Sprake's arms, he succeeds only in kicking the goalkeeper, more than once. And all hell lets loose.

Leeds defenders dive in to jostle and manhandle the Arsenal offenders.

Sprake gets to his feet, aiming to land revenge on Ure.

Hunter confronts McLintock.

The referee hurries to the scene but has very little influence in the mêlée.

A linesman rushes in to help him and is equally as impotent.

Charlton grabs McLintock by the neck, steering him away from Hunter.

Ure tries to defend McLintock from Charlton's handiwork.

Positioned behind him, Sprake aims punches at Ure.

Cooper and Bremner grab Sprake by the shoulders, attempting to stifle his boxing instincts, and Reaney wades in, ready to intervene and help his team-mates.

*

The silver, lidless, three-handled League Cup, is shorter and less impressive to the eye than the FA Cup. And with a much shorter history, it does not pluck the heartstrings as romantically either. But try telling that to the people of Leeds and the United players and staff as the team chair their captain Bremner around the pitch, holding the shining beacon that is the League Cup, their first major honour, in his hands. For today at least, the Football League Cup is the ultimate prize in football!

8 viii

Wembley, so they always reckoned, was 'the Mecca' of English football, and getting there was the dream of every football player and fan in the country. What a load of old bollocks, Wembley Stadium was a dump, a right hole! Not that I let it spoil my March 2nd, 1968 day there though, nothing could have, but it was a big letdown, the state of the place. Our seats, that cost a pretty penny as well, were just long wooden benches in need of a good sand-papering and at least one new coat of varnish - there were splinters all over the shop. This ground had hosted the World Cup less than two years before, what a joke.

My ticket was actually Ces's wife's but she wasn't fussed about going. I can't say I blamed her after seeing Wembley with my own eyes. I was chuffed to be there of course and Ces let me have the ticket for a very reasonable price. 'A pint some time' to be exact, and I'm not hundred per cent sure I ever paid him. If ever anyone wanted more tickets but couldn't get them from the club officially, there was always a chance of getting some from the Leeds players. It was probably against the rules but I doubt there was one single Leeds supporter who minded, it was the Leeds players who'd got the club to Wembley after all. The word was 'See Big Jack' if you needed any more tickets - the players received loads of tickets and had pooled all the spares - Jack was like the box office manager.

And good for him, in my opinion. Jack Charlton was a right entrepreneur, opening his own stall on Elland Road opposite the gates, selling scarves, hats, rosettes and badges and probably anything else he could sell in the Leeds colours. He'd even be there on the morning of home matches which he'd actually be playing in. He went on to open up a couple of proper shops in his name as well - he had one on Roundhay Road (near the Fforde Grene pub, funnily enough, where he was *never* seen and will *not* have been smoking while he wasn't in there!) and Garforth, to name but two. What a star. Eventually the club struck some sort of deal with him so that they opened up their own official souvenir shop in the middle of the Fullerton club house, five-a-side pitch and next to the main gates. Terry Cooper went on to do the same, in town on Lower Briggate, a few years after. I hope any footie boots he sold came in a box and not just wrapped in old newspaper.

Jack was notorious too, for being 'frugal' with money and for cadging cigarettes off people, even complete strangers. Billy Bremner was usually in cahoots with him, as the Leeds squad's 'secret smokers society' with cigs and cigars, and they were said to be two of *the* laziest trainers at the club as well. Gary Sprake was no angel either, he even smoked a pipe as well as cigars - not at the same time, course - and I'd even seen The Don with a cigar once, though I don't think he approved of footballers smoking. I think he was alright about the players drinking, as long as it was in moderation. Billy and Jack would smoke in secret and if someone was about to catch them at it, Jack would always somehow palm his cig onto someone else. Usually Billy, and once in the team bath after a match, legend had it.

At Wembley, Ces warned me to make sure and remember which stairway we went up to our seats, because the stadium is like a huge bloody labyrinth inside. Seeing hundreds and hundreds of folk waving blue and white banners and wearing scarves in the gold, white and blue of Leeds made me feel safe - if I did get lost I'd be in good hands. At half-time I was bursting for a wee so I searched out the Gents. It wasn't hard to find, 'follow your nose' and the hundreds of other desperate Leeds fans wanting to go at the same time. The queue had been so long I needed another wee by the time I'd finished my first.

When you went for a slash in any normal men's public conveniences, the urinal was usually the basic set-up of a white, waist-high porcelain wall with a gutter at the bottom for all the pee to drain away in. It was just about the same at Wembley but with tons and tons more urinals, rows and rows of them in a kind of grid, and back-to-back, like houses. So there I am, standing at one of the urinals in the middle of the huge room, straining to do my necessaries but instead of looking at a wall in I'm actually face to face with some other bloke directly opposite me, also having a wee. And smiling with some relief. It took me a full five minutes for my own flow to even start as I'd suddenly become all nervous as a result.

I was never anywhere near as superstitious as Don Revie - I changed my kegs quite often, for one thing - but I must admit, before the League Cup final even I was starting to think Leeds were cursed and forever doomed to never win anything big. But when Terry Cooper popped up to whack in that bullet of a goal, there and then I was just about convinced there was no such thing as curses, at least not where Leeds United was concerned. The *team* beat Arsenal to win the League Cup, not Lady Luck or Fate or Don's threadbare backside! The fact that we'd won was the most important thing for us all in the White corner. Not the performance, not the prettiness of the play, not the number of efforts on goal and not the fact that some whingeing snobs had to sit through the *horror* of watching working class sportsmen kicking lumps out of each other and committing a lot of fouls.

Even though we were in the same stand as the Royal box, there was no way of seeing the League Cup itself being presented to the team, there were too many people in the way, but at least I'd had a good view of TC's goal and of all the action, even if there wasn't much of it. And I saw the lap of honour of course, which was fabulous. When the referee blew the final whistle, there was Billy jumping off the ground and then doing a forward-roll, Leeds players hugging, dancing, shaking hands, and Norman ('Norman Bites Yer Legs' banner) Hunter clenching his fists, swearing that this trophy would be just be the first of many. And we fans, we were all feeling a part of it, sharing the brilliance, I really believe that. There were men and women around me in tears once that whistle went, and Ces took the Mick, in a good-natured way, and I'm pretty sure he was misty eyed as well when he saw the players celebrating. I know I was but I've never tried to deny I'm a big softie. Me, I felt like I could explode I was that happy, and I'm surprised I wasn't roaring as well. It didn't matter in the slightest that the game was supposedly one of the worst Wembley finals *ever* - Arsenal should take most 'credit' for that anyway - the most important thing was that we never looked like conceding a goal. The only sad part as far as I was concerned was that Harry Reynolds hadn't been there, because he'd been too ill to attend.

Those saps who criticised Leeds obviously had never watched a Lorimer or Giles special before, or Jones trouncing centre-halves, Gray dancing around everybody, or our double agent full-backs Cooper and Reaney racing down the wings on attack, or nullifying opposing attackers. And they won't have appreciated the class of Bremner, finishing off a flowing move that he'd started, or immaculate Madeley floating around the pitch tidying everything up and putting away a few goals too, or our wingers and attackers, Johanneson, O'Grady, Greenhoff, Belfitt, Hibbitt and co in full flight. And then there's the brilliance and bravery of the goal keeping and the tackling and heading of the central defenders, all skills in their own right, big time. There were so many great things to see in this Leeds team. These critics, they were blind and they talked out of their backsides. There was other criticism too, closer to home, but for different reasons. A civic reception was organized in Leeds - this time for actually winning a trophy and not for coming second - in and around City Square and in front of the grubby Town Hall steps. Just because some 'terribly drunken' supporters sang a few naughty songs and trampled on some flowerbeds, the papers told us there had been a full-scale riot. Those poor flowers.

Being laid up in pot some time before, I put on weight, my lungs had been given a long rest and my leg muscles had withered away a bit. But once recovered, I was confident I'd be okay and be able to run all day just like I could before. Of those Leeds players I watched the closest, Billy Bremner always seemed to be the fittest - even though he smoked cigs - and for his age, Bobby Collins had been bloody amazing too, even after his injury. And then there'd been Grenville Hair, who was small and muscular but wiry as well, and he was fast and he looked like he could play until dusk, too. Fit as a fiddle he was, even as a manager like he was now, at Bradford City. So you can imagine the shock when, five days after Leeds won the League Cup, the news broke that Grenville Hair had died of a heart attack after a training session with his players.

He was 36 years old, 36 bloody years old. People say 'God moves in mysterious ways' and all that, like they're trying to make excuses for Him and make rotten luck easier to accept, but the hard truth is that life often can be just rotten and sometimes there's no real justice or reason. 'The good Lord giveth, and the good Lord taketh away'? Do me a favour. Grenville Hair, Rest in Peace.

Modern technology is great. A few weeks after Wembley, the 1968 League Cup Winners were away at Glasgow Rangers in the Inter-Cities Fairs Cup quarter-final. We'd stuttered through to get this far, and Rangers would be the hardest tie I reckoned. It was a sell-out at Ibrox so the Leeds board decided to arrange to transmit the game from Scotland to here by 'closed circuit' television and put it on a special big screen built on the Lowfields Road terrace. I did ask one bloke from the company who were setting the screen up, how closed circuit television worked but he might as well have tried explaining logarithms, in Chinese and from another room to me. Credit to the directors for screening the game. I don't know if it was financially risky to get it screened but there was a 20,000 or so crowd at Elland Road to watch the match, so with luck there'll have been a tidy little profit made plus good public relations. I remember when 20,000 was regarded as a pretty good crowd for a real game of football.

We played to contain Rangers and then take them on the break and grab an away goal. The weather was what you'd expect, just like everyone says it rains non-stop in Manchester, in Glasgow it was either blowing a gale, throwing it down or sleeting. And there were 80,000 mad Scots for the Leeds team to put up with as well. On the face of it, we were really up against it and would do well to get just a draw, but I just had a good feeling due to most of the Leeds Scottish players being Celtic fans, I thought they'd use the hostile atmosphere to motivate them.

In Europe, Rangers had played more games than any other British team without winning any of the trophies. It was our 52nd game of the season as well, already. Not that the players looked tired, they battled for every single ball all night. Sprakey didn't have a difficult save to make all night... neither did their 'keeper, having said that. By the end, The Don seemed very pleased with the 0-0 draw - 'This is the result we came for. Rangers played much as we expected them to, but it isn't over yet. Don't forget we have to take some risks at Elland Road in order to win the tie, and Rangers are an extremely accomplished and experienced side. However, I got one of the forms of result I wanted, a good result, and I think the boys were splendid.' Newspapers agreed and some were nearly complimentary to Leeds as well, saying that the team had struck a severe blow to the pride of all Scotland. Yes I'm *sure* Celtic fans were deeply upset at Rangers not winning.

Two weeks after, it was the home leg. We'd beaten Sheffield United twice in that time, with our Paul Madeley getting the only goal in the FA Cup sixth round home tie, followed by a steady 3-0 League win the Saturday after, Madeley getting one again and Giles two penalties. The Cup tie had attracted 48,000, the League match on April 6th against the same team, got 17,000 less. I always remembered that date because two days before was when Martin Luther King was murdered in Memphis, Tennessee, on the April 4th. What a country America was, Jesus Christ - if you don't like somebody, just pop round to your local gun shop, buy a cheap killing machine and then go out and make that somebody a dead somebody. For the Rangers second leg, I half expected the town crier in the Merrion Centre - Leeds really did have a town crier - to be walking around, shouting 'Beware, oh people of Leeds, hordes of drunken Scotch yobs are invading!' We had the Leeds International Swimming Pool by then too, quickly adopted as 'the Olympics' even though it turned out that architect John Poulson had made the lanes in the pool too narrow for Olympic competition usage.

Rangers had been allocated 3,000 tickets for Elland Road and, like we'd done, they'd arranged for the match to be transmitted on closed circuit television up to Ibrox, Glasgow. Before, Hibs had brought maybe 500 fans but it was obvious the club had underestimated the size of the Rangers following. There were millions of the sods, weird-sounding, foreign-talking, growling, pissed-up freaks all over the place - in Beeston, in the stadium, outside it, *on* it, sitting on the kerb drinking, or sprawled out having kips, coming in on the buses, taxis or staggering from the train station. Some of their mob had kilts on and all, and their fans supposedly wrecked half the pubs in town as well. The total crowd was over fifty thousand.

When I got back after the match, my grandma was waiting up for me, just so she could tell me about all the rowdy Scotsmen roaming round half the night, banging on people's doors and windows, swearing and cursing and throwing bottles as well as urinating everywhere. The referee had even stopped the game in the first half because the Rangers fans were throwing stuff at David Harvey, beer bottles, coins, ball-bearings, the bloody lot. Their captain, John Greig, had to ask their supporters to pack it in. Their behaviour was disrespectful to say the least - the Leeds players were wearing black armbands because chairman Morris had died a couple of days before. At that stage we were 2-0 up, so I don't know if they were trying to get the game abandoned, even before half-time... Rangers started well enough actually, without really looking like they'd score. They battled hard and tried to take the game to Leeds. The fact is, we were a bit fortunate to take the lead with a Giles penalty after Alex Ferguson had hand-balled. Lorimer got a second after latching on to a cross just missed by Greenhoff. I don't know how many Rangers supporters were inside the stadium but it must have been more than three thousand, there were groups of them dotted all over. Seriously, I bet there were ten thousand there, including the ones locked out. Thankfully there weren't any in the little pen at the front of the West Stand, reserved for ground staff, where I was. Good job, there were scraps and scuffles all around the ground.

So, this latest win meant we were A) current League Cup holders, B) Inter-Cities Fairs Cup semi-finalists, C) joint top of Division One and D) still in the running for the FA Cup with the semi-final v Everton in April coming up. In other words, we were going for four trophies. Four bloody trophies! We were over twenty games unbeaten in all competitions, but there were other strong teams to be reckoned with of course.

8 ix

Three days after beating Glasgow Rangers, Leeds were at White Hart Lane in the League against Tottenham Hotspur. It was the first of three games in six days in the 'mad' Easter phase of the season, to go with the 'mad' Christmas phase and the 'mad' end of the season phase. At Spurs, Leeds conceded goals for the first time in seven matches, losing 2-1, their first defeat in 26 matches. And to add to their gloom, with three weeks to go Manchester United took over at the top of the table with a 4-0 win at Fulham. On the Leeds board of directors, Alderman Percy Woodward succeeded

Albert Morris as chairman, he had been vice chairman for over twenty years and was described as a traditional, 'old school' type of businessman. The day after the defeat at Spurs, Leeds visited Coventry City and edged a 1-0 win thanks to a fine and rare Terry Hibbitt goal. It was the first of three hard-fought wins on the trot, with a revenge win over Spurs (1-0, a Lorimer penalty) and West Bromwich Albion 3-1 (Gray, Charlton, Madeley) during the following week. The victories left Leeds looking in a good position to win the Championship for the first time ever, even though in truth, they were not in the best of form.

The League Division One table (top), April 20th, 1968.

1. Manchester Utd	- played 39,	points 54
2. Leeds United	- played 38,	points 53
3. Manchester City	- played 38,	points 50
4. Liverpool	- played 37,	points 48
5. Everton	- played 37,	points 47

When comparing the teams in Division One, man for man Leeds probably were the best, but even the ambitious Revie said that one team winning three trophies in a season was impossible. And here they were, vying for four. Having played around sixty games so far, there were extremely tired and not fully fit players lining up for Leeds. Many were the times when certain men ignored immense pain to play full matches, when just walking without hobbling was an accomplishment in itself. There were players who played despite being ill or who were suffering with broken toes or chipped ankle and foot bones, or swollen, over-stressed knees and fatigued, tender hamstrings. Pain could not be allowed to matter, keeping on working was the most important issue, keeping on winning, keeping on fighting! Revie's preference was to select the same men for each important match: don't change a winning team, don't upset the rhythm, don't tempt Fate by meddling when it isn't needed, and say your prayers every night.

Leeds had a game in hand and could regain top spot on Tuesday, 23rd April, St George's Day, if they won away to second-bottom Stoke City. In theory it would be a straightforward two points, but theory doesn't put the ball in to the opponent's net. Stoke were battling to preserve their place in Division One and thus made Leeds toil. By half-time, the hosts were leading 2-0, both scored by striker Peter Dobing. For the second half, Leeds came out fighting and goals from Greenhoff and Charlton levelled the scores. However, thanks to a combination of the woodwork, poor finishing and superb goalkeeping by Gordon Banks, they were prevented from scoring a third. And to make matters worse, in the dying minutes, Dobing completed his hat-trick to seal the 3-2 win and inflict a severe dent to Leeds' title hopes.

Four days later at Old Trafford was the FA Cup semi-final against Everton. As was often the case against the Toffees, the match was not pretty to watch, nor was it good-natured. The Everton team normally had the 'Holy Trinity' of Colin Harvey, Howard Kendall and a certain Alan Ball in midfield, but not today as Ball was suspended. Nonetheless, a never-say-die attitude generally prevailed with the team capable of beating anyone on their day. In goal for Leeds was Gary Sprake, the highly-rated 'keeper whose reputation had taken a beating a few months before at Anfield due to him incredibly throwing the ball into his own net. And in the FA Cup fifth round tie at home to Bristol City, he was sent off for punching City striker Chris Garland. The referee, however, had not witnessed Garland spitting in Sprake's face first. Here, alas for Leeds, another Sprake incident was crucial to the proceedings. He had caught a cross intended for striker Joe Royle, the young and burly forward who liked throwing his considerable weight around to let goalkeepers know they had a battle on. Sprake, notoriously short-tempered during games, unsurprisingly resented such antics, especially as he spent much of the game injured, hurt in an earlier collision. Shortly before half-time he allowed his temper to get the better of him. As he was in the motion of drop-kicking the ball, he seemed to be trying to exact some retribution on Royle at the same time. As well as the ball, Sprake tried to strike Royle as his kicking foot followed through. The crucial point is not whether Sprake struck Royle or not or if he intended to, the crucial point is the ineptitude of the kick: the ball, like a damp firework, travelled a pitiful twenty or so yards, straight to Everton's Jimmy Husband. He kept calm to fire in a quick-shot towards the unguarded Leeds net, only to see Jack Charlton race in and prevent the ball from entering the net. By using his hands. No goal but the reward of a penalty. Johnny Morrissey duly scored the spot-kick and Leeds' hopes of being the first team to win both the League Cup and FA Cup in the same season drained away. At the final whistle, jubilant Everton fans ran onto the pitch, prompting aggrieved Leeds fans to throw coins, toilet rolls and other objects at them. Two ignominious FA Cup semi-final defeats in a row clearly too painful for some.

For all the superlative displays Sprake had made for his team over the years, his mistakes and occasional lack of concentration were earning him the reputation as Leeds' weak link. This latest gaffe left them realistically with just the Fairs Cup to aim for. The team's form marginally improved in the Fairs Cup semi-final first leg against Dundee at Dens Park on May 1st Paul Madeley was 'Mr Versatile' again, deputising for lead striker Mick Jones, and he got the first goal in the match on 26 minutes, making an impressive personal total of ten for the season. Although Dundee equalised soon after, for the second half Revie ordered his players to ease off to conserve their energy, this was Leeds' 62nd game of the season after all.

Three days later, with just three League games left to play, Leeds were in third place and due to play fourth placed Liverpool at Elland Road. Thanks to Jones smashing a Lorimer cross into the net after quarter of an hour to make it 1-0, Leeds were deservedly in front for most of the match. They also hit the bar, had a strong penalty claim for a Yeats handball turned down and missed a couple more good chances as well. And then it all went shockingly wrong in the match's dying minutes. Six minutes from time, first a scrappy, fortunate goal from Lawler brought Liverpool level and then soon after, another scrappy and even more fortunate goal, this time from substitute Graham, won them the match and brought Leeds' first home defeat of the season. With Manchester City winning at Tottenham, and Manchester United thrashing Newcastle, the late Liverpool goals near killed Leeds' title aspirations.

League Division One (top), 4th May, 1968.

1 Man. City	Played 41	Points = 56
2 Man. Utd.	Played 41	Points = 56
3 Leeds Utd.	Played 40	Points = 53
4 Liverpool	Played 40	Points = 53

Just three days later was their game in hand - away at Arsenal, a team with revenge on their minds after the League Cup bruiser. Sprake and Charlton were injured and worse news for Leeds was the enforced absence of Hunter and Cooper, both called up for England duty away to Spain the night after. David Harvey had shown he was a more than capable replacement for Sprake but three of the famous Leeds back four 'wall' were out while regular right-back Reaney would play on the left with Nigel Davey making his League debut on the right. Revie understandably was furious at having to play such an important match without Hunter and Cooper and he made his annoyance clear to the FA. But, as usual, club managers carried little sway with the game's rulers and his complaints were quickly dismissed.

In a dramatic, entertaining battle, Arsenal took the lead three times, only for the weakened Leeds side to draw level each time through Lorimer, Jones and Giles, and they were virtually camped in Arsenal's half for the last fifteen minutes of the match. Try as they might though, a fourth goal was beyond them and, just seconds from the final whistle, they fell to another late late show, Arsenal getting their winning fourth goal. The next evening, of scant consolation for Leeds, Norman Hunter scored the 81st minute winner in England's 2-1 win over Spain to take them into the European Championship semi-finals.

On the final Saturday of the League, fourth in the table, unable to win the League and already qualified for the next Inter-Cities Fairs Cup, Leeds' last League game, at Burnley, was somewhat meaningless. With the semi-final second leg against Dundee still to play, Revie's team selection was 'unusual' if not wholly surprising. Madeley was accompanied in the centre of defence by Gray, while Nigel Davey would make his second League appearance. Full-back Bobby Sibbald would be making his first full League appearance. It would be Terry Yorath's debut and Jimmy

Lumsden's second ever League game too. Yorath was another of United's Welsh scout Jack Pickard's recommendations. Burnley won the match easily, 3-0. Of eleven League defeats all season, four had taken place in the disastrous last month, while ten of them had occurred away from Elland Road. It was claimed that if Revie's Leeds had played with more intent to win games rather than to just avoid defeat when away from home - in other words, if they had attacked more - then they would have won the title comfortably.

A confident Dundee side visited Elland Road in the Fairs Cup semi-final second leg, the score at 'half-time' in the tie, 1-1. Revie recalled the first team regulars except for Charlton who was still out with an ankle injury - Madeley deputised again. Less than 24,000 attended, the closure of the Gelderd End as a roof was being constructed for the Kop partly responsible for this low crowd. Despite the weekend rest for most of the Leeds players the match still proved to be a struggle, with little in the way of incisive or fluent attacking football until the second half. Was it complacency or weariness? After giving them a stern talking-to at the interval but seeing only slight improvement, Revie believed it to be the latter, though a couple of the players may have been guilty of under-estimating Dundee. The Scots were, after all, fortunate to be in the competition at all due to the Fairs Cup rule of 'one city, one team', plus they had received a bye in an early round. They did though battle well and never made it easy for Leeds. The night eventually turned out to be Leeds', with Eddie Gray in the 81st minute sealing the tie and putting Leeds in the final. His left-foot piledriver hit the roof of the net after somehow piercing the crowded penalty area and beating two Dundee players standing on the goal-line. More good news was that UEFA had decided, due to fixture congestions, to play the two legs of the Fairs Cup final at the beginning of the following season.

In this 1967-'68 season, of the 66 matches Leeds played, Billy Bremner appeared in 58, Jack Charlton in 54, Terry Cooper 60, Paul Reaney 64, Johnny Giles a mere 35, Eddie Gray 50, and Jimmy Greenhoff 55. The busiest of all Leeds men - just - was Norman Hunter with 64 matches plus two for England. Mick Jones played in

38 Leeds games, 30-goal top scorer Peter Lorimer 59 and Paul Madeley 51. Goalkeepers Gary Sprake played 56 and David Harvey the remaining 10 of the entire 66. A lucrative advantage of Leeds' prolonged interest in all competitions of course was the increase in revenue. Whether the public appreciated it or not, professional football was a business and every club had to be run as such. Leeds' sustained financial success enabled the directors to continue with their plans to expand and improve the stadium and make it 'the Wembley of the North'. The summer of 1968 would see the north end of the ground, 'the Spion Kop' on the Gelderd Road side, rebuilt and covered by the new, already under-construction roof. The capacity of the Kop reduced as a result, from 19,000 to nearer 17,000. The new stand encroached on the playing area less than the old one, meaning that the pitch was re-sited thirty or so feet closer to the North Stand, meaning also that there was scope for the south stand to be made bigger too, if desired. The Kop improvements cost well over £100,000.

Chapter 9: 1968/9 - This was our time, Leeds United's

9 i

To hell with Man United, to hell with Liverpool,
We will fight fight fight for United,
'Til we win the Football League!

A great song, it made a change from the usual 'Leeds Leeds Leeds' chant which droned on a bit even though I usually sang it. If fans got bored of singing something then it wasn't really likely to get the players' pulses racing either, that was my way of looking at it at least. The newish song was proof of optimism amongst the Leeds support, that it was going to be our season good and proper. Another reason for looking forward was Yorkshire TV intending to show highlights of the region's matches, on Sunday afternoons. Leeds would be on every show if there was any justice.

The previous season had been a good one - and it hadn't quite finished yet - by any standards, so to hear supporters whingeing about The Don or the team tempted me to slap a bit of sense into the critics, but there was too much violence at football as it was. That wasn't such a joke actually, going to the football was already risky at times, and now there were gangs from various parts of Leeds going to matches with the intention of fighting opposing teams' gangs. A 'disturbing new trend' the papers called it. Course, their publicising it will have done a lot of good. New Leeds chairman Percy Woodward didn't help much either by saying he wouldn't take his grandchildren to Elland Road because of all the abusive and filthy language and atmosphere of aggression there. What a thing to say, as chairman of the club.

Up it went, proudly pinned on my bedroom wall, **the Football Honours 1967 - 68.**

League Division One winners - Manchester City, Runners up - Man. United.
FA Cup winners - West Brom, Runners up - Everton (what a shame!)
League Cup winners - LEEDS UNITED, Runners up - Arsenal.
European Cup winners - Man. United, Runners up - Benfica.
European Cup Winners Cup winners - AC Milan, Runners up - Hamburg.
Inter-Cities Fairs Cup winners - LEEDS UNITED (with luck) or Ferencvaros (without it).
Football Player of the Year - George Best, Man. United.
European Footballer of the Year - George Best.
Leeds' attendance average, home games = 36,828.
Clean Air in Leeds = 7 years.

It had been a good year so far to follow Leeds, at soccer or rugby league. We won the Football League Cup and the RL team won the Challenge Trophy for the first time, at Wembley as well. It was the match when Wakefield's Don Fox missed the easiest conversion ever, with the very last kick of the match. As Eddie Waring said, 'poor lad', even Leeds fans would have sympathised. It wasn't all Fox's fault, it had belted it down all day, the pitch was near flooded; it wasn't nicknamed the 'watersplash final' for nothing.

The first leg of the 1967-'68 Fairs Cup final was to be played at Elland Road on the Wednesday before our League season started. Not only was it a cup final, it was a *major* cup final and against one of the best teams in Europe, the green and whites of Ferencvaros, Hungary's most successful team ever. And if Shankly, Stein and Busby were to be believed they were the finest side in European football too. And being reigning champions of their domestic league as well meant that after this final they'd be competing in the European Cup. So, good as we were, Ferencvaros were tipped to beat us.

The crowd of a little bit more than 25,000 was in my opinion rubbish. Okay, it was the official holiday time in Leeds, match ticket prices had been increased and the match was live on TV, but still. We'd recently beaten Celtic up in Scotland in a friendly and the match reports said we played well, with a more attack-minded approach than previous seasons. With a trophy finally in the cabinet, Revie had apparently given the players permission to 'express' theirselves more. With Mike O'Grady back from injury, I suppose that wasn't so surprising as it would have been like having a new flair player in the squad.

The new liberated, adventurous tactics weren't very evident in the first leg of the Ferencvaros tie though, it was probably too important a match to throw caution to the wind, so to speak. It was a tight match all the way through and the referee used his whistle more than a Bank Holiday train guard, but we managed to grind out a 1-0 win with a scrambled goal from Mick Jones. The win was deserved even though it wasn't a particularly good display, the players hadn't been able to get past or behind the Ferencvaros defenders, all eleven of them near permanently positioned in their own half. If a Leeds move looked promising then one of the Ferencvaros players would chop ours down or obstruct him.

So we were going into the away second leg with a one goal lead which definitely would not be enough to win the cup, if you believed what the experts said. They were forgetting though that Leeds enjoyed being the underdogs. The game might not go ahead anyway, due to trouble in Europe with Commie Russia stamping on countries they'd already taken over, Hungary being one of them. If the match *was* called off then Leeds would be the winners, that's how I saw it anyway. Not that I was hoping for war or revolution or anything, I wasn't that desperate for football glory.

Having 'Shady' O'Grady back was grand news, especially as Jimmy Greenhoff had joined Birmingham for £70,000 soon after the first leg of the final in which he'd come on as sub. It was a decent fee but I'd have preferred he stayed, he had a lot of quality. I couldn't fathom his thinking - he'd played in most of the games the last season, it wasn't like he wasn't getting a chance. *And* the Brummies were in Division Two. It was also looking bleak for Albert Johanneson's career as well, I didn't have a clue what was happening, just that he didn't seem to be involved much any more. I know he liked a drink but whether that was affecting his football-playing, I didn't know. Don Revie would often tell the players to have drink or two after matches, just to unwind and relax, but not to get paralytic. To be fair to Albert, there were always stories about players drinking too much, not just him, and getting involved in various scrapes which the club then had to cover up. A couple of years before, he'd been substituted at half-time in a game, against Notts Forest I think it was, so he stayed in the dressing room and supposedly polished off a whole bottle of whisky. (Some Leeds players liked a nip of it before kick off, to help loosen them up). And that's when it started, when Albert first got a taste for the hard stuff. Leeds players were seen regularly 'on the town', in places like the Windmill Club on North Street and the casino, and loads of different pubs and clubs. There was even a rumour that Billy Bremner had been found asleep on a Leeds golf course one Saturday morning, before a 3 pm match, but the players never really went too far with the drinking. Besides, Don Revie had 'spies' all over Leeds and if a player was seen in an 'unseemly' state i.e. pissed up out of his tree, then the club would know about it soon enough.

Not that any footballer should need more reason to beat opponents other than it's always better than losing to them, but I put a list up on my wall of all our First Division opponents of 1968-'69, with **The Reasons Why We Must Beat Them** title.

Southampton - red & white stripes, Taff striker and top scorer Ron Davies, Terry Paine, Mick Channon, Jimmy Gabriel. Southerners.

QPR - small London club = big headed and cocky Cockneys. Mick Leach, Rodney Marsh.

Stoke - red & white stripes, Gordon Banks, Terry Conroy, Peter Dobing. We owe them big time plus I don't like ornamental pottery.

Ipswich Town - Ray Crawford who's played for England. All country bumpkins.

Nottingham Forest - red shirts, Ian Storey-Moore, 'Slim' Jim Baxter and Joe 'the Jock' Baker who's played for England. And Robin Hood is from Yorkshire really.

Sunderland – red & white stripes, they really hate us. Colin Suggett, George Mulhall. Some of their fans are a bad lot.

Liverpool - all-red, Shankly, Hunt, St John, Yeats. All the abuse given to Albert at Wembley by Scousers. Cilla Black, Jimmy Tarbuck.

Wolves - Derek Dougan and Peter Knowles. The people talk funny.

Leicester - Peter Shilton and record transfer fee £150,000 striker Allan Clarke.

Arsenal - they hate us, some of the supporters are right dogs. McLintock, Graham, Storey and Ure. Red.

Manchester City – manager Joe Mercer, Malcolm big mouth Allison, League Champions. Bell, Summerbee, Lee. Lancashire = red rose.

Newcastle – I hate magpies. Wyn Davies, Bryan 'Pop' Robson. Geordies' foreign language. Ugly black and white kit.
Tottenham - Bill Nicholson, rich club. Jimmy Greaves, Alan Gilzean, Martin Chivers, Pat Jennings, Cyril Knowles, Alan Mullery. Cockneys.
Coventry - Willie Carr, Lady Godiva, the possibly dafter than Wolverhampton accent.
West Ham - snotty manager Ron Greenwood, plus Hurst, Peters, Moore. Cockneys.
Man United – No reason other than nature, but European Cup holders, Busby, Best, Charlton, Law, Stiles. Red, Lancashire. And they really hate us.
Burnley, more Lancastrians. Big mouthed chairman Bob Lord. Ralph Coates, Andy Lochhead, Dave Thomas. Some horrible supporters.
West Bromwich Albion - Jeff Astle, Tony Brown, the possibly dafter than Coventry and Wolverhampton accent.
Everton - they *really* hate us. Some good players and possibly the worst fans going.
Chelsea - FA Cup semi-final, Villa Park, 1967. Cockneys. Most of their players and fans.
Sheffield Wednesday - Don Megson, Jim McCalliog who'd been at Leeds as a kid, Tommy Craig. Their fans hate us probably because we're the best team in Yorkshire.

9 ii

'I took one look and thought he might never play again,' came the articulate voice over the air, followed by the *This Is Your Life* intro music for a fair-haired, bespectacled man: Doctor Matthew McCleary emerges through the curtains and into the spotlight at the front of the vast Queens Hotel banqueting room. Orthopaedic surgeon, Dr McCleary, a small, quietly-spoken man, informs Eamonn Andrews that 21-year old Don Revie had broken three ankle bones and dislocated a joint while playing for Leicester City against Tottenham Hotspur. McCleary was the surgeon to treat him, and he quoted Revie's chances of a return to playing professional football as one thousand to one against.

How, asked Eamonn Andrews, was it only eight weeks after having the pot off that Revie was back playing for the Leicester first team again? 'I think,' replied the surgeon, 'It was Don's grim determination to be a footballer.' Grim determination indeed and a similar determination which influenced the attitudes of the Leeds coaches years later, whenever they were required to treat injured players at the club. Often was the case in the 1960s, that if a supposedly injured player could walk quickly then there was no reason why he could not trot, and if he could trot then he could run, and if he could run then he could bloody well sprint, and if he could bloody well sprint then he was definitely not injured and was available for selection!

Black & white images of the 1949 FA Cup semi-final between Leicester and Portsmouth appear, of Revie scoring the first goal, team-mate Ken Chisholm the second and finally with Revie slamming in his side's third, accompanied by the match commentary '...to sink Pompey lower than a submarine!' Hearty cheers for Revie from the evening's audience. Revie smiles ruefully, the recollection of even more personal misfortune soon after that match clouding his satisfaction. Elsie Revie tells Eamonn Andrews how her husband challenged for a header in a subsequent match against Blackburn, having his nose and teeth smashed by his opponent. The injury caused him to miss the FA Cup final and would threaten his playing career *and* his life.

*

In July 1968, Revie gathered his Leeds squad together in the Players' Lounge at Elland Road to outline his plans and aims for the forthcoming campaign. This was the beginning of his eighth full season as manager but what would emerge on that day was far from business as usual. Standing in front, he addressed the players - 'You're going to win the Championship this time lads, and what's more you're going to do so without losing a single league match.' Club captain Billy Bremner asked if he was in fact joking, while other players wondered, privately of course, whether the Gaffer had taken leave of his senses. So Revie said it again, adding that he was indeed being entirely serious. There were occasions when his men were not entirely sure of Revie's true feelings. For instance, if he was ever distinctly dissatisfied with the team's performance or level of commitment in a match, he would neaten his hair with angry drags of the comb in the dressing room mirror afterwards, remarking that if the players weren't up to the task any more then he would bring in new ones who were. At first those threats were taken seriously but the 'chequebook ploy' eventually wore thin.

The highest compliment the critics seemed able to give Leeds was that they were a powerful 'machine' built by an efficient manager. If that was their best praise then Revie didn't want it. Instead of being admired as a great manager who had built Leeds up from virtually nothing, he seemed to be regarded more as a cold and calculating autocrat, guilty of creating a monster of a football team. Much as he respected Busby, Shankly, Nicholson, Catterick, Mee and even Ramsey, their teams were undeniably built around players with strength and skill *and* bite and steel too, yet it only ever seemed to be Revie's Leeds criticised for their aggressive style. Mud sticks and that's exactly what the FA's 'dirty' tag of 1964 had done. Revie wanted to be popular and to be respected, and he wanted his team to be loved, because they deserved it.

Four days after the narrow home leg 1-0 win over Ferencvaros, on August 7th the new campaign kicked off, and Leeds had seven matches to contest before the return leg in Hungary. The mood within the camp was high confidence, and for every new game the players would enter the field of play believing they would not, perhaps *could* not, lose. An away win at Southampton commenced their assault on the Championship. Despite going a goal down early on, sweet strikes from Lorimer, Jones and Hibbitt (on as substitute for Lorimer) resoundingly won the match 3-1. *The Guardian*'s David Lacey wrote 'Many of the crowd must have wondered how Leeds had earned their reputation for mean mindedness and spoiling tactics...'

Four days later, at home, goals from Jones, Giles, Reaney and Hibbitt brought a 4-1 win over newly promoted Queens Park Rangers, though Leeds had more difficulty than the score-line suggested. And, struggling with knee cartilage trouble, it was to be

Johnny Giles' last game for a while. The injury did not seem too severe at first, more a 'niggle' than anything, but in fact it was a potentially career-threatening one. Fortunately, Giles was treated by specialist Mr S.S. Rose, a director of Manchester City, and his prognosis was good. Rose had helped Jack Charlton's recovery from badly damaged knee ligaments before, a serious injury for a footballer and for which nine out of ten operations reputedly were unsuccessful.

The following Saturday, August 17th, without Madeley and Lorimer as well as Giles, Leeds strove to victory over Stoke, Jones and Johanneson scoring in the 2-0 win. On the next Tuesday, the long journey to newly promoted Ipswich Town resulted in two more Leeds points as goals from Belfitt (in the first twenty seconds), O'Grady and Hibbitt sealed a 3-2 victory. Ipswich had fought back from two down to level early in the second half but a thirty-yarder from Hibbitt decided it. Four wins out of four, eight points out of eight and Hibbitt's third of the campaign. And the next Saturday, at Nottingham Forest, he would be a central figure again.

One of the Leeds players' favourite pre-match pastimes was to play bingo - a fun way of keeping them relaxed and entertained. And there was usually a lot of money riding on it. Before the Forest game, Hibbitt won the bingo and thus pocketed a tidy little sum as a result. As he was one of the younger first teamers, he was paid accordingly too, so the winnings were a welcome bonus. At Forest's City Ground at half time, Don Revie was instructing the Leeds players in their dressing room, within the main stand. The score was then 1-1 and Leeds had not played particularly well. While the players were listening to their manager, Gary Sprake realised he could smell burning and then noticed smoke coming into their room under the door. At first he was told, 'Shut up, the Boss is talking!' but eventually his warnings were heeded. Without any panic the Leeds party made their way out to safety away from the stadium, to a nearby hotel across the River Trent. Hibbitt however, left them to dash back in to retrieve his winnings from his trouser pockets. He returned safe and sound, and that bit wealthier, but had to endure plenty of ridicule from team-mates for not thinking to bring the trousers back with him.

As usual, Dave Cocker, with younger brother Ian, had been at the match. As the flames began to consume the stand in which they were sitting, they realised they were in great danger and so fled into the standing paddock in front of the seats and then on to the pitch, joining hundreds of other spectators there. Dad Les, unaware of his lads' whereabouts or their welfare, spent some frantic minutes looking for them. Because there were no casualties the fire was not regarded as a serious incident but those who escaped it, including the Cocker boys, knew only too well that they had had a lucky escape. As a result, Forest were forced to play their home games at Notts County's ground for a number of weeks as the City Ground underwent repairs. When the main stand was reopened, some Nottingham wags joked that it had been built the wrong way round, facing the pitch.

Four days later, Leeds dropped their first point of the season in a 1-1 home draw with Sunderland, Belfitt getting the goal. Worried about injuries to key players threatening the team's chances of glory, Revie put in a bid for Burnley's Scotland international winger Willie Morgan. But Burnley chairman Bob Lord turned it down and Morgan went on to sign for Manchester United for £117,000. The disappointment of the Sunderland result was short-lived as they beat Liverpool 1-0 at Elland Road, Jones getting the all-important goal, beating the advancing Reds' 'keeper Lawrence on a one-on-one. The two points helped Leeds top the table along with Arsenal who had started the season impressively as well. Midweek, holders Leeds made hard work of beating Charlton Athletic in the League Cup second round, 1-0, before notching up another decent League win at the weekend, over Wolverhampton Wanderers, 2-1, Cooper and Charlton getting the goals.

9 iii

They were all heroes - September 11th 1968. Not my words, the newspapers', local *and* national, on how the Leeds players performed against Ferencvaros away in Budapest in the Fairs Cup final, second leg. I watched it live on the Peacock's television. The pub was pretty chocabloc (choca-Eastern-bloc in fact) but just right, not too sardinesy.

All the Leeds team played heroically, that's the fact of the matter, but especially Gary Sprake, in the best attempt of redeeming yourself since Pickles the dog found the World Cup just after crapping in his owner's slippers. He played fantastically well (Sprake, not Pickles) to keep us in the match, making one unbelievable save, probably the best I've ever seen. The way every one of them battled was what Leeds United was all about for me - the team, the supporters, the city itself. Persevering, resisting, fighting for each other, all for one and one for all. And the harder life gets, the harder you fight to put things right. The team had been expected to just accept what was coming to them, a good Hungarian beating, but times like that were very possibly when Leeds were at their most dangerous. Underestimate or dismiss Leeds at your peril.

Sprakey wore a new kit against Ferencvaros - though it was only a black and white picture - black shirt, black shorts and white socks. He'd worn black shorts in the League Cup Final as well so maybe it was a good omen. I always preferred Gordon Banks's yellow England shirt myself but Sprake could wear anything he liked if it meant he played this well each game. We were 1-0 up from the first leg and Sprake and the lads made sure it stayed that way with a 0-0 stalemate over there. There was no doubt in my mind, at all, that the whole of Great Britain will have been proud of tonight's Leeds United. If they weren't then there was something wrong with them. So up went more stuff on my wall, match reports and other articles. I was running out of wall space, my bedroom was only pokey. There was a Don Revie quote which surprised me a bit - 'I knew we had faced up to such situations before and emerged the victors. But this was the final, the moment of truth, and I wondered for one thing, if the law of averages would work for or against us. I did not admit the doubts of course, and I tried everything I knew to inject confidence into the Leeds players.' I think what all that meant was that The Don, our Don Revie, cool as James Bond, crafty as Harry Palmer, had actually been bricking it!

Some clippings: *United's Finest Hour - The Inter-Cities Fairs Cup was presented to skipper Billy Bremner by its president Sir Stanley Rous, after one of the most exciting goalless draws ever played, in front of 80,000 in the mighty Nep Stadium. The one-*

legged Lord Mayor of Leeds, Mr John Rafferty, himself an ardent Leeds United supporter, will greet the club, which continues to do so well for his domain, in a civic reception. Don Revie with a characteristic example of his detailed conscientiousness, asked the British press afterwards to announce that the entire Elland Road staff and all players' wives or other dear ones, should be at the ground by 7.45 for conveying to the Civic Hall.

United have become the first British club to win this trophy in the ten years of that far flung competition... Certainly the Hungarians gave Leeds United's defence its biggest test yet, swirling through from midfield again and again, on either wing, up the middle, on the ground or in the air... It was significant that Sprake made his save of the match from a thunderous free kick twenty yards out by Novak the Hungarian international right-back and captain. His shot was of such ferocity that it required of Sprake the riskiest save of all - a diving one handed punch. If Sprake had tried to push the ball out with an open hand he would probably have had that hand in splints today. Instead, his lithe leap and powerful punch out sent the ball whirling away, in what will be one of the saves of a lifetime. Leeds United won the final purely because of their indomitable defence, keeping Ferencvaros from scoring last night as well as at Elland Road. There need be no criticism that they won with another deliberate defensive display, they just could not find sufficient ball or openings to attack against a Ferencvaros defence very much on its toes... The real secret of United's success against a better team was simply their never give up spirit in defence. They were always there when it came to the key moment and Sprake can thank his colleagues for a magnificent sustained display of one for all, and all for one. Nobody shirked a thing, even when lungs and legs were straining against the onslaught... So a second cup comes to Elland Road in 1968. As Don Revie said, 'It made a perfect end to last season.' Revie deserves his own tribute for the way he has steered the side which is far from perfect in attack and which has been constantly hampered by injuries, to a couple of coveted trophies against massive opposition.

A couple more cut-out quotes: *Jack Charlton summed up most fittingly why Leeds had the trophy in their hands - 'We won it because we played like England do, giving everything for the team. I sometimes felt we had 22 players, everyone was so willing to come back and cover.' Billy Bremner added 'I'm proud to be in a team like this. We've certainly beaten Europe out of sight - British teams have now won every European club trophy and as our experience increases there is no doubt we can do it all over again.'* I wonder what Billy and the rest of the Scots (who hated the English) thought of Jack's 'England' comment!

*

Aye aye aye aye, Gary is better than Yashin,
Albert is better than Eusebio, And Arsenal are in for a thrashing!

21st September was Leeds v Arsenal and we were honoured enough to have Kenneth Wolstenholme here with the *Match of the Day* television crew. He'd called us 'the number one team in the country at the moment' but that mean nothing as Arsenal were top of the table, and they were still smarting (so the papers said) about the lost 'battle' of Wembley in March.

I suspect it was a deliberate trick by The Don to wind the Arsenal players up: a few minutes before 3pm kick-off he sent two of the Juniors out to parade to the crowd the League Cup and the Inter Cities Fairs Cup. They held a trophy each, in front of nearly forty thousand people, and I was jealous as hell. Not very Leeds United of me I admit but I was angry that two spawny lads who'd done probably sweet FA for the club, so far at least, were getting the glory. I soon softened my opinion anyway due to some tosspot - probably an Arsenal fan - throwing a coin and cutting the head of one of those Juniors, Peter Hearnshaw.

It had poured with rain in the morning so the ground was soaked. There was nothing much you could do to protect pitches against heavy rain bar covering it all up which just wasn't possible, or keep forking it to stop it turning into a paddling pool. There were ways of sponging surface water off but the best measure was to sweep it off onto the surrounding cinder track using the massive brushes we had. Had to be quick and fit to do it though, it was knackering work. It beat carting tons of straw about all night, that was for sure.

The team was announced over the tannoy, and even though the fans sang about him, Albert wasn't even playing. Each player would be cheered when his name was read out. Some cheers more vociferous than others, Billy Bremner's usually the loudest, funny in a way because not too long ago he used get more stick than anything. *Number 1 Gary Sprake, 2 Paul Reaney, 3 Terry Cooper, 4 Billy Bremner, 5 Jack Charlton, 6 Norman Hunter, 7 Mike O'Grady, 8 Peter Lorimer, 9 Mick Jones, 10 Paul Madeley, 11 Terry Hibbitt, and today's substitute, number 12 Eddie Gray.* Getting close to kick-off now and the crowd's lively, warming their vocal chords up nicely. The singing comes mainly from the Scratching Shed end but not completely, all sides of the ground are pretty crammed and noisy, even our side the West Stand, where the wealth usually is. We staff got a typed team sheet before the announcer so I knew already that Norman would be in midfield whilst Madeley was in the centre of defence alongside big Jack.

We're the greatest team in Europe, and Revie is our king, a couple of choruses of *The Whites are going to win* and *We shall not be moved* and then it's on to chanting the names of the individual players. Sometimes it's like the singing is orchestrated - a bloke, lifted up by his mates at the front of the Scratching Shed, conducts the crowd around him when to sing. Since the Rangers game when all the drunken skirt-wearers invaded though, I heard that half the Scratching Shed lads had switched ends and went in the Kop now.

M – I... M - I – C... M - I - C - K - MICK JONES! Jonesy would always look a bit embarrassed but he'd give a little wave to thank his fans. What a great bloke.

Bremner Bremner Bremner Bremner! Not that Billy Bremner ever needed motivating, he wasn't our captain for nothing. And every time he heard his name, his songs, you could see him grinning proudly. This season there was a new song to add to his little collection, too: *His eyes they shone like diamonds, as he lifted the cup from the stand. And there stood Billy Bremner, stood there with the cup in his hands.* Just in case any of the Leeds players felt left out, Leeds fans would try and get them all mentioned if there was time, even the sub. But only time for *Jackie Charlton* (clap clap clap), *Jackie Charlton* today. Then a big roar just before the first kick is about to be taken, to inspire the players on to victory whilst putting the wind up the opponents, good and proper. This is the big one of the League season so far, second versus first.

Even without the midfield mastermind Giles, we had more of the play than Arsenal. Billy looked the liveliest of everyone but he had more than decent help with Hunter and Hibbitt doing well in the centre and O'Grady and Lorimer both out wide on the flanks. Jones was practically up front on his own, though that didn't make it a negative formation as he was seeing plenty of the ball and he looked to have the better of all the Arsenal defence. If he wasn't trying to take advantage of passes from midfield or running in on goal with the ball himself, he was supplying the oncoming midfielders, laying the ball off for them. Looking at him, shielding, dribbling, controlling the ball, fending off defenders, scrapping fairly for every ball that came near him, I couldn't quite believe that he'd needed extra training to improve his control when he first came here.

When the Gunners did manage to mount an attack, Sprake was having another good day - every catch stuck to his hands like glue. Maybe it was something to do with all the chewing gum thrown into his net by his little fan club in the Kop. *Leeds! Leeds! Leeds! Leeds! Leeds! Leeds!* and the Whites press forward as often as they can, and the crowd urges them on even more. Me being more a defensive, tackling and 'holding' sort of player, what I've always liked about the Leeds style is that they don't just clear the ball away from the penalty area, unless they need to, they pass it out of defence or even dribble away with it if they've the space. It all means that Leeds can keep possession and attack and score from just about every position, besides the goalie of course, and even then that's not impossible. The players hardly make a wayward pass or aimless punt, including Sprake who usually throws or rolls the ball out rather than just drop-kicking it with less accuracy.

In the first half, Jack had one of his brilliant giraffe-striding runs from the edge of our penalty area up in to the middle of Arsenal's half. It wasn't all brilliant football of course but it was a good game, and there was a bit of needle too, with Arsenal giving a load of free kicks for fouls away. *Dirty Arsenal, Dirty Arsenal* our lads sing, soon followed by *Animals! Animals! Animals!* Terry Hibbitt was tripped and it looked to me that Jack got a whack in the mouth as well when Leeds had a corner. The culprit was Bobby Gould who looked like he only had one eyebrow. He ran around like he thought he was the cock of the playground. He'd definitely come to the wrong place for that.

Leeds! Leeds! Leeds! Leeds! Leeds! Leeds! every time we get a corner, the crowd goes *United* (clap clap clap), *United!* Even though the Scratching Shed mob behind him give him plenty of grief, Arsenal 'keeper Bob Wilson's not had much trouble so far, and he's dealt with the corner kicks easily enough. It's the same again, except this time the ball is only half-cleared, ending up on our left touchline near the Lowfields terraces. Cooper gets it and you can tell he's trying to take a swing with his trusty left foot and get a cross in, but the Arsenal bloke keeps blocking the chance. So, tricky Terry feigns a kick with his left foot, nudges the ball to his right and then lofts a cross into the penalty area with his right. Long and high, the cross veers inwards but it's gone over Mick Jones and seems just that bit too high and far away for O'Grady as well. Amazingly though, he darts in and then dives forward and *upwards*, to head the ball. Connecting perfectly with his forehead, it's almost as hard as if he'd kicked it and the ball arrows over Wilson's arms, scrapes the bottom of the crossbar and hits the net. A fantastic goal and it's 1-0 to Leeds.

Half time. The players leave the pitch, the Leeds lads in all white with lots of black mud all over them, the Gunners in their usual red and white 'tanktop' shirt, all filthy as well. Hot teas for most of the players, though I wouldn't be surprised if there was a nip of the strong stuff for anyone wanting it. Half the crowd disappears from the terraces too, most of them go to the toilets or get more beers in. There are snacks available too, and gravy drinks, but the prices are nearly as unappetising as the tastes. The grass has churned up big time, as expected, so it's as many ground staff (and casuals, such as I) on as possible to replace divots or flatten any rough muddy bumps and holes. People could be forgiven for thinking that I'd get a thrill every time I get up on the hallowed Leeds United pitch, but the truth is, that feeling's long gone now. It's not much of a thrill any more and the way I see it at least, the more times I go on the pitch to tend it, the less times I'm likely to go on it to play as a fully-fledged Leeds United player.

The second half, the players come out, the same eleven on each side, and all wearing the same mucky kits. The play was much the same too - Leeds taking the game to Arsenal. It's good to see us beat teams convincingly but when the other team is top of the League, you expect a better game of it. I wasn't meaning to put them down but for their sake I hoped that this was just an off day as there wasn't much quality play at all from Arsenal. Maybe they had too many injuries - there was no John Radford, Peter Storey or George Graham or that big sod Ian Ure.

With another one of his regulation headers on the goal-line from a corner, Jack made it 2-0. He's great is Jack; when he scores he doesn't dance around or celebrate much, even though everyone runs to him to congratulate him. He normally doesn't even thank the man who's taken the corner and landed the ball to perfection right on his head for him to score the unmissable goal. All Wilson could do was try and push Jack out of the way; he failed. So that was that, the game was effectively over now, Arsenal were knocked off the top. *U-nited, U-nited, top of the League, top of the League.* The full-time whistle goes, the Leeds supporters cheer and applaud the new League leaders. Both teams' players congratulate and shake hands with each other, as well as the referee and the two linesmen, as they all walk off the pitch and down the tunnel, usually good-naturedly chatting with each other and maybe arranging to have a pint and a natter in the Players' Lounge after. Usually the crowds leave as quick as they can though you sometimes get a few oddballs hanging around on the terraces for no apparent reason. Me, I just want to get in front of the television so I can watch the football results being announced but it hardly ever happens, too much work to do. If the pitch is in a real state, which it virtually always is, we have to do what we can to make it better as quick as possible. Even though it's like trying to plait fog.

Without trying to seem too cocky, even with less than a third of the season gone, I felt only one other team could stop us - Shankly's Liverpool.

Division One table, 21st September, 1968.

1 LEEDS	Played 9	Points 16
2 Arsenal	Played 10	Points 16
3 Liverpool	Played 10	Points 14
4 Chelsea	Played 10	Points 14
5 West Ham	Played 10	Points 14

My own playing career, not a great choice of word that, 'career', wasn't exactly headline material. It wasn't even footline material, if there was such a thing, it was *sod all* material, that's what it was. I still trained virtually every day before going to work, afterwards as well, and I was fitter than the proverbial butcher's dog, I really was. My place in the St Anthony's first team was assured and we won stuff and I usually played well, but no one outside of St Anthony's seemed to take any notice of me. Ces would come and watch sometimes, maybe John too, and I'd ask them if The Don and co knew I actually existed as a football player any more. Ces would say 'They know' and stuff, but I had this rotten little suspicion that I wasn't being taken seriously anymore, or that Ces was trying to save my feelings. Or maybe he didn't want *me* to know that my chances had slipped away, either when my leg and ankle were broken or that I'd let myself go too much, with the drinking and the like. Still, if anyone could seriously blame me for all that had happened to me then they should at least say so to my face, not leave me stewing.

9 iv

A week after their famous Fairs Cup success, Leeds began the defence of the trophy with a 0-0 away draw with Standard Liege. The same evening, West Bromwich Albion made their European bow in the Cup Winners' Cup, also against a Belgian team, FC Bruges. It was a night of shocks there, as not only did Bruges win 3-1 but scores of home supporters invaded the pitch at the final whistle, and Albion striker Jeff Astle needed hospital treatment after being attacked.

In their return from Hungary to the title race, Leeds had earned a point away at Leicester, thanks to a Paul Madeley goal. Liverpool were sitting handily in third place in the table, as if in wait for their two main rivals (Leeds and Arsenal) to falter and allow them to steal the big prize. Late September, in midweek, Johnny Giles returned to the Leeds team in the 2-1 League Cup third round win at Bristol City. Many considered the team's strongest point as the 'engine' of the midfield, the perfect partnership of Billy Bremner and Giles. Bremner would look for attacking positions where he would force things to happen, while Giles would get into positions to guide and persuade things to happen. With Giles recovering from treatment and Leeds already top of the table - on goal average, above Arsenal - it seemed clear that all was looking very promising for the Peacocks. The careful Revie though decided to rest Giles for the tricky game at Manchester City. Despite being reigning champions, City were mid-table and not on good form so Revie's decision to drop Giles should not have signified much of a risk. However, even with a sixteen match unbeaten run behind them, Leeds were outplayed in a spirited City display and lost the match 3-1. And then the critics pounced, as if it had been their sixteenth consecutive game without a win, mainly blaming Sprake, Charlton and Hunter for jittery performances. Colin Bell, with two goals, had been outstanding but also the most wasteful in front of goal. After the match, Don Revie did not seem particularly worried, putting the poor performance and result down to too many of his players being tired or simply off form. Was he trying to conceal his deep concern?

Manchester United had enquired about the availability of a certain Brazilian player on the books of club side Santos and who went by the name of Pele. Nothing would materialise in terms of a famous transfer, but it was a sign that the Old Trafford club were ambitious. Or, some might say, desperate, as the team was struggling in the league. Meanwhile, the Leeds board were more than a little worried that Don Revie would be another target, to replace Matt Busby. The Old Trafford club was one of the richest around and Revie might not be able to resist an invitation. The Leeds directors acted swiftly and prepared to offer him a new, improved contract. 'We have the best manager in the Football League and we want to keep him,' said chairman Percy Woodward, while Revie scotched any 'exit' rumours in the *Yorkshire Evening Post*, saying, 'No amount of money or prestige would take me away from Leeds United. I have had some generous offers from other clubs in the last seven years. Two months ago, I was approached by another First Division club to become their manager at double my current salary. They also included fringe benefits like a house and car. As long as I am reasonably secure, wealth is immaterial to me.' Wealth may well have been immaterial to him but if he ever felt he was being under-rewarded then his directors were always quickly put in the know. His present contract, for seven years at around £7,000 a year, with four years left to run, was far from measly, and now the board were offering an even better deal in the hope of keeping him at the club until 1975. In comparison to the other top managers in Britain, the terms were very generous, and his press statement will certainly have encouraged the directors, yet that new contract remained unsigned for two full months.

After the Manchester City defeat, within eight October days Leeds returned to winning ways with three League wins: two 1-0 victories, at Newcastle and Sunderland (scorers Charlton and Jones) and a scrappy, bad-tempered 2-0 win over West Ham at Elland Road (Giles and an unstoppable Lorimer free kick). They followed that with a midweek - and weak - fourth round 2-1 defeat at Crystal Palace, the holders casually waving goodbye to the League Cup with barely a hint of regret. It may not have mattered too much, but the following Saturday *was* serious, as a young Burnley team outpaced and outplayed them at Turf Moor in the League.

Frank Casper, Dave Thomas, John Murray, Steve Kindon and Ralph Coates enjoyed a fine time to help incur the second Leeds League defeat of the season. Two quick Burnley goals to Leeds' one in the first half helped them hit a thoroughly deserved 5-1 victory. Five goals to one, against the most renowned defence in English League football! And five minutes in to the second half of their Wednesday night Fairs Cup return tie against Standard Liege, the seemingly now shaky Leeds defence had conceded another two goals, albeit against the run of play. Not for the first time in Leeds' European history, both sides had taken to the field wearing all white. Whether it was a mistake or more crude gamesmanship on the part of the Belgian visitors remained undetermined. Revie's boys in blue (and white socks) were now 2-0 down on aggregate with less than forty minutes remaining. It looked like they were releasing their hold on the Fairs Cup as meekly as they had done the League Cup but thanks to a quick response with a header from Charlton and then a 72nd minute free-kick missile from Lorimer, Leeds had drawn level and at least regained some respect by going out only via the away goals rule. But then again, with just two minutes left, the midfield dynamo and captain Billy Bremner was perfectly positioned to tap the ball home after a Leeds corner had eluded the Liege defenders. 3-2 to Leeds and one of the most dramatic Elland Road European ties ever, with Bremner celebrating by grabbing, shaking, punching the net and drop-kicking the ball into the roof of the goal. Their reward would be another tough tie in the next round, with Napoli of Italy. Liege had shown themselves to be formidable opponents and would emphasise that by winning their domestic League Championship.

Leeds' recent less than impressive defensive displays had prompted media comment that their famous back five wall was weakening and had had its day. Of course, Revie knew different, believing only that the defence needed a boost. So the club's defenders – from all the squads - were put through 'refresher' courses by the coaches. Three clean sheets in a row in the League followed, unfortunately their problems now seemed to be in attack, as those games, against West Bromwich Albion, Manchester United (away) and Tottenham Hotspur, were all goalless and caused a slip down the table.

Division One League table (top), November 9th, 1968.

1 Liverpool	Played 18	Points 26
2 Everton	Played 18	Points 26
3 Leeds Utd.	Played 17	Points 25
4 Arsenal	Played 17	Points 23
5 Chelsea	Played 18	Points 22
6 Burnley	Played 18	Points 22

Next up came the visit of Napoli from southern Italy, in the second round of the Fairs Cup. The first leg, at Elland Road, was played on the thirteenth night of November but the only bad luck for Leeds was that goalkeeper Dino Zoff was on top form - Leeds were unfortunate to have only scored twice, with headers from Jack Charlton before the half hour mark, while Mick Jones had two goals disallowed as well as his face punched by an Italian defender for his troubles.

Napoli had earned notoriety over recent years for violent misconduct, on and off the pitch. A journalist's comment in newspaper *Gazzetta dello Sport* regarding games in Napoli went some way to summing up their bad reputation '...visiting players are put through a mincing machine at the end of a game and their remains roasted on a spit.' It is entirely possible that officials and supporters of Napoli enjoyed the infamy. Last season in Naples, for instance, the Burnley party plus English journalists, needed escorting from the stadium by mounted police, an armoured lorry and nine military jeeps. After the Leeds-Napoli first leg, unhappy Revie commented, 'Some of my players said they had fingers poked in their eyes and faces in scrambles, and then there was the punch in the face Jones took and some other unsavoury moments.' He later added, 'We have asked for special observers to be at the game in view of the fact that Naples have been fined twice for crowd disturbances in the last two seasons and the trouble when Burnley played in Naples,' prompting media criticism again, that he was overreacting and guilty of preaching double standards. However, managers of other teams who had played in Europe, especially Italy, expressed support for Revie.

With a 'technically faultless' performance, a fine twenty-five yard strike from Paul Madeley ensured Leeds beat Coventry City (away) 1–0, following it up with a hard-fought but deserved 2-1 win at home to Everton, a penalty from Giles and a well-taken goal from Gray earning the two points, in front of nearly 42,000 spectators.

The Napoli return leg went just as Revie had feared, with the Italian players kicking and snarling their way to victory. Leeds' O'Grady received a booking from the referee, for being head butted by Napoli's Omar Sivori (who then dived as if felled by an invisible assailant). Revie revealed later that he had been very close to taking the team off the pitch as the violence rained in, threatening to cause serious injury to the victims. With stalwarts such as Giles and Bremner and Charlton and Hunter and co in the side, all of whom liked a good old battle, it is unlikely the Leeds players would have really appreciated such a gesture. The Leeds manager and chairman, unusually, were in complete agreement - that despite the club earning good money from the Fairs Cup competition, the risk of serious injury to their players might be too high and that competing in Europe might not be worth doing again. With respect to the actual Napoli-Leeds football match, 1-0 up from the first half, Napoli finally squared the tie 2-2 with a penalty, six minutes from time. The scoreline stayed the same for the thirty minutes' extra time period and so, once again for Leeds United in Europe, the result had to be settled on the toss of a disc. Bremner called that toss and he guessed the outcome correctly. Once again Leeds had won in Europe thanks to the lottery of flipping a coin.

After a creditable 1-1 draw at Chelsea (O'Grady) on 30th November, Leeds beat Sheffield Wednesday 2-0, both goals cracked home by Lorimer. However, an injury to Cooper had necessitated changes to the team - Madeley (who else?) was switched from midfield to left-back, and Lorimer was recalled to the starting line-up after being dropped a short while before. Unhappy at that situation, he had asked to leave Leeds, and so Revie added his name to the transfer list. It would stay there for most of the season. Reports claimed he would be used as part-exchange for players like striker Joe Baker of Nottingham Forest, Hibernian's Peter Cormack or Sunderland's Colin Suggett, but no such deal ever materialised. He probably never intended letting Lorimer leave.

On December 14th - Lorimer's 22nd birthday - Leeds took their unbeaten League run to eight games with a 1-1 draw at West Ham (Eddie Gray). Revie and the players knew very well that they weren't scoring enough goals - they missed more chances than they were converting - but on the positive side, it was also becoming clear that they were the hardest team to beat in Division One. On the Wednesday night, Leeds exploited the freedom and space allowed them by a rather weak team from Germany, Hanover 96, winning 5-1. Lorimer grabbed himself a brace while O'Grady, Charlton and Hunter scored the others. Hanover's coach, Zlatko Cajkovski, praised Leeds as the best English team he had ever seen. Norman Hunter's goal was a sweetly struck shot with his right 'chocolate' foot. Hunter goals, especially from thirty yards out, were only occasional sights, but Hunter *right-footed* goals were very rare.

Four days before Christmas, Leeds most definitely were not in festive mood, they were out for revenge, over Burnley. The players needed little motivation from their inspirational boss to exact it - memories of the 5-1 drubbing in October were more than enough incentive. With the exception of Gary Sprake in goal (only because he had little to do) every Leeds player contributed to a superb team performance which saw them tear Burnley apart from the kick-off. A splendid chip from Burnley's Ralph Coates early in the second half made it 4-1 but only sparked Leeds into increasing the pressure on Burnley even more. Goals from Lorimer (two), Bremner, Jones, Giles and Gray signified a superb 6-1 Christmas cracker of a Leeds win. Seasonal spirit of goodwill was starkly absent at the Division Two match between Millwall and Birmingham City. City won 3-1 and their goalkeeper Jim Herriott was attacked on the pitch by Millwall supporters.

A Boxing Day Elland Road crowd of 42,000 enjoyed a proficient Leeds display against Newcastle and a 2-0 win, a Lorimer penalty and Madeley shot sealing the points. O'Grady had come on as substitute for the injured Giles early on, and whilst the Leeds central midfield was unquestionably weakened, Newcastle never looked like rescuing the tie. Liverpool were still top, by two points, but Leeds had two games in hand.

Their first two new year games were cup ties, against Sheffield Wednesday. The teams had drawn 1-1 at Hillsborough in the FA Cup third round so the Elland Road replay was set for the following Wednesday. Leeds were the country's form team and the bookmakers' favourites to win the Cup. Although they were without the injured Cooper, Giles and O'Grady, a very strong team was fielded as the FA Cup meant a lot to Don Revie. Sheffield Wednesday certainly weren't there to just make up the numbers though. Making only his second start of the campaign, Albert Johanneson hit the first goal of the tie early on but it was an end-to-end tie with both teams going close a few times as well as hitting their opponents' crossbar, and shortly before half-time, Wednesday equalised with a deft, curled lob from Brian Woodall. Early in the second half the visitors took the lead, again through Woodall, and the hosts were forced to push more players up in attack to try for the equalizer. Wednesday defended stoutly, preventing Leeds from breaking through. Finally, after resisting another barrage, the visitors exploited the over-stretched whites' defence to grab a third, decisive goal, through striker John Ritchie. The Cup shock of the round, favourites Leeds were out, falling at the first hurdle.

Their next match, against Manchester United in the League, contained a large slice of good luck. Already fortunate perhaps to be fielding Bremner and Giles who were both struggling with injuries - Bremner with a back problem and Giles with such a badly bruised thigh he could hardly kick the ball, Leeds were leading. A scrambled goal from Jones and an O'Grady cracker from the corner of the Manchester penalty area which soared into the top corner of the net, put them 2-1 up. However, late in the second half, the referee awarded Manchester United a free kick just outside Leeds' penalty area. When George Best instead of Bobby Charlton struck the kick, he had taken the Leeds 'keeper and defence by surprise. And when his chipped shot landed in the Leeds net, their surprise turned to shock, seeing as Best had apparently nicked a point for the visitors. Except the referee disallowed the goal, stating that the free kick was in fact 'indirect' - from the kick the ball must be touched by more than one player for the goal to be given. Leeds' good fortune was definitely well and truly in, especially when it later emerged that unbeknownst to the referee, Best's strike had brushed Giles' head as it floated goalwards.

It was also fortunate for everyone there that there were no serious injuries on the Elland Road terraces. Crowd trouble began well before the three o'clock kick off, with Manchester United fans attempting to invade and 'take' the new Leeds Kop, walking from their allocated end of the ground, the south stand, across the pitch and into the rebuilt north stand. An estimated two thousand supporters were locked out of the ground too, and numerous exchanges were made between rival fans - exchanges of insults, fisticuffs, bottles, coins and other missiles - with nearly fifty people injured. The St John's Ambulance volunteers were kept busy all afternoon, just like the police of course, but afterwards, chairman Percy Woodward surprisingly denied seeing any trouble.

On January 14th Sir Matt Busby announced that he would be retiring as Manchester United manager at the end of the season - FA Cup final day - but would be staying on as general manager. The pressures of football management were becoming too much for a man of his age, nearly 60, and he remarked that it was the perfect time for a younger, 'track-suited' manager to take over. On hearing the news, 43 year-old Revie wagered £10 with Johnny Giles that he himself would retire from football management by the time he was 52.

The next Saturday, Leeds earned a point in a 0-0 draw away at Spurs. Liverpool though outdid them with a 2-1 win at Chelsea to go three points clear Leeds completed one of their games in hand on Friday 24th January, also in London, at Queens Park Rangers. Both teams had exited the FA Cup and so had a fixture-free weekend while the Cup fourth round took place. Revie, keen to avoid the usual end of season match pile-up, took advantage of the situation and sought official permission to rearrange certain Leeds' fixtures. With the clubs agreeing to bring forward from Good Friday their League tie, QPR hosted Leeds on the Friday night. Alarmingly for Leeds, the plan looked to have backfired on them as table-propping QPR gave them a hard time, even hitting the post in the first minute and having a Bobby Keetch penalty saved by Sprake early in the second half. By then Leeds were leading, Jones putting away a parried Madeley shot. Revie commented afterwards, 'I am baffled that Rangers are not near the top instead of at the bottom. We could have lost four or five-one. That little bit of luck had swayed the game in our favour.'

Next up were Coventry City at Elland Road on February 1st, 1969, and a deserved win followed, though the 3-0 score-line flattered them (Bremner 2, O'Grady), while Liverpool beat Sheffield Wednesday at Anfield. Leeds were still in Europe too of course, unlike Liverpool, knocked out in the first round of the Fairs Cup by Athletic Bilbao.

Division One League table (top), February 1st, 1969.

1 Liverpool	Played 29	Points 45
2 Leeds Utd.	Played 28	Points 44
3 Everton	Played 28	Points 40

Leeds flew to Germany soon after the Coventry match for the return tie with Hanover on Tuesday the fourth. Revie would later describe the Hanover team as brutal, even though it was Terry Cooper sent off late in the game. Leeds won 2-1 on the night, 7-2 on aggregate, and mighty Hungarian side Ujpest Dozsa awaited them in the next round.

On February 12th the team took the opportunity to use their League game in hand and, they hoped, gain points on Liverpool to take over at the top of the table. Sections of the media accused the Football League of willingly allowing Revie to bend the rules by the rearrangement of certain fixtures but the FL denied absolutely any wrongdoings or favouritism: Leeds' actions were fully within the rules and were, quite simply, reasonable efforts to prevent fixture congestion later on. The Tuesday February 12th match (versus Ipswich Town) was brought forward from Easter Monday, but it could easily have been called off due to more bad weather that day. Heavy sleet and snow fell throughout the tie, making the pitch heavier and the playing conditions much more difficult. Despite the harsh elements, the pitch was in decent condition, aided immeasurably by the use of braziers to heat the ground and tons of straw to protect the surface from the biting cold. And all the long hours of labour put in by the dedicated groundstaff and casual workers paid off - Belfitt and Jones secured the two points for Leeds in the one-sided 2-0 victory against a moderate Ipswich side.

The next Saturday, Leeds were at home to Chelsea, and Liverpool to Nottingham Forest. With Forest toiling at the foot of the division, and Chelsea faring relatively well in the top half, Liverpool looked to have much the easier task. However, in one of the major shocks of the season, Forest snatched a fine 2 - 0 victory at Anfield while a second half Peter Lorimer strike beat Chelsea, putting Leeds three points ahead of Liverpool.

The week after, February 22nd, harsh winter struck again and Leeds fell behind Liverpool again, in terms of matches played. Sheffield Wednesday versus Leeds was a casualty of the weather but Liverpool's visit to West Ham went ahead. Bill Shankly probably wished it hadn't as they could only gain a point in a 1-1 draw. Tuesday 25th February, Leeds caught up again with games played with their visit to Nottingham Forest at the City Ground, the main stand rebuilt since their last flaming visit. Tonight the only semblance of fire came from Leeds United, on the pitch, as they dealt comfortably with all Forest's attacks and then burned through their defences with ease. Goals from Lorimer and Jones won it 2-0 but it should have been by more. Leeds were now four points clear of Liverpool, both having played 31 games.

The fifth round of the FA Cup saw Liverpool away at Leicester, leaving Leeds an opportunity to extend their lead in the table, with a home game versus Southampton. It was Southampton who looked like champions-elect though, taking the lead twice in the match. Normal service was finally resumed with a Giles penalty, an own goal from Southampton's Kirkup and Mick Jones pouncing on a parried Giles shot to give Leeds the points and the unlucky Saints nothing.

In the Fairs Cup, Ujpest Dozsa, despite their famed fast and adventurous football, defended en masse at Elland Road and only looked to score from breakaway, counter attacks. Leeds had the majority of possession but toiled to make any impact on the opposition's goal. Giles even had a penalty saved in the second half. Late on, the visitors took the lead, star striker Antal Dunai smacking a shot from outside the box in to the top right corner of the net. It stayed 1-0 to the end and few people expected Leeds to overcome the one goal deficit in two weeks' time.

Unusually it wasn't the inclement weather to blame for the next Liverpool postponement but a 'flu bug sidelining eight of Arsenal's players ahead of their game at Anfield. Leeds thus had further chance to extend their lead in the table while the Liverpool players could only hope that Revie's men slipped up at relegation candidates Stoke City. As the adage goes, animals are often at their most dangerous when wounded and unfortunately for Liverpool and most certainly Stoke, Leeds United were one such animal - they owed Stoke for the crucial defeat there last season. This time around their display at the Victoria Ground was quite spectacular, an annihilation of Stoke bringing a stunning 5-1 victory, with goals from Jones, Bremner 2 and O'Grady 2.

Division One League table (top), March 8th, 1969

1 Leeds Utd	Played 33	Points = 54
2 Liverpool	Played 31	Points = 46
3 Everton	Played 30	Points = 43

So impressive was the Leeds performance at Stoke - notably the English contingent - that England manager Sir Alf Ramsey called on Paul Reaney, Terry Cooper, Jack Charlton, Norman Hunter and, after seven years out of international football, Mike O'Grady for the midweek friendly against France at Wembley. As it turned out, Hunter and Reaney did not play in the 5-0 England win but the other three did. O'Grady even opened the scoring and he and Cooper received high praise for their performances.

Liverpool reduced the points gap to six with a steady 2-0 win at Sunderland on March 15th, as Elland Road fell to the weather with the Leeds-Forest game snowed off. On the very same day, at Wembley, Arsenal were playing Division Three side Swindon Town in the League Cup final. They lost, after extra time, 2-1, in one of *the* shock results in football history. Nonetheless, some of the Arsenal players drew strength from the calamity, citing it as the turning point in their careers.

Wednesday March 19th was the Fairs Cup quarter-final return leg with Ujpest Dozsa. Leeds' preparations could hardly have been worse as influenza and cold bugs affected the squad, and Revie's annoyance with Ramsey and the FA was barely contained - 'Whether these illnesses have anything to do with Astle being ill last week when the lads were with the England party or whether it is connected with an injection they received, I just do not know,' he said. 'If we had six, seven or eight down, we would ask the Fairs Cup Committee for a postponement but if we do not lose any more players we will play. With four outstanding League fixtures still to fit in, we can do without another postponement.' Too ill to play, Reaney, Charlton and O'Grady were withdrawn from the squad. Most of the remaining Leeds players were poorly too, but not poorly enough to drop out. Bremner would play at right-back and Bates fill in the gap in midfield. Yorath and Hibbitt were substitutes and Jimmy Lumsden named in the squad. The changes unsettled the weakened Leeds team even more and, in the last 25 minutes of the match, the Hungarian champions-to-be scored twice to win the tie. They deserved it and whilst Revie was gracious in defeat, he was adamant too that had he been able to field a full-strength team, they would have expected to win.

The League visit to Wolverhampton Wanderers on Saturday 29th March followed, one more point collected from a 0-0 draw. Hardly a disastrous result, mid-table Wolves' home record was good, but Liverpool gained a point on Leeds and had a game in hand. Third placed Arsenal were not out of the running just yet either. A major frustration for Liverpool though was the number of postponed games affecting their challenge, the most unpalatable of them being the home match against Leeds, scheduled for 22nd March. Following their game in Hungary, Leeds had ten players ill or injured and so they asked the Football League to call the Liverpool game off. After some consideration, the FL duly did that, bringing about more insinuations of favouritism as a consequence. The Football League clearly could not win whichever choice they made, while Liverpool simply could not win, lose or draw due to so many postponements! Over the next four weeks, to the joy of Leeds supporters, whenever the Whites dropped a point, the Reds appeared equally as wasteful, and their 31st March 1-1 draw with Arsenal looked to have severely hurt Arsenal's title challenge too, even with eight games to go. Meanwhile, Leeds' 0-0 draw at Sheffield Wednesday on the night of April 1st, maintained the gap between the top two sides.

League Division One table (top), April 1st 1969

1 Leeds Utd	Played 35	Points = 56
2 Liverpool	Played 34	Points = 51
3 Arsenal	Played 34	Points = 48

At this stage of the season, the top two teams both appeared to have stopped playing entertaining football, and on Saturday April 5th while Liverpool scraped a 1-0 win at Wolves, Leeds edged by champions Manchester City by the same score-line at Elland Road. The *Guardian* portrayed Liverpool about as inspiring as watching a concrete mixer at work, and Leeds' display was described as, 'Gray and Lorimer were profligacy gone mad and poor Jones had as much support as the average working man's application for a pay rise. Giles and Bremner wove beautiful patterns all over the field but the end product… oh dear!'

Liverpool could only draw 0-0 at Stoke City on April 7th plus they had to suffer the loss of Roger Hunt, taken off injured with a dislocated shoulder. And two days later it was 'as you were' as Leeds' drew 1-1 at West Bromwich Albion, restoring their five points comfort zone. However, Leeds seemed to have much the harder run in of remaining games; they had to face the other three teams at the top, Arsenal, Everton and Liverpool, and all away, plus difficult home games against Leicester City and Nottingham Forest who were both fighting hard against relegation and both incidentally, victors over Liverpool earlier in the season.

9 v

April 12th 1969, it was nearly worth noting in my diary, if I had one - I took it all back what I'd said about referee Ken Burns. Well, some of it. He definitely went up in my estimations after the Arsenal-Leeds match. The Gunners were third in the table, and Liverpool second - and the Scousers had won 2-0 at Leicester the same day. 'That pillock Sprake!' Ces grumbled, the Monday after, 'You'd think he wanted us to lose.' He'd gone to Highbury with John Reynolds, the club laid on a special coach for full-time staff. If I'd got on my knees and begged I might well have been able to go as well, but it would have cost me too much. In the first five minutes of the match, Sprake and Arsenal's Bobby Gould - him with the eyebrow - went up for a high cross. It was breezy and due to the wind, both of them missed the ball. And so Gould decided to kick two others instead, them belonging to Sprake, with a few verbals about his parentage and nationality mixed in to add insult to injury. Sprake got up off the deck and lamped Gould with a proper champion left-hook. So it was Gould's turn to hit the floor now, while referee Ken Burns came rushing in to intervene and probably to send Sprake off as well, and maybe Gould would be joining him. Except Burns is Welsh supposedly and he'd heard Gould's insult. Suddenly the Welsh referee's loyalties are definitely with Wales' international goalkeeper Gareth Sprake and instead of sending them off, Referee Burns gives them both a good talking to and only books them. I was told that at half time in the Leeds dressing room, Sprake was in tears because it had dawned on him how serious the consequences could have been for the team. Anyway, Keystone Cop defending by Arsenal, especially Ian Ure and Bob Wilson in nets, let Leeds in twice on goal and first Mick Jones and then John

Giles got our goals to win 2-1. A great result, and well-deserved too from what I could gather, aside from Sprakey's stupidity. Ces said he was never in doubt that we'd win, he'd been more worried about the coach getting bricked by Arsenal halfwits. Going down by train was even riskier for away supporters, the walk from Kings Cross train station to Highbury was practically you asking for trouble. It wasn't always very safe *on* the football trains either if you were on the same journey as Burnley, Everton or Liverpool nutters, wrecking carriages for fun right back from the 1950's.

Next we were at home to Leicester. Though he never came right out with slagging off Leeds supporters, The Don wasn't exactly great at keeping his feelings to himself about the less than impressive Elland Road attendances. Over the years, they were never great, it was as simple as that, but you could sense he had real trouble accepting it. There was a population of about half a million they reckoned, and I could well see Don Revie ranting about how so many bloody people *didn't* turn up to see the best football team around. This season, there'd been only about six home matches where more than 40,000 people turned up even though we were top of the League virtually all season. Maybe too many Leeds folk were misers or lazy or both, or just plain skint. 38,391 watched us beat Leicester 2-0 on Saturday April 19th - and this was a game that if we won and Liverpool lost, then it meant we were near definite the winners of the League. It wasn't a great game by any chalk but did anyone expect one or really care, as long as the result was the right one? Leicester played alright for a team that was looking like it would be Division Two for them the next season around, but the result wasn't really in much danger. Mick Jones and Eddie Gray got the goals while Liverpool were winning at Ipswich 4-0. You couldn't really argue with that sort of performance from the Scousers, though we were still five points clear of them - we had three games left and they had four. The only way Liverpool could beat us to the League title would be for us to not win any of our games and they to win all of theirs. And one of those games just happened to be Liverpool v Leeds. I couldn't wait for that one.

Ces made sure I was booked on the staff coach, for Monday, 28th April. He'd asked the General Manager Keith Archer specially on my behalf. I said I'd travel in the bloody luggage compartment if needed, I didn't care, just as long as I got there. These games that Leeds and Liverpool had left were rearranged fixtures, due to all the postponements and next Saturday was the Man City-Leicester FA Cup final and League games weren't allowed on that day. Fair enough, as a football fan I always loved FA Cup final day, it was a fab occasion even when Leeds weren't involved.

We were at Everton this coming Tuesday April 22nd and then at Liverpool two days after the Cup final, and then at home two days after that to Nottingham Forest. The club - well, Don Revie more like - and the Football League had taken some stick in the papers for bringing forward a couple of our games when they had chance to. I bet Bill Shankly wouldn't have had to take such crap if he'd been in the same boat. There were only a few managers who the media didn't like much and I think The Don was possibly top of that particular league, at least with a lot of the southern press any road. I listened to the Everton game on the radio at ours with my grandma. Even though Aitch had invited us to the Peacock because he was putting on roast spuds, black pudding and stuff like that specially, this was one of those times I preferred a bit of privacy. Anyway, my grandma had asked me to listen to it with her. I couldn't exactly say no, it wouldn't have been right. I always wondered whether the Leeds players appreciated all those Leeds fans who didn't travel to away games - it was obvious they liked the hundreds and thousands who *did* travel - but what about the tens of thousands of us who had the radio or television only to rely on?

I'd hardly missed a Leeds home game for ten years but had done precious little travelling with them, save for FA Cup trips which never really counted as much in my reckoning, they weren't the bread and butter matches that proper loyal supporters went to. I wish me and my grandma had been rich, then I'd have gone to every single Leeds game possible. Why couldn't my father have been the Earl of Harewood? We hadn't lost a League match since last October but still, having to endure the radio coverage, I was nervous as hell. The BBC didn't help by not having commentary on the match, only 'updates' so it was always 'And here's a special report from Goodison Park' and all that, and you couldn't help thinking *'Shit, someone's scored!'* and *'I hope to God it's us'* when in fact nothing had happened at all, bar a throw-in or one of the players had sneezed or something just as meaningful. The match stayed goalless all the while and it seemed like *nothing* relevant happened at all and Leeds hung on to a 0-0 draw. The reporter said we had a couple of half-chances to score but a draw was the right and fair result. Drawing at Everton was a good point earned any time of the season, and with Liverpool only drawing at Coventry as well, it was a bloody brilliant result, my grandma even did a little jig at hearing that result. Me, my heart felt just for a moment like it might burst, and I had emotion in my throat the size of a pool ball. I nearly gave her a big hug and even a kiss but I didn't, it wasn't something we ever did. Instead I did something just as barmy and jumped out of the door and into the street with my arms in the air shouting 'Yes!' and loads of 'Leeds! Leeds! Leeds!' I didn't care who saw me or what they were thinking. She called me a silly sod for doing it, but was laughing when she said it, and coughing a bit too.

There must have been thousands of Leeds fans at Everton because it was a massive crowd, around 53,000. For once, Everton supporters deserved some credit and all, many of them waited after the finish to applaud the Leeds players - as well as their own, because they'd finished third in the table - though I suppose they'd have applauded a team of war criminals if it meant they'd stopped their biggest rivals Liverpool from winning the League like we near definitely had! Two games left and 64 points for us while Liverpool had 59 points and three games left. But as the next game was against each another, we only needed a draw to win the League Championship.

Liverpool versus Leeds United, to decide the First Division title 1968-'69. This was our time, Leeds United's. We were the best team in England and the match would be the proof, the icing on the cake, the certificate rubber-stamped and the envelope wax-sealed with 'LUFC' imprinted in the *blue* wax. This was what English football was all about, why football was the greatest sport of all and why it didn't matter who you were, where you were born or how rich or poor your family was. And it was the moments like these why I bloody well loved Don Revie and the coaches and all the players and staff and supporters, and Bobby Collins and Jim Storrie and of course Grenville Hair, God rest. Because I knew, I did, I really knew, that all these people were just as proud and excited as I was, wherever they were.

These games were always something special, something *else*. The Liverpool colours were all-red with a little bit of white trim - there wasn't any other strip that stood out as much or looked as threatening. Except for all-white course, *the* all-white of Leeds

United AFC. *The* all-white of Leeds United which Don Revie had adopted as our colours seven or so years before, probably in salute to Real Madrid, which people ridiculed him for. Liverpool versus Leeds - bright red against bright white, under dazzling bright floodlights and on a bright green pitch. This was it, Monday 28th April 1969, and I thanked the heavens I was there to witness it.

The Liverpool fans inside Anfield stadium that night were proper fans, they backed their team whatever, they hardly stopped singing or applauding, there was red and white everywhere (and a fair bit of white, yellow and blue too). And when the Liverpool Kop sing, it's loud and it's proud. True, if something went wrong on the pitch the fans couldn't half moan too, but there was never any doubt whose side they were on. That Kop was massive too, bigger than ours and that wasn't exactly the size of a doorstep. The *trouble* with their fans, the big trouble, was that there were thousands of them locked out and not happy at missing the match which turned out to be the title decider, but not how they wanted it to turn out.

The papers said that Liverpool and Leeds had slugged it out like two mighty heavyweight boxers, that Leeds were magnificent in defence as usual, that Alun Evans up front for Liverpool missed two good chances, that we were happy to defend en masse and intent on attacking on the break only. They said that Liverpool really should have won it and that Leeds set out their stall to stop them scoring and that Tommy Smith was the best player on the pitch, closely followed by Paul Madeley. And they said that at the final whistle the Leeds players turned to the end containing our supporters, to wave to and applaud and celebrate with, and then they walked to the Liverpool Kop as if seeking their approval as well. And the Koppites, almost as one, began to applaud and cheer, chanting 'Champions, Champions' to them. All of that is totally true.

But what you wouldn't see in the newspaper reports was all those locked-out Liverpool supporters' aggression, all the trouble they caused. All the sly cowards hanging around in groups, hiding round corners and in alleys and prowling around all the Leeds cars and coaches. All the cursing, all the insults, all the threatening, all the false praise and all the real spitting, all the violence. Coach and car windows put through, bottles, stones, bricks, ball-bearings, pelting anyone caught up in it all. Coppers not sure who they were protecting or attacking, pushing people around, truncheons always ready for using. There was no word even of the fact that the Leeds players' and officials' coach got bricked and had a window smashed. It wasn't a brick which broke the window, it was a piece of concrete. That was a *fact* because we still had the concrete at Elland Road, it was in the ground staff storeroom where all the pitch and stadium equipment is kept. The reason we still had it was because lucky John Reynolds was on the team bus, sitting with his mate Paul Madeley. Well, John wasn't so lucky really, not lucky at all, seeing as the concrete landed on his lap. There were bits of broken glass all over him and Madeley and obviously, everyone onboard was worried, checking to see if Paul had been hurt. Just Paul, no one seemed bothered about John!

9 vi

On the Sunday evening, the night before this season's biggest game, David Harvey and Johnny Giles watched the film *Rosemary's Baby* at the Essoldo cinema in Ilkley before returning to the hotel for bingo and bowls with their team-mates. Given the sinister theme of the film and Revie's generally odd superstitions, it was surprising that he allowed any of his squad to go anywhere near the film. And at the hotel he unwittingly caused some mirth amongst the Leeds players when discussing the Monday night match. 'If you get anything at Liverpool tomorrow night, lads, I think you'll be home and dry.' The players had heard it all before, because Revie had virtually said it all before, the very same thing prior to every League match for the previous two months.

Leeds captain Billy Bremner had been a worried man prior to the Liverpool match, right up to leading the Whites out on to the Anfield pitch. 'The team was unusually nervous when it went out. I have never known them like they were tonight. It was worse than our FA Cup final. I was nervous. I couldn't sleep the night before, and that isn't me. I even got up out of bed at four o'clock in the morning and smoked a cigarette to try and stop thinking about the game. There was such a lot at stake, of course, and it nearly beat us... Och but it came out alright in the end though didn't it?'

Before the match kicked off, Revie advised Bremner that he should take the team to the Liverpool Kop at the final whistle if

Leeds got the result they needed, to take applause from the home fans. Bremner wasn't keen, he was not so sure the Reds' supporters would be so sportingly gracious. Besides, even talking about it could be tempting Fate. But as probably everyone interested in English football knows, the final score was 0-0 and Revie's Leeds got the result they had hoped for. And reportedly around 25,000 Liverpool Koppites stayed behind to salute them, the new League Champions. 'The reception given us by the sporting Liverpool crowd was truly magnificent, and so, for that matter, was our defence tonight. It was superb in everything,' gushed Revie.

Terry Cooper missed the Kop's marvellous acknowledgment as he was having a shower. Once the rest of the players had returned, about ten minutes later, the champagne flowed in the Leeds dressing room. Liverpool manager Bill Shankly had arranged for the club to provide the bubbly, and he handed each Leeds player a bottle in congratulation. The players could finally celebrate, but not too much though, they had Nottingham Forest to play in two nights' time and a win would give them a historic 67 points, beating the previous record of 66.

Shankly discreetly asked Revie if he could address his players. Above the clamour and chatter of press men and the Leeds contingent, Revie demanded everyone quieten down - 'Mr Shankly wants a word.' In his famous Glaswegian growl, Shankly said, 'All I've got to say to you boys is, you're a great side and you deserved to win it. You didn't pinch it, you didn't fluke it. You're a wonderful team.' High praise indeed, it was one of the proudest moments of Revie's life. Speaking to reporters soon after, however, Shankly was more his usual droll self, complaining 'the best team drew'.

Two nights later, at Elland Road before the third highest gate of the season (46,508) an anxious and erratic Leeds display somehow managed to squeeze out a 1-0 win over Nottingham Forest, thanks to a well-taken snapshot from John Giles, arguably Leeds' best player of the campaign. He had managed to stop a cross-shot from Cooper, then bring it down and under control to turn and shoot in one smooth, swift sequence. The ball flashed high by the Forest goalkeeper's right into the top corner. Perhaps they were a shade fortunate that night to win but no one in football could deny Leeds had won the League on merit. For the record, the valiant runners-up, Liverpool, played their final two games on the 12th and 17th May - losing at Manchester City 1-0 and then drawing 1-1 at St James' Park with Newcastle.

Don Revie - 'All these successes made the past failures more easy to bear and to look back again without anger or anguish.' Leeds had not only won the League title for the first time in their history, they had broken a number of records along the way, too: most points won (67) beating the previous best of 66 set by Arsenal (1930-'31) and Tottenham (1960-'61); most home points won (39); most wins in a season (27); most home wins (18) and fewest defeats (two) beating Arsenal's record of four, again in 1930-'31. Leeds were unbeaten at home, equalling their own best record, set in 1963-'64, and had conceded only 26 goals, a mere nine of those at home. They were the most deserving of champions for many a year, and Don Revie's honour of being named Football Manager of the Year seemed to emphasise that view. Even the press, some of whom had been fierce critics, praised Revie and the team. *Even* the Daily Mirror, who had accused the Football League and Revie of somehow conspiring to bend the rules, said, 'There has been no doubt for two seasons that Leeds are the most well-equipped of all the English teams for the traps, tensions and special demands of the competition they will now enter - the European Cup. Leeds United are the champions, the masters, the new kings of English football - at last.'

Chapter 10: 1969/70 - A hell of a season

10 i

A true and rare thing of beauty, **the Honours List of Football, 1968 - '69**.
League Division One winners - L.U.F.C., Runners-up - Liverpool.
FA Cup winners -Manchester City, Runners-up - Leicester City.
League Cup winners - Swindon Town (Div 3), Runners-up - Arsenal (the shame of it).
European Cup winners - AC Milan, Runners-up - Ajax.
European Cup Winners Cup winners - Slovan Bratislava, Runners-up - Barcelona.
Inter-Cities Fairs Cup winners - Newcastle Utd, Runners-up - Ujpest Dozsa.
Leeds' crowd average, home games = 36,955.
Player of the Year 1969 - Dave Mackay (Derby) and Tony Book (Man City). Eh?
European Footballer of the Year - Gianni Rivera, AC Milan.
Manager of the Year 1969 - DON REVIE, L.U.F.C.
plus the Charity Shield winners of 1969 - L.U.F.C, Runners-up - Man City.
PLUS a new Transfer Fee Record - £165,000 for Allan Clarke, paid by L.U.F.C. to Leicester.
And not forgetting, only six years for Clean Air.

When we bought Allan Clarke, he'd just been on tour with England in South Africa, and he'd caught gastroenteritis. I wasn't medically qualified but I believe the symptoms are that it squirts out of you at both ends probably whenever it wants to. Leeds signed him at his house, while he was in his dressing gown. He said he felt like death warmed up and hardly had the energy to lift the pen to sign the forms. Even better for us was that Clarke had turned down Man United at least once before, and he thought we were on the up while they were definitely sinking.

This year a supersonic airliner, the 'Concorde', flew for the first time and the Yanks had put men on the moon for the very first time too, in the Apollo 11 mission. More importantly, Don Revie said that the new season would see a team win the 'Triple' for the first time in history. He'd told the Leeds players they were aiming for the League Championship, the FA Cup and the European Cup. We needed to win the League again because hardly anyone managed to do that, and we needed to win the FA Cup because we hadn't won it yet and 'Doubles' were as rare as rocking horse manure. And a Triple ('Treble'?) was unheard of. A football team needed to set itself targets, just like people should in their lives. It helps you get out of bed on a morning, for one thing. To Achieve Personal Greatness.

Looking at what The Don had done for Leeds, it was like he'd performed a miracle. When he started the job, eight-plus years ago, he'd inherited good coaching staff and somehow made them even better. And he inherited a couple of good players and sorted them out, made them fulfil their potential, and he brought loads of new young lads in too thanks to the excellent scouting network already in place. None of it could have happened without Harry Reynolds and his money but still, Revie was a genius, and the new season would *re*-prove it.

So this was the season where we'd follow up last season's magnificent League display by being magnificent again, this time in every competition and this time with no slip-ups. The papers said Allan Clarke was the most 'complete' centre-forward in football; he was thin but could look after himself, he was tall but fast, he could head the ball well but had great footwork, and he had a goal-poacher's instinct but could score from just about anywhere, and with either foot. They reckoned he would be the perfect partner for Mick Jones and that he was Don Revie's way of treating himself to a sort of luxury item, like Clarke was a 24-carat medallion or something. A bit too fanciful that I thought, just like one reporter saying Clarke was a 'bespoke Greaves'. No he wasn't, they were nothing like each other except both could score rakes and rakes of goals! Anyway, the team would go hell for leather to cop the absolute lot, and the Elland Road trophy cabinet would need extending.

The season started well, beating FA Cup holders Man City to start with, nabbing the Charity Shield for the first time ever. Both teams had lined up and applauded each other on the pitch, and Leeds did a lap of honour with the Shield at the end. Clarke looked great and though it was early days, I definitely thought we already looked a better team with him here. We had a pretty good run straight from the off after that match, unbeaten - two wins and four draws - continuing till the end of August when we lost 3-2 at Everton. All in all we'd gone 34 League games unbeaten and bettered Burnley's record of 30 matches unbeaten. Burnley had been the last team to beat us, on October 19th, 1968.

Selling Mike O'Grady to Wolves was a surprise to me. True, we got decent money for him - £80,000 - but I wasn't sure why we sold him. He'd had a few injuries, including a mysterious bad back quite often and, I suppose just like most wingers, he sometimes drifted in and out of matches but I liked him, a lot, plus he was Leeds born and bred, east of the city I think. John Reynolds, always in possession of a theory if on the rare occasion he didn't actually *know,* asked me who out of the Leeds squad was the only bachelor. Then he tapped his nose and answered it for me - 'Mike O'Grady. Mike O'Grady's the only one who's not married. Maybe Revie thinks he's a bad influence because he hasn't got a ring on his finger.' We'd won the League with O'Grady, and by a record number of points, so I couldn't see how anyone's marital status mattered. Something else I didn't understand was just about everyone, even the players, calling The Don 'Revvie' and not 'Ree-vi'. I'd given up telling folk off for their mistake, as I definitely was in the minority pronouncing his name how he'd told me, all those years ago when my grandma was a sprinter.

Leeds were the best team around because we had the best players, I genuinely believed it. That wasn't to say I wouldn't have liked to see certain players join us but on the whole, give me a Leeds player over any of the rest. I would never deny that Gordon Banks was a better goalkeeper than Gary Sprake but did that mean he'd have fitted in here better than Sprake, or David Harvey, come to that? You could list the Leeds players and then come up with maybe better players at other clubs who were higher regarded by so-called experts, but brilliant individuals hardly ever made brilliant team players. If they did then you were blessed. Jim Baxter was proof of that, and George Best was on his way to proving it as well. Was Bobby Charlton better than John Giles or Billy Bremner? Was Bobby Moore a better defender than our Norm? Definitely not for his club side. Yeats of Liverpool wasn't better than Jack Charlton, neither was Brian Labone and if there was a harder-working, better committed and more all-round centre-forward than Mick Jones, I never saw him. And that included Geoff Hurst and Jimmy Greaves who was the best goal-scorer of everyone. And I couldn't even think of any better full-backs than Terry Cooper and Paul Reaney, or better goal creators than Eddie Gray and Peter Lorimer (who scored more than most players too) plus the finesse and all-round ability of Paul Madeley.

Aside from *Match of the Day*'s Kenneth Wolstenholme I think, and maybe a few other television commentators, Leeds often got criticised for the way they played. I could understand sometimes why journalists had a go at the team for playing negative football, especially in away games. And when the local paper said the same then you knew it wasn't just southern bias, but being honest about it, I reckoned it was usually because the reporters were either missing the point about professional football and didn't rightly understand how to play it, or worse, they had a gripe with Don Revie or the players.

Leeds didn't make many friends after clawing their way into Division One. Then the FA News made sure they didn't have any friends at all. I never heard Alf Ramsey (or Busby or Shankly for that matter) getting stick for having a tough attitude and if anyone believed England played attractive football all the time then they were daft or blind. Man U and Liverpool definitely didn't, nor Arsenal, Everton or Man City for that matter. The styles of Leeds and England weren't that different, even though Ramsey's side got the nickname 'Wingless Wonders'. He did use wingers at times but not often, while The Don *did*, more often than not, with 'secondary wingers' Reaney and Cooper supporting. It wasn't just them two who could attack from defence though, Norman Hunter would often have freedom to help up front, and always one of the most exciting sights for Leeds fans was seeing big Jack striding with the ball right down the middle of the pitch with much better ball control than he was ever credited with. The number of attacking options we had was brilliant, every single player bar the 'keeper had tons of flair.

First to bloody go was the League Cup. We'd beaten Fulham 1-0 away in the second round but then lost away in a third round replay at Stamford Bridge to Chelsea. 2-0. I wouldn't mind but we'd beaten them easily enough in the League a few days before the 1-1 draw, it was as if Chelsea were only ever bothered about cup competitions and not the League. Maybe it just wasn't glamorous enough for them. The title race was going nice and smoothly again for us though, and our first attempt at the European Cup was progressing okay too: we just scraped through the first round against Norway side SK Lyn Oslo, 10-0 at home and 6-0 away. To be sporting to the Norwegians, even though they'd made it to last year's Fairs Cup quarter-finals, they were only a part-time club. In truth we could have scored double what we did but I was quite sure I'd never see ten goals scored in a Leeds game again, by one team alone or in total.

In the second round we drew old enemies Ferencvaros. Seemed to me that the Leeds players saved their best form for Europe. Put it this way, we were in really good form in the League - we'd beaten Nottingham Forest 6-1 and Ipswich Town 4-0 in our last two home games - but in the first leg v Ferencvaros, we really hit form and went at them non-stop. They must have thought it was like being at the Alamo, they can't have known what had hit them. It was one of those nights when every Leeds player peaked, where we looked dangerous from every part of the pitch. Ferencvaros might not have been as strong as they had been in the past but that was no excuse, Leeds gave them a whipping which should have been more than the 3-0 result. The attendance for the second leg, in Budapest, said it all - only 5,400 - the Hungarian supporters had given up on the match and it sounded like the players had too. We beat them 3-0 again, and one of the younger lads made his debut, coming on as substitute for Eddie Gray - winger Chris Galvin, who I thought had a good chance of properly making it in football.

10 ii

Eamonn Andrews mentions Don Revie's days playing for Hull City and later Manchester City, including the devising of the 'Revie Plan' which even now, 1974, so many years after the event, embarrasses the Leeds manager. He did not create the plan, nor did he claim to have done so, nor did he want all the credit. More archive footage is shown, of Revie's England debut and first international goal, against Northern Ireland, and a glimpse of his FA Cup final appearance for Manchester City against Birmingham City in 1956. He played exceptionally well and the Revie-inspired team went on to win 3-1, but darker events in the match would cause it to be always remembered as 'the Trautmann final' due to the German goalkeeper breaking his neck late in the game but still managing to complete the match. Little wonder that Revie always regarded Bert Trautmann as a hero!

Revie remains seated as more kind words are spoken and more flattering images played; he seems to be struggling to take the occasion in. This event is designed to be fulfilling and to be fun, yet he feels as if he is in the dock almost. And his discomfort continues as Eamonn Andrews again speaks; Revie looks up at him as if expecting yet more humiliating punishment.

*

Saturday evening, 25th October, 1969, and it's *Match of the Day*, on BBC Television's second channel. There has been a keenly contested, exciting First Division match played, between last season's two champions of Division One and of Division Two. A brace of expertly-taken goals from record signing Allan Clarke have won the day. A flicked header from a Gray corner and a one-on-one victory following a long range, defence-splitting Mick Bates pass, signify Leeds beating new boys Derby 2-0.

Derby are managed by Brian Clough and he has developed them in to an impressively strong force, from, bluntly speaking, lower league mediocrity. Now, Clough's Derby County are similar to Revie's Leeds United of 1964. Both teams even had an ageing Scottish 'iron man' leading the team too - Leeds had Bobby Collins in '64, Derby have Dave Mackay in '69, last season's joint Footballer of the Year. Derby also are the first team to have beaten pacesetters Everton this season.

Standing inside the West Stand of the Elland Road stadium, it's chilly and gloomy. The two team managers are being interviewed for *Match of the Day*, by presenter David Coleman. Due to their positioning, the on-screen images give the false impression that Revie stands seven, eight inches taller than Clough. Regardless of their actual heights, there is no sign whatsoever that Clough looks up to Revie in any way. And in spite of their polite behaviour, the victorious Revie and the defeated Clough wear smiles as authentic as ventriloquist dummies'.

The familiar, nasal voice of Clough replies, 'We've been through the Leeds machine,' when asked by Coleman how he thinks his team has performed today. Clough is cool, cool and annoyed - annoyed it seems because he has lost to such a systematic *regime* as Leeds. His remark is not designed to be affectionate or humorous and he makes little eye contact with Coleman as he says it. And none at all with Revie. As he talks he looks away, in the off-camera distance, as if wishing he were somewhere else. He goes on, 'I'm not quite sure why we didn't win. Perhaps it's because *he* works harder than me or he's a better manager than me.'

Revie smiles but it is a smile without pleasure. Coleman seems oblivious to the unfriendly atmosphere, and there will be television viewers across the country thinking Clough's words are intended as complimentary and respectful. They would be wrong. Finally, Clough remarks that he doesn't think Leeds were better than Derby, as there was 'nothing' between the teams, they were evenly matched.

Coleman asks for Revie's thoughts on the match. While the Leeds boss speaks, Clough bows his head, looking down at the floor, looking anywhere other than the face of the man he seems to resent so much, even detest. Revie, apparently puzzled at his counterpart's comments, remarks, 'I just wondered what Brian was on about, as a 'machine'...' His words belie his facial expressions and body language, he is annoyed at his counterpart's clear lack of respect to the Leeds team and to himself.

Coleman to Revie, 'Now you've often said that you want to be respected for your football here at Leeds... Today it was all there wasn't it?' Although the compliment is welcome, Revie does not want to hear it from a television commentator, it should come from the opposing manager, as well as the football authorities and every single team manager who has ever fallen to the strength and skill of his Leeds team. His response has an almost rehearsed feel to it, 'Now they're starting to come on song. When you've nine or ten internationals in your side who can play a bit, eventually they will respect us.' They will respect us... it is more likely hope than expectation.

*

In November 1969, chairman Manny Cussins sold off his luxurious suburban house, 'Three Chimneys' to Leeds United - to in turn pass on to Don Revie. The detached house in Alwoodley, Leeds, had five bedrooms, a four-car garage, two bathrooms and a sun lounge, with annex accommodation too. As the highest paid manager in England too, it is clear the club was treating the manager very well. On the playing side for Leeds United, by Christmas, with nineteen League wins clocked up, Everton were setting a formidable record at the top of Division One, with less than half of the season still to play due to it having commenced early to help England's 1970 World Cup preparations. Leeds were by no means having a poor campaign but had played more games than Everton and won less - fourteen, with ten draws - one recent one coming from a last minute mistake by Sprake to cost Leeds a point at Crystal Palace, the unfortunate 'keeper dropping a 'freak' shot from full-back Sewell into the net. Two days after Christmas, Leeds and Everton met at Elland Road. 46,770 watched a pulsating game in which a second-half Alan Whittle goal was Everton's only reply to two Mick Jones strikes before the interval. 2-1 to Leeds, the title race was not suddenly in their favour though.

Division One League table (top), 27th December 1969

1 Everton	Played 26	Points 41
2 Leeds Utd.	Played 27	Points 40
3 Chelsea	Played 26	Points 34
4 Liverpool	Played 25	Points 32

January 1970 brought another boost to the city of Leeds when Don Revie was named in the New Year's Honours List, for

Services to Football. Posing for photographs outside Buckingham Palace, standing proudly with wife Elsie, son Duncan and daughter Kim, the family is dressed to the nines, with Don in a smart blue suit. It is to be hoped it is not his 'lucky' match day suit as that probably would have been frowned upon by the Queen Mother when presenting him with his award! Ten year-old Kim holds the red-ribbon and Order of the British Empire medal, as light sleet and snow fall from the London sky. There is no inclement weather capable of spoiling this occasion for the Revie family. Don Revie OBE modestly tells journalists, 'My award should be recognised as a club rather than personal achievement, because without the talent, character and dedication of everyone connected with the club, my success as a manager would not have been possible. When I went to Buckingham Palace I collected the award on behalf of Leeds United.'

Division One and Two clubs had entered the FA Cup fray on January 3rd in the third round. Leeds squeezed through to round four with a 2-1 home win over Fourth Division Swansea City (until recently known as *Town*) on January 3rd. The slender win was even more remarkable as Swansea had led for much of the game and later had a man sent off; Leeds' goals came after the dismissal. Everton fared even worse, losing 2-1 at Second Division Sheffield United. Leeds' next League match was away at Chelsea, with over 57,000 people attending, hundreds locked out and with possibly millions more watching the evening's *Match of the Day*. What would be voted the programme's 'Match Of The Season' was captivating viewing, and surrounded by a greyhound track, the pitch was indeed host to a dogged battle. Leeds in white shirts and shorts, and red socks, turned a 2-1 half-time deficit into an amazing 5-2 win. Four goals within twenty minutes of the restart from Cooper, Giles (a penalty), Lorimer and Jones, added to Clarke's first half tap-in, went some way to wooing the football nation and helped demonstrate that the current champions most certainly intended retaining their title.

Two weeks following that rout, Leeds also romped through the Cup fourth round with a 6-0 drubbing of non-league Sutton United, Clarke bagging four goals and Lorimer two.

Interestingly, Mick Jones failed to score. Sutton defender John Faulkner had marked him so well that Jack Charlton recommended Revie sign him for Leeds. Revie did exactly that and 'Max' Faulkner joined the club for £10,000. In the League, Everton's stuttering form had begun to arouse suspicions they would be unable to maintain their title challenge. As well as the defeat to Leeds, they had lost 3-0 to deadly rivals Liverpool in December too. In the coming weeks, Everton's defeats and draws would outnumber their victories. And all the while, Leeds progressed nicely, in the League, the FA Cup and of course the European Cup, about to reconvene on 4th March against Standard Liege, the highly rated Belgian champions.

Since a Boxing Day 1-2 defeat at Newcastle, Leeds had embarked on a fine run. There was the League win over Everton and the crushing of Chelsea, and they had drawn away in tough games at Manchester United, Tottenham, Stoke and Liverpool, and coasted to home wins over Coventry and Crystal Palace as well as giving a 5-1 thrashing to West Bromwich Albion. In the European Cup third round, first leg, against Standard Liege, Leeds won 1-0 away. In all-red, the winner came from Lorimer, driving home a low angled shot which goalkeeper Christian Piot probably felt he should have saved. Maurice Lindley had compiled a detailed dossier on the Liege players, his notes typed up and passed to Revie, and so the players were well informed on the Belgians' capabilities.

Before the second keg, Revie addressed the first team squad. 'It's the first time of asking for you all in the European Cup... The three danger men for me are Semmeling, Van Moer and Takac their outside-left. I think if we can keep these three quiet then I can't see them scoring. This is a tremendous chance of going forward to the European Cup semi-finals.' In that Elland Road tie, on another very heavy pitch, Norman Hunter damaged a knee. (His own). The initial signs were that it was a minor injury but a short time late it flared up again and proved serious enough to notably affect his season, causing him to miss crucial games. Hunter missing any games was a rarity in itself since his debut in 1962. He often remarked that he only ever failed one fitness test (damaged knee ligaments) in his Leeds career, and even that was after Don Revie instructed him to test his knee in a tackle against Les Cocker. And then Revie did not speak to him for three days as a result!

Next up in the European Cup for Leeds was a classic semi-final pairing, the 'Battle of Britain', against the 1967 winners and current Scottish champions Celtic. Revie and Celtic manager Jock Stein were good friends and rivals, in both football and in golf - last year they had attended the 1969 British Open at Lytham St Annes together. Revie - 'It's the draw that we didn't want to face right now. We have a tremendous respect for Celtic and for Jock Stein and we would have been happier to meet in the final.' And he told his players that he would gladly give a year's wages to beat Celtic, adding that he would put the money in the players' pot if need be. Before the draw was made, Celtic had already decided to hold their semi-final home leg at Hampden Park so as to be able to accommodate more of their supporters. Stein had commented that he hoped to avoid Leeds until the final as an all-British final would be a great morale boost to the country. Ticket allocations for the first leg at Elland Road would create major problems for both clubs. The capacity of the stadium was now 48,000 - it was no exaggeration to say that Celtic fans could sell twenty-plus thousand tickets for the game. Unfortunately, Leeds would only provide an allocation of 6,000. And tickets for the match were around double the price of Leeds' quarter-final tie against Standard Liege. The club's General Secretary, Keith Archer confirmed, 'We have to consider our own fans. For these big games we can attract forty-eight thousand fans and they are *our* fans. They have to come first so we simply couldn't give away any more of our tickets to Celtic. I know that Celtic could probably fill half the ground down here, but there's nothing else we can do.'

Maurice Lindley travelled up to Glasgow to take notes on Celtic. After a 3-0 win against Ayr United, he declared, 'I saw enough to realise that this match with Celtic will be the toughest we have ever had to play in almost ten years of European competition.' And on the possibility of the team missing out on the three prizes they were still involved with, one Leeds player said dourly, 'If all that happened we'd be just about the finest bloody bridesmaid in the world.' Interviewed for a television programme titled *United, United,* Jack Charlton shed some light on the pressures of being a Leeds player during their hunt for increased success - 'At one stage if you won three games in a row you'd had a great run. Now, if you lose one in ten you're not doing so well. Everybody's dedicated to winning now and there's not such a thing as not being successful, the whole atmosphere here's changed now. It's all success.'

The Leeds United FA Cup quest continued impressively, with a fifth round home win over battling Mansfield Town (2-0, attendance 48,093) and then a sound 2-0 quarter-final victory at Swindon Town, last season's League Cup winners. Leeds were, well and truly, in contention to make footballing history but the moment the draw was made, Leeds' problems were about to bite. Chelsea were paired with the real underdogs Watford, while Leeds would have to face Manchester United.

14th March 1970, the arch rivals met at Hillsborough. 55,000 crammed into Sheffield Wednesday's stadium, to watch an absorbing tussle between two giants of football. It was as expected, a tough unflinching conflict but nothing like their previous violent, unsavoury encounter there in 1965. Unfortunately, at least from Leeds' perspective, the result was the same, a 0-0 stalemate, nearly as bad as actually losing. The replay took place at Villa Park nine days later, two days after the Saturday League games in which Leeds beat Wolves 2-1 away and Manchester United lost by the same scoreline at high-flying (and new FA Cup finalists) Chelsea. Chelsea had beaten Watford 5-1 in their semi-final. Norman Hunter had to miss the Villa Park replay due to his knee injury so the king of adaptability himself, Paul Madeley, deputised. Paul 'the play anywhere Peacock' Madeley, was the Leeds United Rolls Royce in Don Revie's eyes.

62,500 went to Birmingham to watch the match. Allan Clarke had a headed goal disallowed by referee Jack Taylor while Brian Kidd swung and missed a seemingly easy chance for Manchester United. The score-line stayed the same after ninety minutes as well as thirty minutes' extra time, necessitating a second replay - to be played three days later, at Bolton Wanderers' ground. And at Burnden Park, in front of another fine crowd (56,000), at long last the deadlock was broken. Both sides - Leeds in all-white, Manchester in red shirts and socks, white shorts - had set out on the offensive. After around ten minutes' play, a half-cleared cross bounced out of the Manchester penalty area. Billy Bremner got to the ball before Pat Crerand, and then rifled in a half-volley with his left foot. The ball whizzed in low, skimming the surface before settling into the corner of the net past Alex Stepney's flailing right arm.

Even with such fine array of attacking talent as Best, Charlton, Kidd and Morgan - and Law as substitute - Manchester could not pierce Leeds' defences: the scoreline stayed 1-0 and Leeds had made it to Wembley again. All thanks to a FA Cup semi-final win over Manchester United again, and the winning goal coming from the indefatigable Billy Bremner, again. They would meet Chelsea in the final, unsurprising victors over Watford. Don Revie and Chelsea boss Dave Sexton, each owned an allegedly lucky blue suit and planned to wear them for the final. However, Revie had ripped the seat of his suit trousers and so felt inclined to pay for an identical replacement to be made, hoping perhaps that luck could be tailor made.

10 iii

A 'machine' seemed insulting in my book. It wasn't meant as a compliment, that was for sure, and it implied that Leeds played the same way all the time, like a bloody pneumatic drill, that the players were robots going through the same motions every time. What a load of crap, that Brian Clough seemed full of it. The truth is that when things went right for them, Leeds were the most balanced and skilful side going. They could attack from every angle and score from just about anywhere on the park too. Every outfield player was like a double agent in a way, in that each of them could defend and attack / attack and defend / tackle and create / create and attack, make short passes and long passes, and all the players had the combination of speed and stamina. Aye, when things went right, Leeds were the best team around by a mile, not a machine.

Five semi-finals, FIVE, two FA Cup finals and seven League games. Seven vital League games. That's what we had to play, five semis, two finals and seven League games, from March 14th to April 29th 1970. Fourteen massive games, in forty-six whole days. (Plus, there was thirty minutes extra time in those finals as well). This was the season when Leeds would win the three big ones - the League Championship, the FA Cup and the European Cup. This was it, *the* season. They would prove that they were the greatest football team ever. Except of course, it wouldn't turn out that way. Too many big matches to play, too many injured players or at least not enough fully fit ones. Doctor Adams had said to Don Revie in late March, that five or six of the first team squad were close to nervous and physical collapse. This was the season when, rather than winning the big three, Leeds would *lose* them.

The fixture list well and truly crapped on our parade from a great height, dead right it did. It didn't seem right that the team performing the best in a season was forced to play so many games in so short a time. Liverpool, Man U, Everton, Tottenham, Arsenal, Chelsea, even Burnley over recent times, they'd all suffered like this before, just not as badly as us this season.

March 14 - Man U, FA Cup semi-final = 0-0.

March 21 - Wolves (away), League game = 2-1.

March 23 - Man U, semi-final replay. 0-0. Nail biting stuff.

March 26 - Man U, semi-final replay part two. 1-0, thank you captain Bremner.

March 28 - Southampton (home), League. 1-3, crap, we were losing our grip on the title.

March 30 - Derby (away), League. 1-4, just about sealed the title for Everton, and we were fined £5,000 for fielding mostly Reserve players as well. Paul Peterson and David Kennedy made their debuts (Kennedy got the goal) and David Harvey, Nigel Davey, Jimmy Lumsden, Chris Galvin and Terry Yorath played, while Albert Johanneson, Rod Belfitt, Mick Bates and Terry Hibbitt filled in the other spaces. I bet Everton weren't complaining. Clough did though, surprise surprise, even though his team benefited. It's a wonder he didn't report Leeds for using the Pudsey Juniors as our Junior side this season as well.

April 1 - Celtic (home), European Cup, semi-final. 0-1, a rubbish performance, rubbish goal, we just didn't seem able to get going properly even though Eddie hit the bar. Billy cracked his head, got knocked out in the second half and was taken off, with concussion. He looked in a right state, even paler than normal, chalkier than chalk, and he was wandering around the tunnel and rooms and offices, dazed. After this leg, The Don said 'We never give up hope' after the match, but I think he knew we'd had it. Celtic had one of the best players I've ever seen - Jimmy Johnstone on the right wing, the type every defender hates playing against. Fast, skilful, adventurous, fiery, never-give-in attitude. Terry Cooper had to try and mark him. Norman had a go at him for not kicking Johnstone into the stands but TC couldn't get near him to try.

April 2 - West Ham (away), League game – **the very next day**! 2-2, and poor Paul Reaney broke his leg. That's him out of all our big games as well as the World Cup in Mexico. Sickening.

April 4 - Burnley (home), League game. 2-1, nothing riding on this match, and the Grand National was on the 'telly', so only 24,691 bothered to turn up. But it was a memorable game - Faulkner made his debut and Burnley's goal went in off him, so he wasn't likely to forget his first game in a hurry. Thank the Lord for Eddie Gray's two fantastic goals, and thank technology for them being forever captured on film by Yorkshire TV. One was a lob from miles out which beat the 'keeper, and the other was a dribble round half the Burnley team before toe-ending it with his right foot into the net. As he'd done it, Albert Johanneson was lying in the penalty area, injured, watching Eddie do his dancing. I think that image said something about them both.

April 11 - Chelsea, FA Cup final. 2-2, after extra time, Eddie danced again, all over Chelsea but Sprakey was asleep and gifted them a goal. Some reporters called it a 'pudding' of a pitch, thanks to the Horse of the Year Show the night before. It wasn't that bloody good, it was a disgrace. We should have had the game sewn up - but we didn't. Eddie Gray hit the bar with a right-foot shot when it was 2-2, while Sprake made some good saves in the second half. Half the papers seemed to agree that Leeds had played some of the best football ever witnessed at Wembley.

April 15 - Celtic (away), European Cup semi, 2nd leg. 1-2, Billy took the lead with a scorcher but Celtic were too much for us and Johnstone tortured TC again.

April 18 - Man City (home), League game. 1-3.

April 21 - Ipswich Town (away), League. 2-3.

And April 29 was to be Chelsea, in the FA Cup final replay at Old Trafford.

*

Leeds United were not the first club to be punished for fielding a weakened team in a League match, Burnley had been fined £1,000 nine years before, and Everton £2,000 in 1966. Regarding Leeds' £5,000 fine, FL President Len Shipman, said, 'We took into consideration all their problems and felt sorry for them, and it took us more than an hour to reach our decision because we were conscious that they were struggling especially hard as the season had been shortened. But it must always be borne in mind that the League can, after all, forbid clubs to take part in European competitions if they cannot fulfil commitments at home.'

Nonetheless, Revie had been unrepentant - 'I would do the same again. I can't describe how much those Manchester United games took out of the Leeds players.' On the Derby match, he said, 'The first team players who played for me against Southampton have been ruled out by the club doctor. Five of these players, Jack Charlton, Eddie Gray, Peter Lorimer, Allan Clarke and Paul Madeley were too tired, both mentally and physically, to play in this game.' Another seven players, including Billy Bremner and Mick Jones, were undergoing treatment for injuries at the time too. Leeds claimed to have asked Derby to postpone the match until a later date but their directors had refused. Such a refusal seems to contradict Brian Clough's apparent disgust at Leeds for selecting the reserves. Regardless, Secretary of the Football League, Alan Hardaker, had no sympathy at all for Leeds or for Revie, claiming he had offered them various chances to rearrange games but they had rejected every single one.

*

There were some bare patches on the pitch but the surface was in much better nick than Wembley's. It was cold and windy as well, and yes, it had rained, it was Manchester after all. With regard to the football, the hard truth is, Chelsea nicked the match off us and, though I truly hate saying it, it's possible we got a bit of comeuppance for not finishing them off at Wembley. And that wasn't all Sprake's fault, to be fair to him, but he was replaced by David Harvey tonight. After the match, the papers said Chelsea committed 35 fouls while we, the supposedly dirtiest team in the whole land of association football, committed a disgraceful 11. I must admit, I don't remember *that* many during the match. And to think that the Cockney supporters were jeering Mick Jones big time after he'd gone up for a cross with 'keeper Bonetti in the first half - Bonetti landed badly and jarred his left knee, it looked like he might have to go off injured. Jones hadn't touched him, at all, and Bonetti managed to stay on. Also in the first half, Ron Harris had gouged Eddie Gray in a slide tackle. Whether he was deliberately trying to maim Eddie or not, he did bloody hurt him, that's a fact.

Whatever, those fouls weren't the reason why we lost the match. Well, with the exception of Billy Bremner being kicked in the back of the head, in their penalty area for Christ's sake, by a flying attack from Eddie McCreadie which was so much a penalty even Chelsea fans appealed for it. If someone had committed that on the street, in public, they'd have been put away for assault, but Referee 'Lenient' Jennings just waved play on and he was only fifteen yards away from it. But the nauseating fact of the matter is, even though we had most of the play and created more chances than Chelsea, we didn't make it count and we got sucker punched for it in the end.

In goal, David Harvey did nothing wrong all game until extra time when he went to punch or even catch Houseman's long throw-in. He didn't need to, Peter Osgood was lurking but Jack Charlton beat him to the header. Unfortunately, he only managed to head it backwards towards the back post. There were three Leeds players within six yards of that post - Norman Hunter on the line, Terry Cooper nearby and Eddie Gray standing between two Chelsea players, Cooke and Baldwin, and close to Webb as well. Eddie gets sort of sandwiched and weighed down by them all and can't seem to jump to challenge for the ball. So then it's actually harder for Webb to miss. He scores and they've won the Cup, despite Peter Bonetti making three or four great saves and despite two of the best strikers of a football in the world - Peter Lorimer and Johnny Giles - having weak and wayward shots on goal.

Hunter and Cooper were outstanding, Jones worked his socks off and Billy never ever stopped trying - even after getting his head whacked - but it was painfully obvious that most of the Leeds side were done in. And I mean *painfully*, done in, it was a right battle for most of the players for those two hours. I was badly upset at losing but sort of choked too when some of the Leeds and Chelsea players swapped shirts at the end. I couldn't remember ever seeing that happen before. Chelsea collected the Cup from the various FA suits and the like and then did a lap of honour. Not all of us applauded when they came to our end but plenty did. Peter Osgood was wearing Billy's number 4 shirt at the end, and Webb was wearing Eddie's number 11 as well, though I could have seen it wrong. Webb had tripped Eddie in the first half when he was in full flight approaching goal but after that, Webb had a good game at centre-half. Jack Charlton was so riled at losing the match that he didn't swap shirts with anyone, he just walked off back to the changing rooms, forgetting to pick up his Losers' medal as well.

The replay was watched by over 28 million TV viewers, while attendance takings from the semi-finals and the finals, together with television fees, gave Leeds around £200,000. I doubt it much eased the pain but what a hell of a season it had been for us all at the club.

10 iv

'That's life. We will pick ourselves up from the floor and start again. We have had some practice at that,' said Revie after the most tumultuous and potentially most famous season for Leeds United had ended - perhaps a harsh description - in dismal failure. Bill Shankly was uncharacteristically demonstrative too in his compassion for Leeds' plight, 'It makes you weep when the greatest team of the season fails to win a thing'. On television, working as a match pundit, even Brian Clough praised Leeds, declaring them as *the* team to have *made* the season. In *The Times*, Geoffrey Green famously wrote 'Leeds, like Sisyphus, have pushed three boulders almost to the top of three mountains and are now left to see them all back in the dark of the valley.' Revie was named Manager of the Year again but it was small if any consolation. It had been the most harrowing season ever suffered by the club - possibly the most harrowing on-pitch season ever suffered by *any* club - but the players were told by Revie to go home, take a well-deserved rest and holiday until the next pre-season training.

10 v

The Football Honours 1969 - '70, it should have read like a classic but was more like a horror story.
League Division One winners - Everton, Runners up - Leeds United.
FA Cup winners - Chelsea, Runners up - Leeds United.
League Cup winners - Manchester City, Runners up - West Bromwich Albion.
European Cup winners - Feyenoord, Runners up - Celtic.
European Cup Winners Cup winners - Manchester City, Runners up - Gornik Zabrze.
Inter-Cities Fairs Cup winners - Arsenal, Runners up - Anderlecht.
Football Player of the Year - Billy Bremner, Leeds United.
European Footballer of the Year - Gerd Muller, Bayern Munich.
Manager of the Year - Don Revie, Leeds United.

For the new season, the ground staff had orders to create a new Elland Road playing surface, to replace the old pile of dying earth sometimes described as a football pitch. A new beginning. It meant it was going to be a tough summer for everyone involved, but I was looking forward to it because as well as new grass and turf for the team to start afresh on, it felt like a chance for me to do the same. First we had to dig up the old mud-heap, then re-seed it, then re-lay it with new turf as well as bed it all in with different mixtures of soil and stuff. I couldn't tell exactly of the methods and amounts of materials we used, people like Ray Hardy and John and Ces of course were the clever ones, but I knew the basics of it all because I was part of the team grafting our proverbials off to achieve it all. Back-breaking stuff near enough, even if most Leeds supporters never had a clue how much work we put in or how many aches and pains some of us endured. It was about sodding time Leeds had a pitch to be proud of too, let's get it straight - the stadium itself, with the Kop especially, was looking better each year but the pitch had always stayed the same, embarrassing. Not Derby standards but bad enough.

We dug up the pitch, the top of it, about a foot all over, and kept the bottom six inches. Then we laid tons of peat, sand and ash down in the 'hole', which would at last improve the drainage - then we replaced the six inches of the original soil, and then levelled it all off with ash, sand, peat and soil mixture. I lost count of how many sacks of seeds we used, but I know they weighed fifty bloody kilograms each those sacks - about eight stone in normal terms. Or *abnormal* terms more like, seeing as we had to carry the things on our own. I don't think I ever worked as hard as I did in those days of remaking the pitch but once the grass started to peek through and grow after a week or so, and green replaced grey and brown, I know I wasn't on my own thinking that it had all been worth it. Pride replaced pain! Four weeks it had taken, four weeks of the hardest labour I've ever experienced, but it was worth it. Even now, when I see the Leeds pitch in brilliant condition, greener than I thought natural green actually was or could ever be, I'm proud that I was part of the team who created it. It was, is, a thing of beauty, even if some of the events on it have been far from pretty over the years.

Out of the house, right foot first, think the thought again, *To Achieve Personal Greatness, Perseverance Works*. Do some stretches and bends on the pavement, a trot up our street and onto the patch of waste ground. Star jumps and crouches to brace my calves, then I'm on Elland Road in seconds. Song and rhythm helping the beat of my footsteps.

We've got the best team in the land, we've got the best team in the land...

Forcing each word out, growling, barking, grunting, repeating lines over and over.

We've got Gary Sprake at number one, we've got the best team in the land.

We've got Paul Madeley wherever he wants, we've got the best team in the land.

We've got Paul Reaney at number two, we've got the best team in the land.

We've got Terry Cooper at number three, we've got the best team in the land.

Past the Scratching Shed, the shops and houses, the training pitches, the giant Greyhound Stadium stand, the workshops and factories and under the railway bridge.

We've got Billy Bremner at number four, we've got the best team in the land.
Advertising hoardings as big as the screen at the Rex.
We've got Jackie Charlton at number five, we've got the best team in the land.
We've got Norman Hunter at number six, we've got the best team in the land.
All the way along Elland Road until it rises in to Churwell Hill, under another railway bridge while I'm looking out for my old, old friend the Morley Milestone.
We've got Peter Lorimer at number seven, we've got the best team in the land.
Right round the New Inn, careful not to fall over any stray drunks or bottles at the back, and back down the hill I'm heading, under the railway bridge and the billboard sign.
We've got Allan Clarke at number eight, we've got the best team in the land.
We've got Mick Jones at number nine, we've got the best team in the land.
We've got Johnny Giles at number ten, we've got the best team in the land.
We've got Eddie Gray at number eleven, we've got the best team in the land.
Past the nice Cottingley houses and cemetery and land and where the council's planning to build two great big sod-off high-rise blocks of flats and a ton of houses.
We've got Mick Bates and the rest, we've got the best team in the land.

And then it happens, without rhyme or reason, the smallest of incidents which has a big impact on me. As I'm running, near the crematorium graveyard un-funnily enough, I hear this little cracking sound like a tiny twig being snapped, and with it a vicious pain in my left calf muscle like a bullet's daggered into it.

Chapter 11: 1970/71 - 'A dazzling decade of success' and yet...

11 i

There it was, the first time I'd ever noticed it, sprayed on one of the Lowfields Road walls, in white, foot-high letters - *DEATH TO ALL MANCHESTER FANS.* I didn't know whether the graffiti meant City or United. By the end of the day I didn't care either, and I thought it one of the most unfunny things I'd ever seen because just a few hours later and life's all gone badly wrong. I'm not talking about torn calf muscles or fractured bones, I'm talking a life that's suddenly torn and broken.

'I'm sorry to advise,' the doctor said, 'but your grandmother's condition is extremely serious.' He told me the nurses would make my grandma as comfortable as was possible and that all 'we' could do was wait and see if she regained consciousness. And that I shouldn't raise my hopes too high. She had had a blood clot on the brain, at the back of her skull where she'd banged it, falling down some stone steps at the side of the River Aire in town. She'd cracked her head open. A woman had found her lying there unconscious, at about eight in the morning. Unconscious on her own, and she'd not woken since. That's about all I knew, about all anyone knew, because no one saw her fall or had been there to help her when she did And she had her purse with her, intact, so she'd not been mugged or anything. The woman who'd found her was from Kirkgate Market's offices as well. Because of the blood and my grandma being so cold and pale, the woman thought my grandma was dead, there and then. That poor woman had to be treated for shock, she'd got herself so anxious.

I'd been at work, doing all the little and not so little jobs to help get the stadium back to ship-shape for the new season beginning in August. This particular day, with brush and big pot of gloss at my side, I was re-painting barriers on the terraces when I heard the news. I'd been painting them red too, for God's sake. It was Ces who waved me down to the north-west corner tunnel, whistling, signalling me. I realised later why he hadn't shouted me, it was obvious.

I got to the hospital quick, John gave me a lift. I wanted to blame someone, anyone, but I couldn't, sometimes there is nothing *to* blame, it's a simple rotten fact of simple rotten life. Seeing my grandma lying there lifeless in a hospital bed, I'm thinking that the existence of God definitely is not part of the deal. God didn't exist, how could he, letting such a lousy thing happen to two nothings like my grandma and me? I could see her through an interior window, she was lying in a side room, separate from the rest of the bed-ridden patients in the ward.

Eyes closed, her head propped up on a pillow, like she was as stiff as a waxwork. No movement, no twitching or anything like that, not even eyelids flickering or eyeballs moving, there wasn't much sign she was breathing either. The blankets looked like they had been shaped around her, *moulded.* It was stifling hot and a not-so-faint smell of bleach and chemicals was stinging my eyes, making me feel more nauseous.

The nurse walked with me to my grandma's room. Despite the heat I was shivery and I didn't want to go in but I knew I had to, I had to try and be a man about it, deal with it like a responsible adult. Except I was hardly a responsible adult whichever way you looked at it. I felt like a lost little child, that's the truth, a twenty year-old child. I couldn't look at my grandma, not into her face, I was scared to. I couldn't believe any of it was actually happening, it was as if I wasn't really there and it was all just a bad dream. I mean, I'd seen her earlier on, just a few hours ago, and she'd been right as rain. Now look at her.

The nurse suggested I sit close to the bed, touch or even hold my grandma's hand, telling me that just because my grandma was unconscious didn't mean she wasn't aware I was there. I had to snap out of it myself and show my grandma that everything was going to be alright. There was only me of her blood who gave a damn after all, only me who cared. God only knew where her son – the spineless bastard also known as my dad – was. Probably only

God cared too because I never bloody did. I was told it could help if I spoke to my grandma. There might not be any physical sign but there would be some sort of a response, if only on the inside - her 'inner spirit' would know I was there. I wasn't anyone to question what a nurse said, but how did *she* know that, how did she know anything about me and my grandma?

Then I'm on my own, holding my grandma's cold hand, her freezing-cold hand, and finally I'm talking to her. 'It's me, Gran, Jimmy, I'm here… I'm not going anywhere till you get better.' My throat was as dry as anything and I couldn't swallow and it hurt when I tried to. I was hurting all over, my throat and mouth and head ached so much. I was sweating hot but I was cold inside and my stomach felt like I'd been punched, or kicked where it really hurts. There was so much I wanted to say, so much I wanted her to know. I wanted to say sorry, sorry for everything, anything, I'd ever done to upset or hurt her. I wanted to tell her that I did know, really, how hard she'd always worked to bring me up well and how difficult it all must have been for her. I wanted to thank her for everything – her care, her help, her sacrifices – and to tell her that no matter what pretence she'd put on, I always knew she liked having me around even when I was a real pain. I wanted her to stay so I'd get the chance to prove she was the most important thing in the world to me, over everything else - over Don Revie, Leeds United, St Anthony's, Ces. I wanted to tell her that I loved her more than anything else ever, she was the only thing that mattered. But I didn't say it, I couldn't, because we never did.

A mad rush and I suddenly can't stop myself crying. I wasn't just crying, I was wailing, whimpering, and saying all sorts of stuff to her, hoping she'd answer me. I even swore at her, that should work I thought, should cause some sort of reaction. It didn't. But I kept on at her, nagging, mythering her, whingeing, ordering her to wake up. Because I didn't want to be there and because I didn't want to lose her and I didn't want to go back to the house on my own and I didn't want to have to tell everyone what had happened. It was all useless and I was drowning, in my own uselessness and the feeling that there was no point to any of it. I thought about shaking her, grabbing her to jolt her awake. 'Please don't go, Gran, it's not your time, you've got ages, you've got years…' with tears and snot sliding down my face, tickling my jaw, dripping down my neck, drenching my collar. 'Wake up, listen to me!'

I kissed her cheek, it was soft but cruel and cold and the skin looked dry and yellow and grey. She *wasn't* my grandma any more, she was just a stranger now, a sleeping, waiting stranger. She looked so vulnerable and frail, so alone. It dawned on me, so quickly that it made my heart jump and made me shudder, that there were people waiting for her, people waiting to keep her company and to look after her. People in heaven or wherever we go when we die. Angels, ghosts, spirits - and of course, my mum would be there waiting for her. I felt light-headed with a strange reassuring impression that they were looking out for me too, like I was about to fall a long long way but someone would be there to catch me.

I sat at her bedside for an age - probably less than an hour, in reality. It was alright saying *keep fighting, never give in* and all that, but what was the point of fighting something that you had no chance of beating?

And then the strange noises started. The only thing human I could compare them with was the sound of hawking from the back of your throat to spit, but these were longer, harsher noises. Frightening, almost animal noises. Guttural, deep, deep breaths, almost snoring, almost growling. Long, unpleasant breaths making me more nervous each time one began and then stopped - the breathing was slower, irregular, almost like a small engine fading, cutting out, giving up.

The nurse hurried in, she must have noticed my panic even though I could hardly move I was so scared. I half expected the nurse to tell me to leave so she'd be able to examine my grandma in private, but nothing of the sort. Nothing of the sort because the nurse *knew* exactly what was happening. So did I, deep down. 'She's been waiting for you,' the nurse said. 'You're here now, and she's finally decided to go, it's her time, James love, it's her time. Her body is shutting down.' She sat at the other side of the bed, took hold of my grandma's right hand and spoke to her, quietly, telling her it was alright to leave now, that everything was calm and there was nothing to worry about any more. That James was here and he wants only what's best for her. This lovely nurse seemed nearly as upset as me.

I sit on the near side of the bed and hold my grandma's left hand again like I did at first. I've no idea what she's going through but I can't rid the fear from myself that she's in pain and that the quicker this is all over with and finished, the better. The quicker, the better. I'm willing for it all to finish quickly, I'm willing the pain to leave my grandma alone and to leave her in peace. I'm actually willing my grandma to hurry up and die. Her breathing slows down, the sounds get softer until they're not that unpleasant and more like gentle ocean waves or trees in the wind. Then her jaw drops so so slightly, opening her mouth a fraction, as if she's about to say something. It's only a tiny movement and it is not life. In fact, it is death, and the nurse sighs, a smile on her face and tears in her eyes saying sorry, and telling me my grandma has gone.

I don't know what time I got back home but it was dark. I couldn't think clearly and as well as being horribly tired, I was scared, no, *terrified*, of waking up in the early hours with a shock, remembering everything that had happened.

I never let on to anyone because it would probably have been a bit too odd to understand, but I slept in my grandma's bed that night. The room was musky and smelt of lavender and dust, and there were far too many blankets, but I actually slept well, as if everything was peaceful and was going to be alright.

11 ii

'You move on from Manchester City to Sunderland then finally to Leeds. It was here in Leeds that Don Revie the star player began in 1961 the new career as manager. And in a dazzling decade of success, you transform a team which is struggling at the bottom of the Second Division into one of the world's greatest club sides...' Mercifully, Eamonn Andrews does not mention the disastrous year 1969-'70, the season which had promised so much but delivered nothing but heartache for Revie and his players.

*

In April 1970, Paul McCartney left The Beatles and soon, for many, the dreaded rumour that the band had split up became official. And the World Cup in Mexico brought more disappointment to the country as Sir Alf Ramsey's England team were dumped out of the competition - by the 1966 losing finalists West Germany. Holders England had been two up in the quarter-final but ended up losing 3-2, after extra time, with the seventieth minute substitution of Bobby Charlton alleged to be the main reason for the defeat and manager Ramsey thus getting most of the blame.

On the Leeds front, with approaches from Birmingham, Juventus and Torino for his services - plus the persistent rumour that he would take the Manchester United job 'tomorrow', Don Revie was clearly a much sought after man. Torino had been dedicated to recruiting him for a long time and had reportedly offered him a four year contract worth around £100,000 tax free, with two years' salary paid up front and deposited in a Swiss bank account. But Revie was well aware of the unsettling affect such conjecture and gossip could have on the morale and camaraderie at Elland Road and, while he was flattered by other clubs' interest, there was still much to do at Leeds. 'How on earth could I preach loyalty to the players if I tossed everything aside just as soon as a big offer came along?' he said.

Whilst he had performed near miracles for the club, there was still room for development, the standards could be lifted even higher, for real football history to be made. And so, improvements were made to the facilities while the pitch was re-seeded and £200,000 spent on the north-west corner of the stadium, filling the gap between the rebuilt Kop and the West Stand. The pitch investment would prove excellent value, making it worthy at last of a top class team, and to their credit, the board's plans for ground developments weren't finished.

Nine years and two months after Revie commenced his own new role as Leeds player-manager, Hull City were hoping for a similar renaissance with a certain Jack Charlton as their player-manager. Charlton's potential as a top coach was emerging, and he was impressed by the approach, but he too believed there was still more to do at Elland Road - 'I'm honoured that a noted league club should regard me as the type of man worthy of consideration for a managerial job, and I hope somebody will still think of me in that light in two or three years' time for then I feel sure I'll be keenly interested. But just now, Don Revie believes I can still play in top class football for some years and he's the man whose judgement I accept in everything associated with the game... At Leeds we have come up from the depths together and left behind the times when we suffered bitter disappointments, and the important thing is that we have come through it all as a team, so nobody could induce me to break up that kind of happy combination... I believe there is a lot of time in life when one can get down to managerial work, but one's years as a player are short and precious and I want to make the most of them.' In fact, Revie believed Charlton could carry on playing until he was forty, as he had no weight or fitness problems and possessed the outlook of a 25 year-old. Charlton himself wanted to be remembered at his best and so would finish his playing career only when he felt, physically and mentally, the time was right. Hull then turned to Arsenal's Terry Neill.

In August 1970, in time for the forthcoming season, Leeds United became the first ever club to install a 'police station' within their stadium grounds while the Football League's Alan Hardaker urged the civil authorities to take a harder stance against trouble causers at matches because, he said, sooner or later someone would be killed. In October, Jack Charlton joked in a television interview that he kept a little black book to list the names of certain players he intended getting his revenge on for past skirmishes and quarrels. He later denied the existence of such a book but the FA deemed his comments as bringing the game into disrepute. He would face a Joint Commission of the FA and the League for his remarks.

Two specific Leeds matches stand out in the 1970-'71 campaign, memories and consequences of which will never fade from many minds. Both games were aired on *Match of the Day* as the programme's main features, and both made for compulsive and, for some, excruciating, viewing. The first was close to Valentine's Day, 1971, in a match proclaimed as gloriously representative of the eternal romance of the FA Cup: Colchester United versus Leeds, in the fifth round of the Cup, the day before Valentine's Day, the 13th of February.

In just short of a decade's tenure as the Leeds boss, Revie's team had played nineteen games on the thirteenth day of various months over the years. Not that he suffered from triskaidekaphobia, there is superstition and then there is clinical obsession. Besides, Leeds had lost just one of those games. So far this season the Cup draw had been kind, drawing them against lower league sides each time - Rotherham United of Division Three in the third round (winning the home replay 3-2 after a 0-0 draw), Division Two Swindon Town in the fourth (4-0 home win) and now Colchester United in the fifth. Colchester, a tiny club with an average gate of less than three thousand, currently in the top half of League Division Four.

Mick Bates replaced injured Billy Bremner while Paul Madeley stood in for long-term injury Eddie Gray on the left wing. Gray had endured terrible luck with injuries, culminating in a seemingly minor injury to his ankle in December against Liverpool. At first it was thought he had just sprained the ankle but X-rays showed a fracture, necessitating a week in hospital and ten weeks on crutches. Bremner too was forced to tolerate an unsettled season due to recurring injuries. Paul Reaney on the other hand, had worked him self to a good level of fitness after breaking his leg at West Ham last season. It was not an entirely trouble-free season for him though - October saw his return to first team action but he dropped out after just two games, as his mended leg felt weak and still gave him pain. He returned in December, ironically coming on as substitute for Gray in that Liverpool game.

First Division high-flyers Leeds United flew down to Colchester for the match at Layer Road. Although it was a cold and windy Saturday, the conditions were better than most other venues in the country, with postponements affecting the day's fixture list. Shortly before kick-off, while the Leeds players warmed up on the pitch, as usual, Norman Hunter and Jack Charlton discussed their prospects. With the surface ridged and bumpy and the wind swirling, and with former England forward Ray Crawford leading the Colchester line against them, and with a partisan crowd crammed to capacity inside the tiny ground, Hunter and Charlton agreed that they would need to 'get stuck in' as it was going to be one hell of a battle.

The opening five minutes of the game are indeed a battle, and Leeds struggle to even get out of their own half - Colchester set off with clear intent to 'rattle' them. Just as the attendance for the match had swelled to sixteen thousand, the Colchester players seemed to have grown in stature too, *they* look like the famed honours-chasing First Division team, not Leeds. Their early pressure is near relentless and when a Leeds player actually gets the ball at his feet, he has precious little time to do anything with it as opponents hassle him at every opportunity. The referee seems to prefer the more physical game too and only occasionally blows his whistle for a foul, usually made on a Leeds player. That is not to say Colchester are a team of hackers and cheats... they are not, they are a well-organized, disciplined and physically fit team. Colchester supporters have no respect for reputations either, chanting 'You're a load of rubbish!' at the Leeds players.

After around a quarter of an hour comes the match's first scoring chance. Mick Mahon has a run in on the Leeds goal. He smacks in a good low shot which Sprake does well to push away for a corner-kick. Nothing comes of that attack but it that won't be the case for long. Near the right-hand Leeds corner, Dave Simmons, Colchester's big target-man, gets to the ball before Jack Charlton. Simmons is better-known for his heading ability and for throwing his weight around, but he shows good footwork to keep the ball and skip by Jack Charlton with it. The defender thrusts out a leg to try and jab the ball away from Simmons but succeeds only in tripping him. The referee blows his whistle, a free-kick is awarded and Simmons and Charlton jog into the penalty area, sharing a good-natured chat. More players take positions around the area and get ready for the free-kick. Brian Lewis takes it, and the well-struck cross swings in close to and across the Leeds goal. Charlton and Simmons jump to try and head the ball but it misses them both by inches and should be a straightforward catch or punch for Sprake, or failing that, a header clear for Norman Hunter. The two Leeds men need only to communicate and the problem is easily resolved. Instead, they hardly move and watch like spectators, as the ball flies in towards them. Their indecision proves decisive, allowing Crawford to steal in and pounce to head the ball firmly into the near top corner of the net. It's 1-0 to Colchester, and no more than they deserve. Leeds have yet to pose any serious threat on the home side's goal. Johnny Giles and Peter Lorimer have hardly touched the ball while Allan Clarke and Mick Jones have made little impact.

Although more a hopeful punt than a calculated pass, ten minutes later a long and lofted cross from just inside the Leeds half floats towards the visitors' goal. As it approaches, Reaney and Crawford jump together to challenge for the airborne ball. It's fifty-fifty - and both players actually make contact with it, Crawford heading the ball, against Reaney's ribs. It drops softly to the ground while the two players land in a heap, with the ball nearby, minding its own business. Sprake scrambles out from his goal-line to collect it, unfortunately - for him - Crawford's legs are much closer and he spots a chance. Still lying on the ground, he swings his left leg to kick the ball, albeit with very little power. His kick deceives the advancing Sprake and the ball rolls slowly by him. It rolls, rolls, rolls, twelve, fifteen yards, towards goal. Colchester fans behind the net would suck the ball into the net were they able, while Leeds supporters pray it is heading wide. The ball gently collides with Sprake's left-hand post - the inside of the post - and its journey is at an end as it comes to a halt, just across the goal-line. Striker Dave Simmons rushes in and whacks the ball into the net, just to make sure, but it is Crawford's goal and it is 2-0 to Colchester. The Leeds men in the tiny pitch-side dugout would be cringing with despair, were it possible to feel any smaller or more uncomfortable in such a cramped space. Soon after, their mood is not helped by Allan Clarke failing to hit the target with two half-chances. Half-time arrives.

The second half commences and Leeds look more determined, more confident and more agile. And the overall play, from both sides, is even faster and more frenetic now. In the 54th minute there is another significant mistake in the Leeds defence. Another long cross comes in from the Colchester right, one yard inside the Leeds half. The football is high in the air for some time, and Gary Sprake should be able to judge it easily. But again his indecision is final and the ball bounces high towards the Leeds area, close to the penalty spot. Admittedly, it is not the easiest of situations for a goalkeeper but a player with as much expertise and experience as Sprake should cope comfortably. Instead, he hesitates and when he runs out to catch the high ball, it's too late. The unfortunate Reaney is made to look foolish too, as Simmons beats both players to the ball to head it before either of them can intervene. The ball loops over Sprake and bounces in to the empty net. Fourth Division Colchester 3, First Division Leeds 0. Carthorses 3, thoroughbreds 0!

Jones is having one of those games where very little goes right. He latches on to a low Lorimer cross but his shot is weak and off target. Although they are three goals up, Colchester show inexperience by continuing to attack, leaving spaces at the back instead of 'shutting up shop' and defending en masse. With room to advance and run with the ball, Paul Madeley has a thirty-yard shot deflected for a Leeds corner. Terry Cooper takes it, the penalty area packed with ten Colchester men marking nine Leeds. And just out-jumping all around him, Hunter connects with the ball to score a rare headed goal, giving Leeds a glimmer of a chance to save the game. In the 73rd minute, with Leeds on the attack and showing real urgency at last, a fine left-footed strike from Giles makes it 3-2 to the hosts. Charlton is moved up in to the front line to add weight and height to the attack as an emergency striker. It's now all Leeds, but still not in the typical 'Super Leeds' style, more the long-ball, 'kick and hope' play.

In the 79th minute Charlton has a great chance to equalise. A strong Lorimer cross comes in and Charlton stoops to meet it. His bullet header ought to hit the target, trouble the 'keeper or at least go close, but it squirts yards wide of Colchester's left post. And a minute later, six yards from his own goal, U's defender Brian Garvey meets a low cross a fraction of a second before Mick Jones, sending the ball goal-bound. It looks like it will be a goal but luckily it's straight at goalkeeper Graham Smith and his reactions are sharp. He makes a smart save. Seconds after, Jones strikes a poor left-foot shot wide and Hunter wastes a decent chance, skewing a free-kick high and wide from just outside the area.

And so the referee blows his whistle for full time. Colchester players and supporters are ecstatic. It's a major shock result in British football of course, but on the face of it all the only *real* shock at Layer Road is how poorly Leeds played. Dick Graham's Colchester are through, and rightly so. 'There's no excuse,' said Revie afterwards, 'Colchester didn't play above themselves, they are a very difficult side to beat here. They played very well and that's the story of the match'.

*

On 17th April, 1971, League leaders Leeds would meet West Bromwich Albion at Elland Road. Arsenal and Leeds had been virtually unstoppable at the top of the table for most of the season, and seemed to be running away with Division One. At one stage, Leeds held a seven point lead over Arsenal, though the Gunners had a couple of games in hand. A home win today was imperative for Leeds if they were to maintain a serious challenge; West Bromwich meanwhile, had possessed the worst defensive record in the division. A comfortable Leeds victory was expected, though Albion had a powerful, proven strike force, two players would regularly featured in the lists of top goal-scorers. Tony Brown and Jeff Astle had upset the odds and opposing defences many times before, while the team had taken a point in impressive performances at Everton, Liverpool and Tottenham. For Leeds, Mick Bates replaced unwell Peter Lorimer, the sole absentee from an otherwise full strength line-up. Nigel Davey, a local lad from Garforth, was number twelve and on the bench.

From the start, Leeds were on the offensive, hoping to get an early goal and thus weaken Albion's resolve and damage their morale. Perhaps the Leeds players were too keen, or perhaps they had under-estimated their opponents, because the Whites looked edgy throughout, especially in defence. The usual incisiveness of their passing and fluidity of their forward play was lacking also, whilst the Leeds midfield were struggling to mark their authority on the game. Full-backs Reaney and Cooper too, were making little impact on the wings, and central defenders Hunter and Charlton looked uncomfortable each time West Bromwich counter-attacked. They were jittery, either due to nervousness or fatigue. Fortunately, Sprake in the Leeds net looked to be in good form, and he had a busier than expected afternoon, as Albion mounted various assaults on his goal with relative ease.

In the nineteenth minute the game's first goal arrives, following a mistake by Jack Charlton in the centre circle, inexplicably losing possession of the ball with a stray pass just inside the Leeds half. Albion break away swiftly, a quick couple of interchanges ensue and Tony Brown is free and in the clear outside the Leeds area. Running a few yards with the ball at his feet, he looks up towards Sprake's goal and slams the ball home with a low, well-struck right-footed shot. 1-0 to Albion. Up until that mark, Leeds had already been caught offside 'umpteen times' according to *Match of the Day*'s Barry Davies, including once when Clarke and Gray had been running back to their own half. Even though Clarke's argument that the ball had deflected off an opponent and thus did not signify an infringement seemed a valid one, offside was given. His protest was ignored by referee Ray Tinkler but in fairness to Mr Tinkler, Clarke was the only one who complained. Half-time and the 1-0 score-line remains.

In the second half, Nigel Davey replaced Mick Bates, and Terry Cooper moved up to left wing. Leeds looked livelier and were attempting to pierce their opponents' back line by whatever route possible. But Albion stood firm while continuing to be dangerous on the break. Sprake was playing well even though Tony Brown wasted a great opportunity to score again by shooting tamely straight at him from five yards - it looked easier to score.

On the Leeds right flank, seven or eight yards from the Albion goal-line and just inside the penalty area, Eddie Gray shimmied and swayed to deceive the defenders and place a right-foot, head-height cross in to the box. Mick Jones, loitering with intent on the six yard line, gets to the ball first and, with a powerful and accurate flicked header, the ball soars past goalkeeper Jim Coombes in to the far corner of the Albion net. A superbly taken chance but alas for Leeds, it doesn't count - the linesman had raised his flag almost immediately Jones connected with the ball. The striker had encroached into an offside position as he waited for Gray to cross and he had been off by a yard or so. It was a hard decision to accept but it was the right decision.

A few minutes later, running shoulder by shoulder, Allan Clarke and centre-half John Wile chase a through-ball. Clarke gets to the ball first but Wile is right with him and just inside the area, he collides with the Leeds striker. Clarke is sent sprawling while the football rolls harmlessly through to Coombes as he dashes out of his goal. The crowd believe it's a foul and make the referee aware of it. Clarke believes it is a foul and tries also to make the referee aware of it. Commentator Davies suspects it is a foul too, though he does point out calmly to viewers that no other Leeds players seem to be appealing for a penalty. The referee waves play on and the game continues.

A beautifully struck, missile of a volley from outside the Leeds area seared in on Leeds' goal from inside-left Bobby Hope. It arrived through the crowded penalty area, and Sprake did well to see it as well as block it. The ball rebounded off him and landed at the feet of Colin Suggett to casually tap into the net. Suggett though, was at least a yard offside and it is still 1-0 to West Bromwich. Quickly, goalkeeper Sprake takes the resultant free-kick, passing the ball to his left to Hunter. Hunter paces down the left flank, reaching the halfway line with the ball at his feet. He pauses, in search for a team-mate to pass to whilst keeping tight possession of the ball. He spots Clarke in attack and attempts a diagonal pass to him, but only succeeds in finding Hope's backside. Luckily for Hunter, the ball gently ricochets back to him. He traps it and again looks for an available Leeds man while the other Leeds defenders vacate their own penalty area and make their way to the half-way line. To avoid being caught offside, the Albion players in attack follow suit. Back to the play in the Albion half - Giles signals to Hunter that he wants the ball. Hunter acknowledges and hits the pass towards him, but Tony Brown nips in to intercept the lay-off. The ball hits his left boot and rebounds into the Leeds half.

Paul Reaney, positioned way over on the opposite flank, stands just inside the Leeds half - he is the only Leeds player in that half. Colin Suggett, casually making his way back from the forward position he had occupied less than a minute before, is the only Albion player in that Leeds half - and he is at least five yards behind Reaney and therefore at least five yards offside. As soon as the football enters the Leeds half, the linesman Bill Troupe waves his flag for offside. Players of both teams stop in their tracks because they recognize that Suggett is indeed offside.

Except for Tony Brown, who continues to run as he is watching the ball and nothing else. He tears after the loose ball while all the other players wait for referee Tinkler to blow his whistle and corroborate the linesman's decision. But the whistle blow does not come - Mr Tinkler deems that Suggett is not interfering with play and therefore the player is not offside. And so play is waved on, though Brown momentarily halts his run when he too sees Suggett is offside. But then he sets off again at the absence of the referee's whistle. In the centre circle Suggett, the player adjudged to be not interfering with play, sees Brown's run and swivels around to sprint towards the Leeds goal. At the far side of the pitch, big centre-forward Jeff Astle shows a decent turn of speed too and chases after his team-mates. He races half the length of the pitch, with Reaney close by, but not close enough. Still in possession of the ball, Brown progresses into the penalty area. He looks up and sees Astle ready to accept a pass in his stride. Brown's timing though, is imperfect, and he casually taps the ball slightly forward to Astle who is two yards in front of him - and therefore two yards offside as well. A second offside infringement within half a minute, yet it is adjudged again by Referee Tinkler to be legal. Astle receives the pass and rolls the ball into the net past the helplessly stranded Sprake. 2-0 to West Bromwich Albion.

'And Leeds will go mad. And they have every right to go mad... Don Revie, a sickened man, look at him looking up to the heavens in disgust,' cries Barry Davies. And following the referee's two contentious decisions in this small arena in the south of Leeds, West Yorkshire, a tiny vista of mayhem begins. Twelve angry men, of various ages, run on to the pitch to remonstrate with the referee. Some of them might well have had more violent intentions in mind, too. Fortunately, no assaults are made. When the game eventually restarts, Clarke nets for Leeds in the 82nd minute to make it 1-2 but it is too little too late, WBA hold out to win and steal the points, while Referee Tinkler is escorted off the pitch by police officers to protect him from any possible danger. Viewers could be excused for thinking he had been arrested.

It had been one of the most controversial, notorious football matches ever played in England, and the match result just about decided the fate of the 1970-'71 season's League Championship. As if the immediate result were not grave enough for them, the consequences of the crowd disorder would have more serious and far-reaching effects on Leeds United. Chairman Alderman Percy Woodward, never slow to lambast the loutish aggression of British football terraces in the past, was furious - at the actions on the pitch - 'It is appalling that nine or ten months' work by all of us, should be destroyed by one man.... I am not blaming the spectators. There was every justification for it. I am sorry it happened but there it is.' The Lord Mayor of Leeds, Alderman Arthur Brown, himself a former professional referee for many years, and who had watched the match from the Elland Road directors' box, said. 'I can find no defence for the referee.' Not everyone agreed though, Leeds City Councillor Bernard Atha for one, calling Woodward's comments 'disgraceful'. Revie, when asked about the crowd trouble, responded, 'Can you blame them for what happened today?' adding later, 'I have never been so sick at heart. The ref's decision on Suggett, the worst I have seen man and boy, was wrong and it wrecked nine months of hard work at our club. I regret the crowd scenes like anybody else but, by heaven, I can understand why they cut loose. Astle was also offside, in my opinion, when he took the pass from Brown to score.' Albion manager Alan Ashman also commented, 'I would have been choked to have been beaten by an offside goal like that in any match, but these things happen and we just have to swallow them.' Referee Tinkler defended his actions, 'I am completely sure that Suggett committed no offence. He was in an offside position and the linesman had flagged him, but he was not interfering with play.'

Comments in the Daily Sketch, from the linesman Bill Troupe - who was felled by an object thrown from the crowd for his troubles - contradicted Tinkler's viewpoint: 'Suggett wasn't just a yard off-side, he was a good five yards and in my opinion must have been influencing play. He didn't touch the ball but he set off in support of Brown so there was a clear intention of interfering with the course of the game.'

League Division One table (top), 17th April, 1971.

1 Arsenal	Played 37	Points = 58
2 Leeds Utd	Played 39	Points = 58
3 Chelsea	Played 39	Points = 48

Even though Leeds went on to win their remaining three fixtures, including a 1-0 home win over Arsenal, the mortal wound to their title hopes had been made in the West Bromwich game; Arsenal went on to win the title with a last minute win at Tottenham in the last League match of the season. The consequences of the defeat to West Bromwich Albion and the contentious referee's decisions and the fans' actions went deeper than just a ruined title challenge, negative press and increased notoriety for Leeds fans. Because of the pitch invasion the club was punished severely by the FA - too severely plenty said - forced to play their first four home fixtures of the next season at neutral venues.

*

Although their 1970-'71 season contained those two shock (and shocking) defeats, Leeds' campaign was not a disaster. As well as registering a record number of points for League runners-up (64, twelve more than third placed Tottenham Hotspur) in March the club announced a record profit of £171,951 for the previous season. Seven Leeds players were said to earn between £10,000 and £12,500. *And* Leeds managed to win the Inter-Cities Fairs Cup too. They were 'Champions of Europe' once again, albeit not in the European Cup. Arsenal meanwhile, unflatteringly, were described as only 'middling champions' by some media. A quite nonsensical comment, as well as the League they won the FA Cup too, beating Liverpool after extra time.

Three days before the West Bromwich nightmare, Leeds had been away to Liverpool in the first leg of the Fairs Cup semi-final. A surprise inclusion in the side was Billy Bremner who had been out of action for more than two months. Renowned for scoring crucial goals, Leeds' very own copper-topped Captain Marvel played as a third attacker rather than his usual 'midfield general' role. For Leeds, the first British winners of the Inter Cities Fairs Cup, the Anfield tie was their fiftieth in the competition, and they had scored 99 goals along the way.

Bremner as captain, having won the coin toss, decided to make Liverpool play towards their Kop, crammed with over 20,000 supporters. Just as Leeds liked playing towards their Gelderd End Kop in the second half of Elland Road matches, Liverpool preferred to do the same at Anfield. So, a minor psychological advantage won by Bremner already, and it did seem to work: all Liverpool's pressure failed to break the deadlock. Leeds' confidence was growing and Liverpool's unbeaten home record was increasingly under threat. And just after the hour mark, Leeds were awarded a free-kick on Liverpool's left. Johnny Giles floated the ball high in to the penalty area. It seemed the ball would elude everyone, probably explaining the defence's slack or complete lack of marking which left Bremner free to lurk alone just inside the area. Probably the smallest man on the pitch, he demonstrated yet again a marvellous heading ability which belied his size.

Gauging the flight of the ball, he dashes a few yards inside the area and launches himself, twisting his body mid-air to try and plant as much of his bodyweight into the ball as possible. Connecting well, he smashes the ball with the top of his head towards Liverpool's goal, its power and trajectory beating goalkeeper Ray Clemence to open the scoring. Yet another stunning piece of skill and finishing prowess from Billy Bremner which stings the Liverpool faithful into wounded silence. The goal is enough to win the match and indeed the two ties to put Leeds into the final; the second leg of the semi-final resulting in a 0-0 stalemate.

A young Liverpool fan, in a letter published in one of the tabloid newspapers, recounted an incident occurring in the second half of that Anfield match. The boy, at the front of the Kop for the match, described how the ball had landed near the corner flag next to the Kop, for a Leeds throw-in. Billy Bremner went to retrieve it and take the throw-in, while thousands of Liverpool fans sang 'We all hate Leeds and Leeds and Leeds'. In addition, a spotty and full of rage teenager went further with his own vitriol, shouting directly at the Leeds captain - 'And we really hate you Bremner, you ginger bastard!' On hearing the not so pleasant tirade, and with the ball in his hands, Bremner instantly grinned and then adroitly bounced it off the lad's nose, saying 'Well there's another reason to hate me - I've made you even uglier.'

With a 2-2 draw (goals from Madeley and Bates) away at Juventus and a 1-1 draw (Clarke) in the second leg of the final at Elland Road, Leeds won the Fairs Cup for the second time in their history, this time thanks to the Away Goals rule. The Turin leg had been delayed for two nights, eventually being played on the evening of Friday 28th May, torrential rain having caused the first attempt to be abandoned. There had been off-field problems for Leeds as well which had threatened to disrupt Revie's preparations for the big match. Normally, he did not allow the players' wives to travel or stay with the team on European visits, his view being that the fewer distractions for the players, the better. However, for the Juventus game, he had relaxed the rules a little, allowing the wives to stay in a separate hotel. Unfortunately, the arrangement was not agreeable to some of them, and so a contingent complained. Word somehow reached the media and quickly rumours of unrest and disharmony began to circulate. Reports even claimed that so incensed was Revie by what he saw as disloyalty and ingratitude, he threatened to resign as manager. The Leeds directors would not allow that to happen of course and so Revie got his way while a couple of the players' wives returned to England.

Juventus benefited financially from that Wednesday abandonment as 46,501 tickets had been sold, gate receipts being worth around £100,000. In Italy, tickets were not refundable if a game passed a certain stage in the second half, the fans would be forced to fork out again if they wanted to attend the re-scheduled tie. Around 45,000 did exactly that. It was a week to forget for Eddie Gray. Practically a whole season to forget in fact - warming up for the first match, he fell awkwardly on the waterlogged turf, suffering the excruciating injury of a dislocated shoulder.

The return leg was played at Elland Road on the balmy evening of June 3rd. The 1-1 score-line meant that Leeds triumphed thanks to scoring more goals away in the tie than their opponents. Quite understandably, Juventus felt aggrieved at losing on the Away Goals rule, because they had not actually lost a single game in the competition. Leeds had, in the second round away at Dynamo Dresden, 2-1, on that occasion the Mick Jones away goal taking them through. They made easier work of their other opponents, beating Norwegian side Sarpsborg 6-0 on aggregate in the first round, Czech side Sparta Prague 9-2 in the third, Vitoria Setubal of Portugal 3-2, and Liverpool 1-0 in the penultimate round of the competition. The Fairs Cup had not featured high on their list of trophy priorities to begin with, but by the end of the season it turned out to be an extremely significant target.

11 iii

When the crappiest sort of luck hits you, I think it's safe to say that you either sink or you swim. With me, I was sinking, it all felt like I was up to my neck in it and drowning, everything had changed so much and so rottenly. Having said all that, I was lucky because I'd have been well and truly done for without friends' help. Proper, true friends. Ces and John, and Aitch, and just about everybody else in our street, supported me and guided me when my grandma died. The funeral, the insurance, the money, the rent, the paperwork, the obituary thing in the paper, the Peacock for the wake, and so on and on and on, all taken care of thanks to teamwork just about. It had all seemed to be never ending and I didn't even want to get out of bed most mornings, there just didn't seem much point. It was like I'd lost all my energy and enthusiasm. So Ces and John took it in turns at battering on my house door each morning, even some Saturdays when we weren't even due to work I was only just 21, I didn't know what you were supposed to do or how you recovered from being left on your own. I couldn't even play football to help kick out the stress because I had to rest my calf muscle-tear until autumn time.

Till the funeral, I'd never known my grandma had so many friends. In truth, it might surprise some folk but that fact made it all a bit more uncomfortable for me as there were dozens of them. Everyone of them was so nice and sympathetic, lots of them I'd never met before, I didn't know what to say or how to react but I think I did alright, I don't remember anyone criticising me for something I should or shouldn't have done. There were a lot of well-meaning things said by people who only meant well, even though a lot of it was soppy claptrap about my grandma dying being 'God's will' and that she'd had 'a good innings' and 'at least she went peacefully', but I didn't bite, none of them was trying to cause offence. They were only trying to help me, of course, those friends of my grandma. And now they were my friends as well.

Sometimes things happen, even if they happen away from your own personal world, that manage to shock you and maybe shake you out of personal dark times, to make you realise that you're not the only one with problems and that others have it a lot worse. On January 2nd 1971, 66 people died and over 200 were injured at the Rangers-Celtic match at Ibrox. Metal barriers next to passageway ('Stairway') number 13 collapsed, causing a pile-up of people, most of them dying from 'compressive asphyxiation'. Even though it was all that way away in Scotland, it felt closer to home as it could easily happen at many an English ground.

We all make mistakes, every single one of us, but Tinkler's wrong decisions in the West Brom game weren't just mistakes, they looked deliberate, as if he wanted to bloody spite us. And we should have had a penalty and all. When some of the fans got on the pitch I really did expect him to get lamped. He was lucky he didn't, that's a definite, because he'd deserved one.

Trouble at football matches was getting more and more common. You wouldn't hear about it on the television or radio so much, and the papers missed more than they actually reported, but there were always stories. Pub talk, terrace talk, talk at work, talk amongst the St Anthony's fellas. There were regular incidents within the ground but most of it was outside Elland Road, or in town and around Beeston and Holbeck. A mate of Aitch's called Steve, liked to tell a few tales in the Peacock of his travels watching Leeds. I listened in during one afternoon lock-in we had - I was playing pinball and this Steve was holding court round the table just next to it.

'We were away at Spurs, season before last when we won the League. More often than not for Cockney games we'd go on the Service train because there's hardly any hassle, no one takes much notice of the normal trains, unlike the football Specials or the Wally Trolley coaches. We heard that the police had been having a lot of bother at Chelsea and West Ham matches whenever teams from the North played there, so they were trying to do something about it. They linked up with Leeds constabulary to set something up.' Sup of beer. 'So they decided it would be a good idea to put these two plain clothes policemen in with us on the Service train. Trust me, 'plain clothes' isn't that good a choice of words, their plain clothes meant a big overcoat over full police uniform, with blue shirt, dark blue tie, serge trousers, black shoes polished to fuck so you could see your reflection in them, the lot. Half wits, I'm telling you - God knows how they catch any criminals!' Sup of beer, drag of cig. 'Anyway, they sort of joined up with us, I don't know if they picked us out or what, but we got drinking with them on the way down to London. We had our own supply plus there was a bar on the train, even that early on in the day. You can't turn a drink with your mates down, whatever time, because you'll never get it back, doesn't matter what time it is. These Bobbies were both well over thirty, it wasn't just their clothes that stood out, they both looked like they'd had a lot of late nights. But fair enough, they knew their football and they weren't doing any harm and neither was we, that's the point, and I think they'd worked out for themselves that we were going to watch football and have a good day out and all, nowt more. They didn't mind a slurp either, which was a bit of a surprise, I admit. I don't think they'd realised that we were on to them - I don't think they ever realised, even when we arranged to meet them in the Clarence pub in Trafalgar Square after the match. We drew nil-nil by the way. These coppers bought most of our beer in there, maybe there was a London Met tab put on for them, I don't know.' Sup, burp, drag. 'We got the last train back to Leeds from Kings Cross with them, some time after ten. Straight into the buffet car, straight into the bar and straight into the McEwans Export lager.

We tried but didn't quite manage to empty that bar - we put in a sterling effort, mind. One of the Bobbies, Dave I think his name was - I'm not sure *he* knew his own name by then - couldn't take his drink very well... we had to carry him off the train when we got back into Leeds station, about three bells. If ever I miss the last bus home on a Saturday I have a kip on the Sunday papers piled up next to City House. Comfier than they look. And this was in January, I wasn't risking freezing my bollocks off walking home, so I slept on them Sunday papers again. A few hours later I woke up, frigging cold and damp, and it wasn't even daylight. And this Dave was sleeping like a baby, curled up next to me, complete with thumb in his mouth! Wouldn't surprise me if he'd peed himself as well. Top bloke though, top top bloke. Hope he didn't lose his job or anything, you need as many good coppers as possible.'

And then this Steve started singing something that I'd heard at the odd match or two from the Kop but was never able to make out the words properly - *'The River Aire is chilly and deep, Ol-u-wale. Never trust the Leeds police, Ol-u-wale.'* Oluwale was some black tramp who got killed for his troubles by two representatives of West Yorkshire's finest, the police. I didn't think Steve was making any of it up, I mean it wasn't as if he was trying to convince anyone that he and his mates had kicked ten bells out of Spurs fans *and* the police force in its entirety. You definitely did hear some proper tall stories mind, from others.

In September, Leeds were playing Chelsea at home - obviously there was no love lost between us and them anyway, so there was plenty of scrapping, as you'd expect. Mainly in town near or in the train station. Then in October we had Man U at home. A 50,000 crowd, plenty of arrests and all, again. The Evening Post reported on it, saying Man United had 'many youths wearing crash helmets, heavy boots and wearing red', with lots of them ejected from the stadium. There were fights all over the place and the New Peacock (the 'other' Peacock) supposedly got trashed - windows smashed, furniture bust and records stolen from the jukebox. And the Imperial Hotel on Princes Street, Holbeck, licensee William Horsfield supposedly had £100 worth of windows smashed, and lots more breakages as well. I must admit, I didn't know that pub but it sounded like it was a bloody palace with that much damage-worth supposedly being made. According to people who lived around there, trouble connected to the football was common, every time

Leeds had a home game they reckoned there was always loads of violence and vandalism. They should move house then, or have tried living in our street, especially when Glasgow invaded. I didn't want to sound callous or anything, but there were innocent people getting bombed to pieces in Northern Ireland, trouble at the football didn't seem that much of a big deal to me.

Anyway, the club eventually outlawed helmets at matches as well as turning away blokes with steel-capped boots on. And any women wearing them I suppose. They banned banners as well, and instructed the police to look out for 'aggressive clothing'. I always thought police uniforms were just about the most aggressive clothing you could see.

Chapter 12: 1971/2 - 'Excellence was everywhere'

12 i

The Football Honours 1970-'71.
League Division One winners - Arsenal, Runners up - LEEDS.
FA Cup winners - Arsenal, Runners up - Liverpool
League Cup winners - Tottenham Hotspur, Runners up - Aston Villa.
European Cup winners - Ajax, Runners up - Panathinaikos.
European Cup Winners Cup winners - Chelsea, Runners up - Real Madrid.
Inter-Cities Fairs Cup winners - LEEDS, Runners up - Juventus.
Football Player of the Year - Frank McLintock, Arsenal.
European Footballer of the Year - Johan Cruyff, Ajax.
Crowd average, home games = 38,922.
Years to wait for Clean Air in Leeds = four.

Not the best reading, true, but a few years back I'd have given my right arm for it. At least we won *something*, even if Johnny Giles grew a moustache which didn't suit him at all and spoiled the photos it was so bad. Winning the Fairs Cup meant I could remember the season my grandma died with a bit of comfort, even though the final did take place a full year after.

12 ii

Due to those West Bromwich Albion misdemeanours, Leeds United were forced to play their first four home games of the 1971-'72 campaign on neutral territory. The referee received no punishment whatsoever for causing them. This was another item discreetly excluded from Revie's *This Is Your Life* edition, the programme produced to praise Revie, not to upset him. Leeds were not the only club embroiled in controversial incidents and crowd trouble, but the presence of the BBC cameras at Elland Road that day ensured they were football's 'enemy number one' and the television coverage served as the Football League's chief witness for the prosecution. At Old Trafford, after a knife-throwing incident in February at their match with Newcastle, Manchester United were also banned from playing at home, for two weeks, their August home game against Arsenal switched to Liverpool's Anfield.

On the eve of the new campaign, with the attitude of, 'If Arsenal can do it then so can we...' the Leeds players were told of what their aim for the '71-'72 season was to be: the Double of the League and the FA Cup. Revie told the *Evening Post*'s Don Warters - 'Teams as good as the one we've got come round once in a lifetime, so enjoy it while you can'; confidence rather than arrogance. But by the third month of the season, the comment seemed almost delusional. Twelve games played and Leeds were eighth in the table, six points behind leaders Manchester United. Plus they were out of the UEFA Cup at the first hurdle in September, and their exit from the League Cup wasn't long coming either.

The newly created UEFA Cup competition had replaced the Inter-Cities Fairs Cup, in which Leeds and Spanish side Barcelona had fared the most successfully over the years. So, never afraid to invent more money-spinning games, UEFA arranged for a play-off between the two sides to decide the trophy's permanent owner. Barcelona had won the trophy three times, Leeds twice. The match, held at Barcelona's huge Nou Camp stadium on September 22nd, created less prestige than UEFA originally hoped, with just 35,000 people attending. Barcelona won 2-1, with Leeds' goal scored by Joe Jordan, signed from Morton for £15,000 in October 1970. A few hundred ardent Leeds fans made the trip to watch the match but it is unlikely their disappointment at the result lasted much longer than the return journey home time.

Jordan's early days at Leeds had been uncomfortable to say the least. In addition to relentless ribbing from his new team-mates for 'unusual' dress-sense - an oilskin coat and an Arran wool sweater his mum knitted being the main offending articles - he had been kicked in the mouth in a Reserves match at Coventry and his front two teeth ended up in the muck. They were followed soon later by the tooth at each side whilst he was forced to wait days for dentures. He had been a Morton team-mate of the one and only Bobby Collins. While Collins was at Morton, he would stay with his parents in Glasgow, visit his Leeds-based family whenever he could as well as sometimes train with his former Elland Road teammates. It was on one such occasion that Don Revie asked if there were any players north of the border who he could recommend. 'Aye,' Collins had replied, mentioning a boy called Joe Jordan 'who's got a real chance' and who played football like a man.

In the summer of '71, 'Goal' magazine declared that the new Leeds season would be the last throes of a great side, while Peter Morris, in *Team Makers - a Gallery of the Great Soccer Managers* warned that Revie's 'family' did not have long left as a team and that if he were to depart it could cause the club's swift decline to the low-point of the early 1960s. Privately, the worry that the present squad could not stay at the top much longer was a real one for Revie. Players were getting older and slower, and perhaps losing the desire too, and some were hindered by persistent injuries also. The beginning of the end of his 'Super Leeds' squad was approaching and there was very little he could do about it. With every day and every new setback, his anxieties simply grew. In the early days of his managerial career, he rarely got more than four hours' sleep each night. Ten or so years later, his sleep suffers all over again, but for very different reasons - achieving success rather than trying to avoid failure.

Those four neutral venue games proved to be more *inconvenient* than heavy punishment - Leeds went unbeaten in them: 0-0 with Wolves at Huddersfield's Leeds Road ground, 1-1 with Spurs at Hull's Boothferry Park, and victories against Newcastle (5-1 at Hillsborough) and Crystal Palace, 2-0 at Leeds Road again. The team's problems were away from home - officially away - although they did beat Manchester City at Maine Road 1-0 on the opening Saturday. By late October they had lost at Sheffield United 0-3, Arsenal 0-2, Huddersfield 1-2 and 1-3 at Coventry, all in addition to the defeats to Barcelona and 1-0 to West Ham in the League Cup (after extra time in a replay) and 4-2 on aggregate to Belgian side Lierse SK) in the UEFA Cup.

Responding to criticism that the club thought it was too big for such 'minor' competitions as the League & UEFA Cup, Revie said, 'We never opt out of anything... Anyone who thinks we opted out is thinking entirely along the wrong lines.' Nonetheless, the negative press continued unabated for some time. That 2-0 defeat at Arsenal prompted the Sunday People's Mike Langley to write 'Don Revie squirmed through a grim afternoon in the glass-fronted trainers' box, hunched, chewing incessantly and peering into a worrying future. For he could only see another season of comparative failure for Leeds United, the team that for the past two seasons has always stumbled to second. This time, on this form, they probably won't even do that.' It is though reasonable to argue that injuries to key players upset the Leeds side's balance. Allan Clarke, Mick Jones and Eddie Gray all missed matches, while Jack Charlton, Terry Cooper and Johnny Giles had occasionally been rested.

Not only was the team said to be fading, certain individuals were alleged to be on their way out too. Billy Bremner responded to rumours about his own fitness, 'Right now I'm fitter than I have ever been and I'm enjoying my game more because I've increased my work rate. I'm more determined to win things and I'll tell you this, Billy Bremner is far from finished.' He did admit however that the Leeds squad had discussed how to improve the situation, the players generally having tired of the detailed and deathly dull dossiers from which nothing more could be learned about their opponents. Some of the Leeds players even struggled to stave off sleep in those dossier sessions.

The 9th October defeat at Coventry also saw Eric Nicholls in the Sunday People portray Revie's 'Leeds lions' as having been reduced to 'toothless cubs'. But, *wounded beasts* and all that, four Leeds League wins in a row then followed, at home to Manchester

City 3-0, Everton 3-2 and Leicester 2-1, plus a fans' favourite 1-0 victory at Manchester United. Superb goals from their trident strike force of Clarke, Jones and Lorimer - with a trademark thunderbolt volley - watched by millions of *Match of the Day* viewers signified the double over Manchester City, and they had beaten Liverpool 1-0 in the League in September too. However, a 13th November 2-1 defeat at Southampton spoiled their League run: notably, Leeds seemed to *save* their defeats for teams less fancied to be challenging for honours.

Division One League table (top), November 13th, 1971.

1 Manchester Utd.	Played 17	Points = 26
2 Derby County	Played 17	Points = 23
3 Manchester City	Played 17	Points = 23
4 Sheffield Utd.	Played 17	Points = 23
5 Leeds Utd.	Played 17	Points = 21

Also this month, Leeds had all but bought left-sided midfielder Asa Hartford from WBA for in excess of £200,000; he had even trained with his new team-mates. A quick, intelligent, hard-working and skilful player, Hartford had all the qualities Revie wanted in a Leeds United player. However, due to a past heart condition, Hartford was to fail a medical and the transfer collapsed. Despite cardiologists giving the all clear, Leeds were warned off the transfer for insurance reasons. A great move ruined for the player and for the club, Hartford would become one of the most consistent players in the League for years to come.

Leeds went unbeaten in the League for nine games as well as easing through the third round of the FA Cup in mid-January 1972. The eye-catching run included a November 2-0 walkover at Nottingham Forest, an impressive 3-0 home win over Brian Clough's Championship hopefuls Derby and an excellent 2-0 win at old rivals Liverpool on New Year's Day, in front of nearly 54,000 spectators. It completed the double over Bill Shankly's men: 'It has always been an ambition of Leeds United to come here to Anfield, play well and win well. Liverpool must be the hardest to beat at home in the world,' beamed Revie after goals from Jones and Clarke won the points. Shankly did not entirely agree on Leeds' qualities - 'We played them off the pitch until they got their first goal after sixty minutes. We were unlucky. You can't call Leeds an attacking team... they keep the ball well, their passing is accurate, but they're negative like continentals. The one man who gave us trouble was Eddie Gray, he was taking men on and beating them.' The draw for the FA Cup fourth round would give Shankly chance for revenge.

In the League, a Sprake blunder gifted Chivers the winner and Spurs the points in the 1-0 defeat at White Hart Lane to spoil Leeds' run and meaning they still had not reached top spot.

Division One League table (top), 29th January, 1972

1 Man. City	Played 27	Points 38
2 Leeds Utd.	Played 27	Points 36
3 Derby	Played 27	Points 36
4 Man. Utd.	Played 27	Points 35
5 Arsenal	Played 27	Points 33
6 Wolves	Played 27	Points 32

February 5th, 1972, the FA Cup 4th Round - Liverpool 0, Leeds United 0. With around 56,600 making it Liverpool's highest attendance for over ten years, the hosts had most of the possession and attacking pressure. There were few clear-cut chances though, while a combination of good goalkeeping by Sprake, solid defending by Reaney, Cooper, Hunter and Madeley (in for the ill Charlton) and inadequate finishing by Liverpool kept the scores at nil. Whilst *Match of the Day* and media reports said that Leeds were well worth the draw, John Giles' comment was probably fairer - 'We got away with it.'

In the same period as Rolls Royce was declared bankrupt, the government declared a state of emergency on February 9th as a response to the miners' strike. This meant FA Cup replays had to be completed in daylight due to power cuts and the three day working week. Ahead of the Liverpool replay, Leeds' Keith Archer said, 'The electricity board cannot guarantee us lighting for a night match, as on safety grounds we have no alternative but to make it a two-thirty start.' After a relatively slow start, tickets for the match sold out. And in addition to nearly 46,000 inside the ground, thousands were locked out too. A hundred or so supporters managed to perch on the Peacock pub rooftop to get a view (of the

Kop end of the pitch at least) while a few others tried watching from nearby trees and stand roofs.

At the final whistle of the Elland Road replay, having officiated both ties Referee Gordon Hill applauded the two teams off the pitch, commenting later, 'Two of the greatest games a referee could wish to control… the teams played like real professionals in the truest sense of the word.' Thanks to expertly taken goals by Allan Clarke in each half, Leeds won 2-0. This defeat to Leeds was their third of the season for Liverpool, and Revie was proving to be a proper thorn in Bill Shankly's side.

Less than two weeks later (with a stalemate at Everton in between) millions of television viewers in addition to a crowd of over 45,000 at Elland Road saw second in the table Leeds annihilate fourth-placed Manchester United, 5-1. All the goals were scored in the second half, though none of them were spectacular; it was the Whites' snappy passing and fluid approach play which undid the Red Devils. Mick Jones notched his first ever League hat-trick with Clarke and Lorimer (with his left foot) scoring the others. Just a few weeks prior, Manchester had been top of the table but were now stuck in a dismal run of form, despite a line-up including Best, Charlton, Morgan and Kidd. Best mysteriously disappeared from football soon after the Leeds match, in dispute with manager Frank O'Farrell.

After the match, Brian Glanville wrote in the *Sunday Times*, 'The spectacle was almost that of the matador toying with a weary bull, the delighted roars of the crowd at each new piece of virtuosity the equivalent of the 'oles' of the bullring.' Revie, with his long-held admiration for Real Madrid, enjoyed the Spanish connection, and Leeds fans were indeed heard cheering 'Ole' while the season was suddenly looking promising. After a mediocre first half-season, Leeds were now riding high and Don Revie told journalist John Sadler, 'When we came into the First Division they slung a terrible, cruel tag around our necks. They called us the dirtiest team in the land. That was a lousy label to give a team of youngsters. We were booed on every ground, booked for almost every hard tackle, it's only now that we've managed to live it down.'

Next up was the FA Cup fifth round - away to Second Division Cardiff City. Leeds were expected to win but Revie, still haunted of course by last season's humiliation at Colchester, warned that Cardiff would be no mere pushovers. There would be a big and partisan crowd of Welshmen roaring them on, and the players would 'chase everything and fight like tigers'. He was, right. For the match, Madeley would deputise at right-back for the not fully match fit Reaney, who was substitute. 'People get agog about Paul Madeley's ability to play in different positions that they tend to forget he's a world class player. However, you cannot exaggerate his value. Having him at the club is like having three men in one. He can do any job, Paul just goes out and does exactly what you want him to do. I never need to worry about him,' - said Revie.

And so, on 26th February, on a rainy Wales afternoon, close on 50,000 people attended Ninian Park to watch Cardiff play Leeds, most of them hoping for another shock result. In spite of the conditions though, Leeds put on a near faultless performance. There were no nerves, no complacency, no frills - with a goal in each half, the second a typically sweet strike, man of the match Johnny Giles steered Leeds into the next round. Cardiff played well and gave the favourites a hard game but Leeds deserved the win. Revie remarked that his players showed their true character and professionalism in such adverse conditions, and that they believe they can win every game they play.

Saturday March 4th 1972 - *Match of the Day*'s Barry Davies - 'To say that Leeds are playing with Southampton is the understatement of the season. Poor old Southampton just don't know what day it is…' Leeds had thumped Southampton 7-0 at Elland Road. The scorers were Clarke two, Lorimer three, and Jones and Charlton one each. Because Don Revie and Saints manager Ted Bates were good friends, as the rout took place Revie sent word to his players to 'take the heat off' Southampton as he did not want to cause any more embarrassment for Bates. Heeding the Boss's instruction, the Leeds players began to play 'keep ball' instead of trying to score more goals. And with the fans all around the ground cheering, crying 'Ole' with every Leeds pass again, various ball-flicks and tricks ensued. Southampton barely got a chance to touch the ball. So Ted Bates' players weren't embarrassed now, they were humiliated.

For the Leeds management and directors, the one disappointment about the Southampton game was the attendance of less than 35,000. One week later though, nearly 9,000 more turned up for the League game against Coventry. Mid-table City made the match hard for Leeds and just one goal settled it. That goal was scored by Jack Charlton, and in his 600th League game for the club.

A week after his 38th birthday, Paul Trevillion made his Leeds debut, against Tottenham Hotspur in the FA Cup. Rather, the *influence* of Paul Trevillion made the debut. Actually from Tottenham, Trevillion was a self-professed 'lunatic genius' most famous for his *Gary Player Golf Class* drawings which appeared in newspapers all around the world, and well-known too for *Roy of the Rovers* and *Eagle* comics artwork, plus his eternally popular *You Are the Ref* puzzles in football magazines since the late '50s. A mutual love of golf brought him and Don Revie together

Keen to capitalise on the positive press bestowed on Leeds of late, the captivated Revie listened to the ideas of this madcap Londoner. Consequently, ahead of the Spurs quarter-final, the Leeds players would perform warm-up exercises on the pitch before kick-off, wear tracksuit tops with their names emblazoned on the back and distribute free footballs for a few lucky fans on the terraces. Each player would wear jazzy, numbered sock tags too, their team number in white on dark blue soft leather-like material, complete with white hanging frills beneath.

Closely observing the Leeds players in training, Trevillion had likened Les Cocker's rigorous and detailed manoeuvres to Busby Berkeley's amazing screen choreography of old Hollywood movies. Such a sight deserved to be seen by a wider audience. The Leeds players did often have hundreds of fans regularly watching them in midweek training but nothing like a match day crowd. And seeing as the Leeds board raised ticket prices by as much as fifty percent for the Cup tie, the fans certainly deserved some kind of bonus anyway. But as they prepared to distribute the new garments and accessories to the players, Revie became anxious that the publicity stunt would bring them bad luck. He suggested they postpone the idea. Trevellion however, was insistent and so the twelve Leeds players, each carrying a plastic football and wearing pristine white personalised tracksuit tops, strode on to the Elland Road pitch to line up in the centre circle and salute the crowd on all sides. Twelve grateful individuals were soon to be in possession of those footballs, and after each game, many of the sock tags would go the same way too, or be snatched up by eager and sharp-eyed ball-boys. The majority of Leeds supporters warmed to the scheme, though hardly surprisingly, some in the media were less approving of such 'gimmickry'. The sock tags, 'target' balls, tracksuit tops and warm-up routines effectively carved entries into football folklore, and Trevillion wasn't finished.

The match: Pat Jennings, the big Northern Ireland international with famously big hands, played in goal for Spurs outstandingly well. His performance prevented a drubbing and kept his team in serious contention in the tie. Tottenham in fact took the lead shortly before half-time, albeit against the run of play, with a fortunate goal - a cross intended for Chivers floated too high and over him, over team-mate Alan Gilzean and over Jack Charlton as well. With his view obstructed by the three players, Sprake saw the ball too late and it swirled into the net despite a last-ditch lunge from Hunter. It was the first time Leeds had been behind in that season's FA Cup but it wouldn't be for long as desperate Spurs defending was unable to stop Clarke stretching to toe-poke the ball home for the equalizer after a game of football-pinball in the muddy penalty area. The ball fell kindly for Clarke - nicknamed 'Sniffer' thanks to his fine ability to sniff out goal scoring opportunities in the tightest of situations - and he was never one to decline such invitations. Later, early in the second half, an innocuous Martin Peters foul on Cooper brought a Leeds free kick on the left, yards outside the Spurs box. Lack of concentration and organization allowed Charlton to rise unchallenged and thrust a net-rippling header past Jennings. It proved to be the winner, 2-1 to Leeds, in a captivating match which *The Observer*'s Hugh McIlvanney wrote that Leeds' football had been 'breathtaking in its scope and fluency, alive with dazzling improvisations,' and 'scarcely a weakness to be seen and excellence was everywhere'. The semi-finals draw paired Leeds with Birmingham - managed by former Peacocks defender Freddie Goodwin - and Arsenal would play Stoke City.

Paul Trevillion decided that Leeds should release another pop single, but this time the aim would be for it to really impact on the hit parade - and it should be released in time for the semi-final and not, as was customary, just for the final. Caring little about protocol he contacted Les Reed, writer or co-writer of various hits over the years, including Tom Jones' *It's Not Unusual*. Trevillion took only a few minutes to persuade Reed to pen a song for the club and the single *Leeds United*, backed with *Leeds! Leeds! Leeds!*, written with Barry Mason, was released in April 1972. Sung by the players and a smattering of supporters, sales were very healthy indeed and the single eventually peaked at number ten in the charts.

12 iii

By April 1972, we'd sold two of the 'understudy' players - Terry Hibbitt and Rod Belfitt. Both had been great servants to Leeds and it was sad though understandable why they wanted to move on, because they'd get more first team action elsewhere. Hibbitt went to Newcastle for just £30,000 which was a snip, while Belfitt went to Ipswich for £80,000, decent money. There were three League games to play before the April 15th FA Cup semi-final, plus two more within the week after it. No rest for the wicked, some idiots would say. First up was Derby away, on April 1st, 1972. I watched the highlights on *Match of the Day*. There weren't many highlights at all, Derby made fools of us, beating us 2-0, their second goal an embarrassing fluke. Leeds used another kit variation - yellow shirts and socks, blue shorts with a thin yellow stripe down the side. I liked the kit but not the performance.

Top of League Division One table, April 2nd, 1972

1 Derby - played 36, points 51.
2 Man. City - played 36, points 50.
3 Leeds Utd - played 36, points 49.

4 Liverpool - played 36, points 46.

The Wednesday after the Derby defeat, we were back on track with a home 3-1 win over Huddersfield (Jones, Lorimer, Gray). There were over 46,000 there for that one, I was impressed, though it probably had a lot to do with Derby losing on the Monday before, to Newcastle 1-0, putting us back in with a chance of the title. It was a week that *possibly* showed that the Football League wasn't biased or unfair to any specific club, as they treated them all just as crappily. Derby played us on Saturday the 1st April, Newcastle on Monday the 3rd and then on the 5th, they were drawing 0-0 away at West Brom when we beat Huddersfield. That left us one point behind with a game in hand.

On Saturday April 8th, we gave Stoke a bit of a seeing-to with a 3-0 win at their place (Jones two, Lorimer). It would have been a great way to warm up for the FA Cup were it not for Terry Cooper breaking his leg. It was reported as a harmless-enough looking challenge against Stoke's John Marsh, but turned out to be a bad break. By rights, his injury would have given Nigel Davey a chance to take his place except poor Nigel broke *his* leg in a home Reserve game against West Brom as well. Two great Leeds men having their careers just about ruined on the same day, the same way, I felt sick for them.

Hillsborough, April 15th 1972, FA Cup semi-final. Birmingham's striker Bob Latchford, a bit of a bruiser and not a bad goal-scorer, had been talking to the papers, spouting on about how he was going to physically intimidate Gary Sprake in the match. The Don was genuinely worried as Sprake was prone to do something stupid when rattled, but he was more worried about their teenage 'prodigy' Trevor Francis, a real sharp goal poacher, and their winger Gordon Taylor. Luckily for Leeds (but not Sprake) it would be David Harvey playing anyway after Sprake got injured against Huddersfield Town. Harvey wasn't as spectacular a 'keeper but he was brave and reliable, sometimes that's all you need in nets. Don Revie, interviewed before the game, said, 'There's something different about an FA Cup semi-final and until you have experienced it you do not realise what it's like. On the morning of the match, the fact that you are only ninety minutes away from Wembley hits you all of a sudden, it can be a nerve-racking feeling. The tension continues to mount as the morning goes by and hits a peak when you get to the ground. We have been at this stage five times in the past seven years and feel we are well equipped for the big occasion and the tensions. It must be an advantage to us.'

No disrespect to Birmingham who had some good players, but *of course* we had advantages over them - they'd been at home in every round and they hadn't really beaten anyone decent, this was to be on neutral territory (and in Yorkshire) and they were inexperienced in a big way compared to us. We were the first big team they'd been drawn against in the Cup. Our players were instructed to exploit Birmingham's left and right-backs' over-willingness to push forward, which left the defence exposed on the wings meaning our wide men would have more space to float crosses in earlier and not necessarily from the dead-ball line. Those wide men men would be Eddie Gray on the left and Peter Lorimer on the right, neither in need of much telling when or how to whip perfect passes in to the strikers.

Possibly for the first time ever, Leeds wore all-yellow complete with the new sock tags and the newish badge of 'LUFC' old-style writing, while Birmingham wore red shirts (with a wide, white stripe down the front) white shorts and red socks. Before kick-off, City copied our pre-match routine of warm-ups on the pitch, presumably in an attempt to wind up the Leeds camp. It probably worked Ces said, and was the only thing City got right all day. More fool them then. But fair dos, they started the match quite well and got the first shot in, even if it was tame and straight at Harvey in goal. It woke us up - we started to take control. After about twenty minutes. Giles ran with the ball out of our half and passed it forward to Jones. Jonesy laid it off for Bremner on the left-hand side who quickly and neatly switched the ball to our right flank to the overlapping Reaney, a few yards from the corner flag. 'Speedy' Reaney controlled it, and with two defenders blocking his own chance of hitting a cross in, passed it diagonally backwards and inside to Lorimer on the edge of the penalty area. Lorimer lashed in a pinpoint cross for Clarke to head, at the back post. 'Sniffer' Clarke nodded the ball across and in front of City's goal to the oncoming Jones to firmly plant an easy header past the 'keeper. It was clinical, like a technical blueprint drawing put in to motion.

1-0 and I knew then, one hundred per cent, that we were on our way to Wembley again. We scored another in the first half, a well-taken goal from Lorimer himself, feeding on a brilliant long ball from Eddie Gray, and we got a third goal after the break, from

Jones again after Gilesy had beaten three defenders to the ball and somehow stroked a perfect little cross in. The entire Leeds team played well, really well, but I think Jones gave Birmingham the most trouble, they just couldn't handle him.

I watched from the seats with the 'employees' coach load, but seeing how bloody mad and brilliant it was in the Leeds end behind the goal when we first scored, I wished I'd been in with the standing fans, even at the risk of getting shoved and knocked about to kingdom come. The whole day was fantastic and it was a superb performance, almost surgical how Leeds sliced the Birmingham defence apart. So many Leeds fans there too, the whole day pumped me up with pride and good emotion. I got well and truly tanked up in the Peacock that night but four days later we all crashed back down to earth when mid-table Newcastle beat us 1-0 in the League at their place. No excuses, we were a team supposedly chasing the Double so it was a game we should have won, Newcastle had nothing to play for even though they had beaten Derby not long before. We played West Brom three days later and grabbed a 1-0 win there, thanks to a Giles penalty, but I couldn't help thinking we'd blown our chances by then.

12 iv

Although Observer journalist Tony Parson likened a Leeds side without Terry Cooper to gin without tonic, the Whites were able to replace him with another fine international in Paul Madeley. Despite declining the opportunity to join England's 1970 Mexico World Cup squad (in place of Paul Reaney) Madeley had finally gained his first cap in 1971, at right-back, with Cooper playing on the left. Leeds had other fitness worries ahead of the FA Cup final, Giles being the main concern, troubled by a groin injury. And Clarke, Madeley and Reaney had all picked up minor knocks in the 2-0 win over Chelsea the previous week, while Gray probably would not be fully fit. As a precautionary measure in the days before the final, Revie banned even the playing of golf, the players were forced to rest and put nothing at risk.

For the 1972 European Championships qualification stage, England had been paired with West Germany, the victors going through to the June finals in Belgium. The two legs were to be played on 29th April (Wembley) and May 13th (Berlin), so the domestic League schedule was altered to make way for international call-ups. Most First Division clubs were affected, specifically Leeds as they were vying for the Double. The fixture changes meant that they would have to play the Cup final on Saturday 6th May and then finish their Division One campaign just two days later, Monday May 8th. Leeds' two most important games and the destiny of English football's two most prominent competitions, were to be decided within less than three days of each other. Leeds *and* Arsenal asked for their final League game (away to Wolverhampton and at home to Liverpool respectively) to be rescheduled. Football League Secretary Alan Hardaker refused both requests, stating that such a change would harm not only England's preparations but also those of the two English teams involved in the two-legged UEFA Cup final (Wolves and Spurs). That despite those two teams playing the second leg of that final on May 17th, well over a week after the FA Cup final. Hardaker, whose loathing of fellow Yorkshireman Revie was hardly a secret, reportedly offered Leeds a compromise with respect to the England players' commitments. But bearing in mind that he had refused to allow the title decider to be played four days after the FA Cup final instead of just two, 'compromise' seems a rather generous description.

For the FA Cup final, Revie was faced with one of the greatest dilemmas of his managerial career. Both goalkeepers were fully fit, so who to choose, Harvey or Sprake? In the week before the big day, he chose to discuss the quandary with Paul Trevillion. Harvey, Revie said, made every save he ought to, whereas Sprake would make some saves that he shouldn't but then would miss ones that he should too, some of Sprake's saves were beyond Harvey's ability, beyond most goalkeepers' in fact. *However*, Harvey was in a good run of form and had never let his manager down. In truth, Trevillion did not need to say much, Revie would arrive at the correct decision. On the Thursday, two days before the final, Revie took Harvey to one side to tell him that he would be playing in the match. When asked how Sprake had reacted to the bad news, Revie said, 'Gary accepted it. It is all part of the family spirit at this club,' but the reality is that Sprake was stunned at the rejection and did not take the exclusion at all well.

The Centenary FA Cup Final between Arsenal and Leeds United took place on Saturday May 6th 1972. It was the competition's hundredth year but only the 91st actual final due to cancelled competitions during the World Wars. In the Leeds changing room prior to kick-off, Revie spoke to his players passionately and forcefully. He told them not to let themselves down, to be honest and to play to the best of their abilities; they were the best team around and, providing they followed the instructions, they would be taking back to Leeds the trophy which was rightfully theirs. 'Forget Arsenal's strengths, yours are unbeatable!' It was time for the Leeds team to make history, time to prove to the doubters and to those who accused them of losing their nerve, of choking, at crucial times.

'It is never easy to get the better of Arsenal because they are extremely well organized. Arsenal are never more dangerous than when they are pinned deep in their own half. They have the ability to take opponents by surprise with quick incisive counter attacks,' Revie told the media. Those incisive counter attacks almost always involved midfielder Ray Kennedy who had an almost uncanny ability to score crucial goals. However, he would only be named as substitute and so Revie's hopes of winning the Cup gathered even more momentum.

12 v

I'd been to Wembley Stadium before, four years earlier, and that was Leeds versus Arsenal too. Today the teams wore virtually the same kits as they did in the League Cup final. I missed our last Wembley match, v Chelsea, when the Horse (and Cart) of the Year show made the pitch look like the surface of the moon, only with grass on it. This time around it was in beautiful condition and the weather had been alright, with a bit of damp in the air making it a bit slippy but nothing serious. The ground staff there had got their act together this time, though to be fair to them, it won't have been their fault the last time. No, it'll have been the money-grabbing tarts who ran the Wembley show and who never spent anything on improving the facilities for the fans, like the seats or the bogs which were the same as my last visit. At least they'd been cleaned since then though, I think.

On the day I'm sure there'll have been scrapping and trouble between us and Gunners fans somewhere but I never saw any, walking up Wembley Way in the massive throng of thousands and thousands of fans, of both sides. It felt a really good atmosphere - lively, loud, good-humoured - people mixing without any bother, singing and clapping and chanting and waving their banners and flags about. There was some taunting and stuff but it had all been friendly enough. Me, with a white silk scarf round my neck and, would you *Adam and Eve it,* a bright blue waistcoat on plus on each wrist a scarf (both wool and white with blue-yellow-blue bands). I blended in with all the other Leeds fans, mainly because it was like everyone was trying to outdo each other in the wearing your team's colours stakes. It's truly uplifting is walking up that road towards the twin towers with your fellow fans, *Marching On Together,* ready to give as much as you can to help your team win the best trophy going.

As well as proper football supporters going to the game, and the coppers and the vendors and Wembley officials plus poor ticket-less unfortunates begging to buy one, I saw a couple of big time weird blokes as well. Well, they were weird in my book at least, looking like Captain Mainwaring near enough (in his bank manager clothes) with black jackets on, glasses and yep, bowler hats. A fella nearby called them 'God's Squad' and told them to 'bugger off out of the way', waving their placards about, not doing much except getting on people's nerves. The first one was 'SEEK YE THE LORD' in big black print - one of our lot asked which seat he could be sought in - and then a few yards later was another with white print on black this time - 'AFTER THIS THE JUDGMENT'. I just hoped whoever was doing the judging wouldn't be too hard on bad spellers, *judgement* always had two ees in it at my school. At least 'THE END IS NIGH' didn't make an appearance. *Normal* football placards and banners outnumbered the holy ones massively, and probably every type of hat in existence was on show as well, in place of those bowlers. Either in white and blue, or Arsenal red and white, there were flat caps, woolly bobble hats, berets, paper and card helmets and pirate hats, even top hats, everywhere you looked.

And millions of scarves, mainly Leeds ones from where I was looking. SUPER CHAMPIONS LEEDS banners, SUPER LEEDS flags, FA Cups made out of cardboard and silver foil. ARSENAL FOR THE CUP and KING CHARLIE. Leeds rosettes with little silver FA Cups as the centre-piece, blue and yellow ribbons and all within lovely white satin material on the edges.

I watched everything in a state of complete sobriety, not a drop of alcohol had touched my lips. I wanted to stay clear-headed so as to soak in the whole occasion and the sights and sounds and the band and Tommy Steele and *Abide With Me,* and most importantly, I wanted to study and remember the whole match in detail, the tactics and strategies and the moves and runs, all the individual battles taking place on the pitch. But afterwards, after it was all done and dusted, most of the actual match stayed as a blur, no matter how hard I tried to remember it. I might as well have got tanked up before the game, seeing as I forgot so much so easily. One of the beauties of soccer on telly though is that the FA Cup final gets screened live on both sides as well as the highlights shown on the night and on Sunday afternoon so I could re-watch it and then forget it all again. A few weeks later I even bought the LP of the commentary.

Even the advertising hoardings around the pitch add to the occasion for me. Odd, I know. *Gola Sports Shoes* (yellow writing on black) and *Winfield Woolworth* in red on white. *Midland Bank* (white on black), *Norwich Union Insurance*, black on white writing. *Evvaprest Trousers* in light blue on white and *Van Heusen*, whoever they were, big yellow letters on black. *Daily Mirror* (black on white), *Bet With William Hill* (also black on white), *Go Esso... Buy Esso* and *Enjoy Wrigley's Spearmint* (both black and white), *Embassy the best in smoking* (white on red), *Vision Hire Rent Pye TV* (yellow on black), *Rothmans King Size* (more black on white) and *John Player - Champions of Sport* in white on black.

You can hardly hear yourself think when the teams walk out from the tunnel on to the pitch at about quarter to three. Cheers, chants, whistles, songs, horns blowing. The Leeds twelve look bloody great in their white socks and blue tags, white shorts and white tracksuit jackets with the blue collars and trim and LUFC in old style script writing on the chest plus the player's name on the back in blue. What I'd have given to be out there with them, with one of those jackets with my name on it. The shirts are white with crew necks and the same LUFC script badge on the left chest. Arsenal have red socks, white shorts and a less than impressive-looking red training top on. We'd out-dressed them before the match as well, with the Leeds players having specially made to measure suits for the day whilst the Gunners wore whatever casual clothes they liked. And I always thought it was Londoners supposed to be stylish and us oop Northerners the scruffy ones!

The Don leads Leeds out, Bertie Mee his Arsenal, both smartly dressed in nice suits. Don Revie's is dark blue, surprise surprise. If we win the Cup today then Don will be the eighth League manager to have won it both as a player and then as a boss - the list includes Matt Busby, Bill Shankly and Joe Mercer. With the players there's a lot of hair and sideburns on show on both sides, they look like they're auditioning for Mungo Jerry or something, especially Mick Bates who's sub, and Bob McNab, Arsenal's left-back. Peter Lorimer waves to someone in the stand near the royal box as the teams walk out in lines on to the pitch. Jack Charlton had said something along the lines of 'Sod the stupid superstitions, I'm not interested anymore' but here he is last in the Leeds line out on to the Wembley turf. He'll be 37 on Monday, the oldest one in the final, and he'll be marking the youngest, 21 year-old Charlie George.

Leeds United: 1 David Harvey, 2 Paul Reaney, 3 Paul Madeley, 4 Billy Bremner, 5 Jack Charlton, 6 Norman Hunter, 7 Peter Lorimer, 8 Allan Clarke, 9 Mick Jones, 10 Johnny Giles, 11 Eddie Gray, 12 Mick Bates. Arsenal: 1 Geoff Barnett, 2 Pat Rice, 3 Bob McNab, 4 Peter Storey, 5 Frank McLintock, 6 Peter Simpson, 7 George Armstrong, 8 Alan Ball, 9 Charlie George, 10 John Radford, 11 George Graham, 12 Ray Kennedy.

The Scottish lads on both teams seem to get on well with each other, smiling, sharing laughs, whereas none of the other players seem to be talking much at all. David Harvey apparently is the only non-international for us, he's wearing a white t-shirt under his green shirt, and the number one on his back is in a blue, not as dark as the usual team numbers. Clarke and Giles passed fitness tests this morning while for Arsenal, regular goalie Bob Wilson is out injured so Geoff Barnett's playing, I've no idea what he's like as a 'keeper but he's certainly got more hair than Wilson. The players and managers meet Prince Philip on the pitch, the massive royal band troops off. The Queen's in her seat looking down upon the proceedings and looking lovely, even though her outfit and hat is a pastel red. She wore red in 1965 and all. Tory Prime Minister Ted Heath sits a few feet away on her left. I'm surprised he even knows what football is. The teams warm up in their half of the pitch, passing balls to each other or taking shots at the goalkeeper or sending high crosses in for him to jump and catch. This is the moment when Leeds fans warm up their vocal chords too, raucous like. And we sang more and louder than the Cockneys and that's a fact, the TV coverage proved it. 'Leeds! Leeds! Leeds! Leeds! Leeds!', 'Oh when the Whites, go marching in, Oh when the Whites go marching in, I wanna be in that number, Oh when the Whites go marching in!', 'David, David Harvey, tra la la la la, la la la laa.' 'Oh Eddie Eddie, Eddie Eddie Eddie Eddie Eddie Gray!' 'Super Jack! Super Jack!' 'Billy, Billy Bremner, Billy Bremner is our king.'

The Cup final referee is David W Smith and he is being paid fifteen guineas for his afternoon's work. Captains Frank McClintock and Billy Bremner share friendly chat and jokes with him in the centre circle before the coin toss. I'm not sure who wins the toss but the teams keep the same ends and Arsenal kick off. And away we go, the Centenary FA Cup final 1972, Leeds United v Arsenal. Within five seconds there's a foul, by Allan Clarke on Alan Ball. Norman Hunter always said that the first one's a 'freebie' but this was more an accident than anything else, I reckon. Clarke's foul isn't a serious one but it was committed so early you can tell people will be worried the game will be a war and not entertainment. And less than two minutes later McNab chops Lorimer down in what does seem a nasty challenge, the defender missing the ball as if he meant to so he could leave his mark(s) on Lorimer's right shin and ankle. He gets booked for it and rightly so, the tosser. Matters calm down and the match turns out to be fast-paced and keenly-fought. Minor confrontations occur all through the match but that's how football should be, a bit of bite but no malice involved at all.

Eddie Gray has so far been well shackled by Arsenal, or fouled as a last ditch effort to stop him when he's had the ball. The Gunners are terrified of him though he hasn't had much chance to dance yet. Allan Clarke has been marked tightly too but he looks super fit and is striving very hard to get the better of a very good defence. In midfield Alan Ball has been much more involved than

Billy Bremner *and* Johnny Giles, though there hasn't been much threat from him attacking-wise. For us Lorimer has never stopped and looks dangerous on the right wing - McNab has a hard afternoon in store, especially after already being booked. In defence, Norman Hunter has had the better of John Radford while Jack Charlton has beaten Charlie George to every single thing coming their way, by land or air. To be fair to the Arsenal strikers, they haven't been fed one decent pass yet, while Clarkey and Jonesy are always prowling and marauding in our attack, like they're big cats hunting. Frank McLintock looks pretty unbeatable though, I reckon, and Simpson is no slouch alongside him. I think McLintock is Scotland's Bobby Moore.

Twenty minutes or so in, as George gets the ball in our half and quickly passes it, Norman sort of runs into him and concedes a free kick, fifteen yards outside the Leeds penalty area. Ball and George stand over the ball, preparing, or pretending to prepare, to take the kick, discussing their plan. But McLintock jogs up into the fray so Ball passes it short and square to him. McLintock shoots and connects well as his shot arrows in waist-high through a crowd of players into the area, curving at the last instant as it's about to hit the target. The swerve deceives David Harvey and he moves wrongly to his right but then suddenly corrects himself to dive forward and slightly left. He manages to grab the ball, no fumble or panic. It's a good shot and an even better save. Maybe it's not just the ball that he's seized but the moment too, the *day* even.

By the 25th minute, Frank McLintock has beaten Clarke to the ball again and Norman has done the same with George as well. I notice that McLintock likes to support the Arsenal attack, on the wing at times, while for us Gray and Lorimer switch flanks regularly. And we're on the attack again - it's a proper end-to-end match - Paul Madeley at full-back strides forward and links up well with Bremner on the left wing. Madeley dashes to the by-line and manages to get a low but weakly-hit cross into the area past Arsenal's defenders. It rolls gently across the area in front of goal but there are no Leeds players close enough to take advantage.

Half an hour's gone and bar a couple of good touches, John Giles is not having a good game. He looks tired and is possibly limping (left leg) while any passes he makes seem to be hard work for him. And he's given the ball away more than any other Leeds player. Normally you can count the number of mistakes Giles makes in a month of games on one hand - today he's already lost possession two or three times. He might be injured, no he *is* injured, I think Mick Bates should be brought on to give him a rest. There's Monday night's game to think of as well after all. I've noticed other things too, like the fact that the Arsenal full-backs Pat Rice and McNab especially like to go to ground quickly, diving in to slide-tackle or nip our players' ankles from behind. Right from my school days, Mr Hatfield always said the best defenders stay on their feet as much as possible - diving in often gives the attacker the crucial, split-second advantage. Our defenders were a great example of how to defend the best way, and it's the same with Bobby Moore and even Frank McLintock. There's such thing in football as being *too* eager and I think today the Arsenal full-backs are exactly that. Our back five have hardly done a thing wrong in this half, and Paul M has supported the attack even more than Paul R. Madeley looks so composed, so quick and strong, I wouldn't be surprised if he got a goal, even from left-back.

The midfields have just about cancelled each other out, though Ball seems to have got more tackles in and made more ground than all the others. Up front, Jones has been quiet until just after the half hour mark when Lorimer puts in a good cross which Jonah jumps marginally too soon for. He wins the header but the ball flies well over the crossbar. Soon after it's back up at our end - Jack, running towards his own goal but under pressure from George concedes a corner kick. The kick is lofted in and I have to admit, it's a pearler, a pinpoint pass to Ball waiting on the edge of our area. He volleys it, clean as a whistle, low and on target. It's the best effort of the game so far but luckily for us, Reaney is waiting on the goal-line to stretch out his right boot and (just) clear the ball away.

Right back down to the other end of the pitch and we're on the attack now. The more tired certain players get, the more open the play is and the more scoring opportunities occur. Tiredness is even more likely when it's a hot day, like today even though it's rained and is still cloudy. Allan Clarke has run from near the halfway line with the ball. He reaches the edge of the area and a breakthrough looks possible, even with three defenders trying to stop him. Finally he's half tackled and the ball rolls to Jones who swings his left foot at it. It's not the best of connections but is a good, grass-cutting shot towards goal which, even though it's not the hardest of strikes, beats Barnett in goal. Unfortunately for us it beats the goal as well, skimming the outside of his left hand post and going out for a goal-kick. A few seconds later, near the half-way line, Norman is booked for a high and late tackle on Ball who needs treatment from the physio. Norman has probably committed the most fouls so far in the match but that was no where near as malicious as McNab's on Lorimer. The ref probably got it right though and he's having a steady match, he knows that football matches are about the teams, and not him.

We get a free kick eight yards outside the Arsenal penalty area after Clarke is fouled. We shout 'Lorimer, Lorimer', we know he possesses the hardest shot in football, measured at over seventy miles per hour apparently, but it's Giles who's standing over the ball, 'Lash' is a few feet away. Arsenal form a defensive wall and we can see pushing and shoving going on as certain Leeds players join it. Tempers are getting frayed, specifically Charlie George's as he's trying to get at Allan Clarke for sneakily yanking his long hair!

Giles wastes the free kick, weakly skewing the ball as he tries to lay it off square. He definitely isn't the fantastic architect and schemer we know and love today, his pencil's a bit blunt. The kick is easy meat for Arsenal with a defender rushing out from the wall to intercept the pass but somehow the ball goes loose again and bounces to Lorimer a yard or two away. He sends a fizzing snapshot in on goal which bounces awkwardly in front of Barnett who's very nearly caught unawares but he parries it out, just, for a Leeds corner-kick. 'Leeds! Leeds! Leeds! Leeds!' all around again, but the corner amounts to nothing.

Soon after there's more Leeds pressure after McNab slices a clearance straight up into the air. With Lorimer's amazing volleying skills, even though the ball is nearer the corner flag than the goal, Arsenal have suddenly got problems: he whacks the ball in the general direction of the goal. Typically, Clarke has sniffed a chance, ready to pounce, but the ball seems to dip away from him at the last moment. Twisting his body and near crouching, he manages to get his head to it. The header is not powerful but it is on target and it beats Barnett in goal, only to brush the crossbar and then land safely for Arsenal.

It's half-time. Don Revie rushes down the side of the pitch to get back to the tunnel and the dressing room. I'm thinking maybe he's spotted an Arsenal weakness that he needs to explain to the lads urgently. It's been very tight, keenly contested and whilst Leeds have had marginally the better of the chances, Arsenal have possibly had more possession and their central midfield has had a better time of it than ours. The defences have both done really well, with McLintock their best and big Jack well on top for us. There were even chants of 'Charlton for England' late on. You'd never think he was 37, he looks as fit as anyone, and better than most too. I can tell people are nervous around me, there's no lively chatter or laughter and the like, it's more as if people are talking to each other in hushed voices, as if being loud might somehow disturb the team's chances.

I went to the bog but found it very hard to produce anything when I finally got to the urinal, I'm not very good when there are hundreds of blokes milling about in close proximity. I'd have been rubbish in those films they show at the Plaza, I really would.

Second half - the teams switch ends and it's our turn to kick off. Nothing much has changed as far as I can tell - no substitutions or tactical changes. Billy Bremner was about to commence an attacking run with the ball but Charlie George clumsily brought him down. Billy sprang up off the deck ready to have a tangle but then realised it hadn't been a deliberate foul (George being near enough half a foot taller might have had something to do with it as well). Making friends, Billy puts his arm round Charlie with the referee warning the Gunner that no more fouls will be tolerated. Billy's trying to help Charlie keep out of trouble but there's no point, the big long-haired lug isn't listening and is arguing with the referee instead. So the ref books him for being gobby.

Arsenal are playing well now - they're strong and fit and capable of beating most teams but what they lack in particular, in my opinion, compared to us at least, is pace and flair on the wings. We've got Gray and Lorimer, the Gunners don't have anything close, though it has to be said that their defenders have contained Eddie and 'Lash' pretty well so far. There's about fifty minutes gone and it's all so even, difficult to pick a winner. McNab got forward well and ended up getting on the end of a cross in our penalty area but he wasted it, heading into the side-netting which he should have nodded square across goal where a striker would have had a great chance. It's a let off for us, no denying it, though I'm still confident we'll win. Soon after, Clarke loses out to McLintock in their half again, getting his foot to the ball and prodding it clear before Sniffer can control and shield it. The ball runs to Ball in the centre circle, inches from the halfway line. He scurries forward twenty yards and then taps it to George. Ball carries on running, expecting a one-two return from George but it doesn't arrive as Charlton has easily dispossessed him and casually shifts it in to the stride of Madeley a few feet away on our left side. Madeley runs diagonally with the ball, his graceful pace taking him over ten yards in quick time before he strokes a fifteen yard pass with the outside of his right boot to Lorimer in the centre circle. With no opponent near him he has time to suss out his options and who to pass to. Cantering with the ball for ten yards, he decides to knock it, diagonally, to Mick Jones midway in the Arsenal half on the right flank.

Jones seems to idle and dawdle with the ball at his feet just about, making very little progress as Bob McNab blocks his way, waiting to challenge him with another biting tackle. But really, Jones is testing him, gauging the situation, seeing what McNab will do, seeing if he can catch him off guard. He'd do well to achieve that normally, but a sudden burst of action sees Jones running with the ball directly into the penalty area. McNab is no slowcoach and can match Jones for pace, but he makes a mistake - instead of staying on his feet and keeping up with Jones' run, he decides to try and win possession outright with a slide-challenge. He fails to connect enough with the ball though, only slightly scuffing it, nudging it just a few inches. The ball remains in Jones' stride. And even though McNab springs back up from the floor to just about catch up with him again, he is at a disadvantage now. *And* the ball bounces just nicely for Jones as it nears the by-line. McNab puts in another stretching, sliding last-ditch challenge but it's too late, Jones has already hit a dangerous cross in towards the penalty spot. He was quite fortunate that the bounce went in his favour, and McNab told him so, in no uncertain terms. Well bollocks to Bob McNab, he should have stayed on his feet, then he wouldn't have had anything to gripe about.

Two defenders rush out hoping to block whatever attempt on goal the onrushing Clarke makes. 'Sniffer' Clarke, probably the best all-round striker in English football if you ask me, seeing the ball drop more sharply than expected, decides to head rather than kick it. And he throws himself at it, slamming a brilliant, bullet header in to Barnett's left side of the net. The 'keeper got nowhere near it, I doubt any one could have done, it's a fantastic finish. CLARKE, ONE-NIL!

For a few seconds it's almost deafening, dizzying pandemonium where we are and wherever I look, with Leeds fans shouting, jumping about, swaying, hugging, falling, getting back up again (even in the seated bits), waving their, our, colours in celebration. Blue, yellow, white. White, blue, yellow. Yellow, white, blue. Everywhere I look, scarves scarves scarves, flags flags flags, banners banners banners. Multiplied by thousands. Cheers, shouts and cries, a million and more times over! 'We shall not, we shall not be moved, it's like a team that's gonna win the FA Cup… and we shall not be moved!' 'Oh when the Whites, go marching in… oh when the Whites go marching in, I wanna be in that number, oh when the Whites go marching in!' 'Super Leeds! Super Leeds! Super Leeds!'

I didn't see how many of our white shirts ran to congratulate arms-aloft-Allan Clarke but it might have been all of them. I'm pretty sure the green shirt of David Harvey stayed put in his goal, but you never know. And then we supporters get involved again, we get in on the action, hoping to help the Leeds players, hoping to keep them focused and intent on keeping a clean sheet. Do that and we've won the FA Cup, for the first time ever. So up and out it comes, stronger, deeper, louder, harder than possibly ever before - 'Leeds! Leeds! Leeds! Leeds! Leeds!' on and on, pumping, pulsing, almost like it's a war cry, a savage spine-tingling, exhilarating war cry. And all the while the Arsenal supporters stay still, as if they've been stunned into silence.

Things are calming down now, there is still ages to go. I don't even see the ball returned to the centre-circle or Arsenal kick off the game again. But we're singing again, and the longer we sing, the stronger the chances of our hopes becoming reality. 'And you'll never walk alone…' is eventually drowned out by more 'Super Leeds! Super Leeds! Super Leeds! Super Leeds!'

Lorimer nicks the ball off McLintock on the edge of the Arsenal penalty area. He's just about through, it's a chance to make it 2-0. He shoots… and goes nowhere near to making it two as he's been fouled. We have a free-kick in a threatening position. 'Oh my lads, you should have seen their faces, going down to Elland Road to see Don Revie's aces! All the lads and lasses there, all their smiling faces, going down to Elland Road, to see Don Revie's aces!' But the free-kick amounts to nothing, play quickly moves on. Near the touchline on our right wing, Alan Ball is frustrated at not being able to gain possession of the ball. He hacks Bremner from behind, giving Billy's left leg one hefty crack. Billy hits the deck and is definitely hurt, though he may well be playing for time too so as to have a little breather. Ball has walked away but rushes back and tries to drag him to his feet. He's letting his frustration get the better of him and he could be in trouble with the referee if he doesn't watch out. Bremner notices that Ball is more than likely going to get booked so he gets to his feet, grabs and shakes Ball's hand in hope of dissuading the referee from doing it. Ball is a lucky fella, it works. Watching it on the telly later, someone shouts from the teams' benches, 'Let's keep sanity!' It sounds like Revie to me.

Alan Ball and George Graham are still working hard in midfield but rather than making real progress they're more just cancelling out Bremner and Giles. I'm even surer now that Giles could do with a rest and be substituted by Bates, he still doesn't look right. A few yards outside the left corner of our penalty area, Ball passes to Peter Simpson who evades a Bremner challenge and passes to Graham. He quickly switches it back to Ball who takes a couple of scampering steps before hitting a right-foot shot, low and hard. It's going wide though, until it takes a deflection that is and reaches Charlie George. He never needs to think twice about taking a pot shot on goal and, swivelling, he hits a great right-footed shot on the turn which beats Harvey in goal easily, only to thud against the crossbar. The rebound bounces to Simpson but it's too high and too quick for him, as soon as he's hit it he knows he's fluffed it, skying it over the bar.

Maybe Charlie George's bad luck there was to do with him wearing RED football boots. The big girl's blouse. As far as I knew, our very own Terry Cooper was the first to play in boots that weren't black or brown - he started wearing white boots (made by Hummel) a while back, and we all know how much good luck they bloody brought him. George's shot could be Arsenal's last serious effort. They're pushing forward a lot and hitting a load of crosses in but big Jack seems to win every single one of them, it's bloody great. And while the Gunners attack, they leave gaps behind them meaning that we have more territory to exploit. We suddenly get a three-on-two situation but Clarke cocks it up by slicing a left-foot shot high and wide, and then Gray brought a good tip-over save from Barnett a few seconds later.

Ray Kennedy replaces John Radford but there's no sign of The Don making a substitution for us. I don't like it, Giles is almost anonymous now, through no fault of his own, fresh legs wouldn't do us any harm especially when it's a class player like Bates we're talking about. In the 82nd minute Gray is put clear through on goal after a clever little pass from Lorimer. He could pass it to Clarke on his left who's free but instead he shoots at goal and it's weak as soapy water and straight at the 'keeper. In the 85th minute Lorimer shoots from the corner of the area and hits the outside of the post, it probably wouldn't have beaten Barnett but still, while the ball's at Arsenal's end of the pitch it's good news as they can't equalize then.

The ninetieth minute mark arrives and there can't be much to add on either. Norman Hunter intercepts a sloppy Simpson pass midway in our half and sends it to Giles. He returns it to Norman who then jabs a pass out to Jones on the right wing again, not far away from the Arsenal area. He only needs to keep possession of the ball and stop Arsenal from getting it then the FA Cup is ours. And Jonah is aware of this, he knows the game is nearly over, he's heard the shouts from the Leeds bench, he may have even seen the electric scoreboard clock. But maybe he wants to banish any possible suggestions that Leeds United like to deliberately waste time, that they are negative and too professional, whatever that means, and that they're happy as always with a 1-0 victory. Or maybe he senses a chance to score a second and definitely seal the tie. And so he races with the ball at his feet towards the corner of the Arsenal penalty area.

He eludes McLintock by nudging the ball past him, and now he's through on goal just about, though wide of their left goalpost. Barnett rushes out and dives towards his feet, hoping to snatch the ball away. He succeeds, just, the momentum of his frame causing our striker to fall over him, back side first. Jones lands awkwardly, his left arm is twisted and tucked under his body weight. And he crushes his left arm as he hits the turf, emitting a yelp at the sudden terrible pain in his arm and elbow. Barnett shouts an insult, believing he is feigning injury. Jones has *never* feigned injury. Play goes on but Peter Lorimer notices Jones is in a bad way but there is nothing he can do to help.

A minute later and we've soaked up another weak Arsenal attack and have kept possession of the ball, in our half. And then the referee blows his whistle for full time. 'Ee aye adio, we've won the Cup!' Jack Charlton has his arms aloft, he's smiling big time, it's the only major domestic trophy he hasn't won before. Though Clarkey got the goal and Jones set it up brilliantly, big Jack is my man of the match, he's been near perfect. And the proper bloke and proper sportsman that he is, he hugs Alan Ball to commiserate with him. Captain Billy Bremner, with arms bent at the elbows and fists clenched, is also delighted, shaking hands with as many players as he can. John Giles celebrates with Mick Bates, chatting excitedly with him and sharing the moment - Bates still has his tracksuit jacket on, just looks thrilled to be there, he has no qualms about not playing in the match and looks as pleased as any of the eleven victors. Norman Hunter joins them and the three men hug. However, the scene close to Arsenal's goalposts is a completely different story.

Les Cocker, with his small black Stylo Matchmakers holdall to hand, crouches by the prone, distressed Mick Jones. It's horrible to watch, even though you can't see for certain what the injury is. He's lying there, in agony, his face as white as his shirt, and he's whispering to Les Cocker. It's like he saying his final farewells, it's horrible. More and more people are buzzing around Jonesy now - photographers, cameramen, Dr Adams, Wembley stretcher-bearers - and the sodding band troops by him within a few feet! Cocker barks at people to stand back and give them room to breathe, even threatening them to stay away.

On television, David Coleman mentions that Jones could be suffering from a dislocated shoulder – in fact he'll learn later that it's his left elbow that's been badly damaged. Bobby Charlton is briefly interviewed and mentions what an achievement it is for his 37 year-old brother Jack to be winning the Cup and in such a great side. Jack is still walking around the pitch, absorbing the occasion, grinning proudly, but then a photographer informs him that something serious is afoot with Mick Jones, so he runs back across the even more crowded pitch towards the Arsenal goal to find out what has happened. He gets there and, realising it's a nasty injury, he kneels down to comfort Jones while Les Cocker tries bandaging and securing Mick's left arm down to his side. 'M. I. … M. I. C. … M. I. C. K. MICK JONES!' from the crowd.

Clad in a dark grey pin-striped suit, our Dr Adams is helping out. And Don Revie is there now too. The Doc and Les want to take Mick Jones for treatment straight away but Jones, even though he's in excruciating pain, wants to get his medal and meet the Queen. The Don listens to the player insisting he meets the Queen. Revie knows how important this occasion is to a player, any player, and so gives Jones his permission.

David Coleman tells his television audience what a tragedy for Leeds this is, at the moment again of their greatest triumph. They've taken the FA Cup for the first time in their history and yet again, bad luck has struck, what with the First Division Championship to play for on Monday night. They will have to play without Jones, one of the greatest influences in their attacking play… The new FA Cup winners begin to climb the steps to collect their prizes, Jones not among them.

The winning team is Leeds United, and we are the singing, winning, united Leeds supporters - 'When the Whites go marching in, oh when the Whites go marching in…' Billy Bremner reaches the top of the steps to where the trophy and medals presentation takes place, where the FA Cup stands on its ledge, directly beneath Queen Elizabeth and the other regal and not so regal guests. Billy, quite like Bobby Moore in 1966, wipes his right hand on his shirt to rid it of sweat and grime, to make himself presentable for the monarch. Immediately behind him is Jack Charlton, eager to meet the VIP's, anxious to smarten his straggly, thinning hair. Billy walks along the platform, not noticing - or maybe even ignoring - Prime Minister Ted Heath, to meet the Queen. Her Majesty and Our Captain shake hands and she warmly congratulates him. Ted Heath and Jack Charlton act like good old friends and Billy, with the blue 4 on his back to the watching world, takes a few seconds to compose himself and make sure too that everything is in order. And then, grasping the two solid handles swathed in pure-white silk ribbons, he turns around and lifts the beautiful trophy high in the air. It glints and dazzles and captivates. He declares to the watching world - amidst a mighty roar from the stadium crowd - that Leeds United are the 1972 FA Cup winners, in its one hundredth year.

There is probably no need but BBC commentator Coleman guides the television audience through the Leeds players as they each are presented with, in small individual boxes, their awards. 'Jack Charlton receives the Winner's medal and also the plinth.

Johnny Giles the architect of so much of the Leeds play. Paul Reaney who missed the final two years ago, who kicked off the line today. Paul Madeley… Norman Hunter… Eddie Gray… David Harvey, who showed Don Revie to be right in picking him. Peter Lorimer and Allan Clarke the goal scorer, and finally the substitute Mick Bates.'

Bates enjoys the longest audience with the Queen as she asks him about Mick Jones' condition whilst handing over two medals. Over on the pitch, Jones walks with Dr Adams in front of the goalposts with photographers buzzing all over, rushing in front and around them, turning towards them, walking backwards and trying to get good shots of the stricken striker. And then the Arsenal team collect their Losers' medals, followed a few seconds later by the referee and his linesmen receiving their own individual awards, too. Down at ground level, Adams and Jones now stand waiting, not entirely sure of what to do or what they are *allowed* to do. Mick Bates joins them.

Dr Adams desperately does not want to accompany Mick Jones up those steps, he is adamant that he has not contributed anything to Cup Final day and has not earned the privilege of meeting royalty. Eventually, Norman Hunter rushes up in response to Dr Adams' urgent appeals for one of the Leeds players to help Jones. Climbing the steps, leaning over the adjacent waist-high wall, well-wishing Leeds fans stroke Jones' head, gently pat him or applaud and cheer him.

'And in fact Mick Bates has got Jones' medal by the look of it, but Jones will go into football history here at the Centenary Final. Being helped by Norman Hunter to go up and be officially presented with his medal by Her Majesty the Queen.'

Mick Jones later revealed that he nearly collapsed three times in those few minutes of reaching the royal party and dignitaries. As he climbed the steps, his wife Glenis was there with some of the other players' wives, leaning over the wall. Dressed in pretty pink and red but she was in a terrible way too, crying, distraught at her husband's suffering and his ghastly, pale appearance. The Queen clasps his good hand in both hers and apologises for not having his medal. She asks how he is, smiling kindly but probably not really aware of how badly hurt he is. Prince Philip looks on with great concern and then asks Jones if it's his elbow he has damaged. Mick Jones acknowledges.

'M. I. … M. I. C. … M. I. C. K. MICK JONES!'

While the Leeds team minus one pose for photographs, Jones is placed on a stretcher and covered with a grey blanket. Once he's being taken care of in the Wembley treatment room, it will need four doctors to hold him down and re-set his elbow.

'We want Revie! We want Revie!' we cry. The Don stands with Billy, holding the Cup between them for the cameras. 'Ee aye adio, we've won the Cup!' The Leeds-crammed terraces are a shimmering ocean of white, blue and yellow scarves and banners. Our players wave and salute them, this is mutual glory and adulation.

Scant chance for the players to celebrate their Cup triumph was provided though, relaxation and rest being the order of the weekend, as decreed by The Don, something which, not to put too fine a point on it, pissed most of them off a bit. They were professionals after all, and grown men, they wouldn't overdo the partying, they'd have preferred joining their families and friends and the staff to enjoy their success. Anyone would have. So, while the players were being transported to the Mount Hotel in Wolverhampton, the directors and employees were having a celebration banquet at the Café Royal on Regent Street in London's West End. At the Leeds players' hotel, Wolves striker Derek Dougan presented the Golden Boot award to Allan Clarke for scoring the winning goal, two nights later, he'd be doing his best to stop us getting the point we needed to win the League.

Unfortunately, in addition to Mick Jones and Terry Cooper who were crocked and must have been bloody miserable about it, it's likely that one specific Leeds first teamer will have been even more anxious. A few minutes after the Cup final had finished, Don Revie had to tell Eddie Gray that his father had been taken ill, initially with a suspected heart attack. Gray senior was kept in hospital for most of the week for observations. Later that week he'd suffer a relapse. Poor Eddie and younger brother Frank, stuff like that always puts football and the like into stark perspective. Nothing matters as much as family and loved ones, not one single thing.

We only needed a draw to win the Double. England boss Sir Alf Ramsey had apparently given permission to play the Wolves game on the Wednesday night, but without their English contingent. So, excluding Mick Bates who hadn't been capped for England, and

Terry Cooper who was injured weeks before and Jack Charlton who had retired from international duty, we *only* had England players Reaney, Madeley, Clarke, Jones and Hunter. Thanks a bundle Ramsey and Hardaker and the rest of you tossers in charge.

The Division One table before that Monday night.

1 Derby	Played 42	Points = 58.
2 Leeds	Played 41	Points = 57.
3 Man City	Played 42	Points = 57.
4 Liverpool	Played 41	Points = 56.

Like I said, we only needed a draw - we had a better Goal Average than Derby and Liverpool needed to win at Arsenal by a good margin, *if* we lost. The media reckoned it would be straightforward for Leeds not only to get one point but the two points, even so close to a knackering Cup final two days prior. Not me, we rarely did anything simply plus there were other important factors that the media seemed to ignore. For one thing, the players were very tired, as you'd expect. And Wolves' players weren't, they'd had much longer to rest. Mick Jones was out, obviously, while Allan Clarke and Paul Madeley needed pain-killing injections to play, and Eddie Gray was suffering with his thigh problem again, his leg had to be strapped up from knee to groin. In the all white kit together with all the white bandaging, he looked like a Mummy. Wolves were generally tipped to lose the match, pretty powerful motivation on its own if a team has any pride, plus there was the fact that as long as they didn't lose then they'd move up to ninth in the table. We were unbeaten in the League at Elland Road but had lost *eight* out of the twenty away games, and we'd scored 72 goals in the process but only 18 of them came away from home. Very importantly too, in my opinion, was that Wolves still had the second leg of their UEFA Cup final to play, nine days later. The players would be fighting for their places, none of them would dare *not* to play out of their skin and manager Bill McGarry would tolerate nothing but total commitment from his team. And finally, there were allegations Wolves players would be bribed to give Leeds the game.

Those bribery rumours - that Wolves players would be offered money to swing the result - came *before* the match. They were rumours of *possible* dirty deeds, it didn't even make sense; they were rumours about rumours! I wonder if anyone considered that it might be bastards creating the rumours, to unsettle the teams or make trouble. Or maybe it was just another racket aimed at making a killing at the bookies, seeing as Leeds were the clear favourites to get the required result and win the League. Someone somewhere was up to no good yet it was Leeds getting slated and slandered for the unfounded accusations.

On the morning of the Wolves-Leeds match, Bill McGarry gathered his squad together, on the Molineux pitch. He spoke to his players about the rumours of possible bribery attempts, warning them that they must play to beat Leeds, play till they dropped and play as if their Wolverhampton futures depended on it (because they possibly *did*). Anyone not giving their all could leave the club, it was as simple as that. The integrity of the club and its good name rested on their performance in this match, if anything untoward was suspected of them then it could ruin the club.

Course I could well be accused of being biased about it all but my honest opinion is that the only thing ever proven about bribery and stuff was that *if* Leeds really did ever try to fix matches or bribe players then they were totally, seriously, utterly shit at it.

Changes to the FA Cup Final line-up: Mick Bates replaced Mick Jones, slotting into central midfield while Billy Bremner moved up into the attack alongside Allan Clarke; Terry Yorath was named as substitute. I felt even worse for crocked Nigel Davey now, as I'm sure he would have got a chance somewhere along the line tonight as a 'natural' full-back. And how we could have bloody done with Asa Hartford. But regardless of all the selection problems and fixture fiasco, Don Revie's comments after the match summed it all up pretty well - 'I thought we should have had three clear penalties. It was definitely handball twice. It's just too much. When you get decisions like that going against you, what can you do? But I was proud of the team even in defeat. I don't know where they got the energy from in the second half.'

Wolves played well, really well, especially their 'keeper Parkes, but even most of the media seemed in agreement that we'd been badly done to. They took a two-goal lead and Billy got one back for us but despite masses of pressure of near misses, the score somehow stayed 2-1 to Wolves. It was horrible, like receiving all the Christmas presents you've ever wanted and then seeing them all stolen two days later. Liverpool, who only managed to draw 0-0 at Arsenal, must have been kicking themselves too as the League title had been waiting for them to claim it near enough. So, in the end, somehow, Derby were crowned League Champions.

I wouldn't have minded staying in to watch *Star Trek* but I had to work, to help set up and then clear up afterwards. They were expecting a busy night. Fair enough, I thought. The plan was that there was a civic reception in town for the players and then they'd ride on an open-top bus back to Elland Road to parade the FA Cup around the pitch to all the fans. The Queens Hotel in Leeds City Square was the Leeds United focal point again - the bus would set off from there then go along Wellington Street, Gelderd Road, Lowfields Lane and Road and then on to Elland Road and in to the West Stand car park.

The next day the procession and all the celebrations were in the *Yorkshire Post* and made it to *Look North* and *Calendar* on television. None of them mentioned the trouble. Nothing much happened to spoil the party in City Square; well okay, some fans got a bit boisterous, climbing on bus shelters and up the various nearby statues but none of them meant any harm by it, they just wanted to get a better view. On the bus top deck, Jack Charlton is smoking a cig and he doesn't care who sees, other players hang over the sides waving, smiling, catching scarves and hats thrown to them by fans. Poor Terry Cooper's at the back, seated, looking left out a bit and looking as ashen faced as Jonesy had on Saturday. Jonesy's there too, looking quite relaxed oddly enough, with his left arm in a white sling. There were 1,500 fans congregated in City Square, the reports said, and 35,000 at Elland Road. God knows how many more had stood on the pavements to cheer the bus home into Beeston.

Despite The Don's comment - 'I have waited and sweated a lot of years for today but it has all been worth it. This is the second happiest day of my life, the first was when we beat Liverpool to win the Championship' this night was far from as pleasant as it should have been. I have never understood some Leeds supporters. Why the hell they thought it right to cause trouble on tonight of all nights was beyond me. Every football team in the land had 'undesirable' supporters, so it's not as if I was slagging our lot off more than was necessary. Besides, I had more right than most because I had to bloody clear up after the tossers! On normal home match days *you would not believe* the number of empty wallets and purses we have to fish out of the stadium toilets - the Gents' *and* Ladies' - and the signs might well warn 'Beware

Pickpockets!' but it seems they're ignored. Either that or the people who do take notice of them are being robbed when they're reading them.

A mate of mine was on the Kop terraces when the open top bus reached Elland Road. He had his little instamatic camera for the proceedings and one of the photographs in particular is a bit surreal: it's like a tiny, shiny, UFO is floating along Elland Road just inches over the Scratching Shed stand roof. It was the FA Cup itself standing on a plinth on the top deck of the bus. Weird and beautiful at the same time! The radio announcer was cranking up the atmosphere as the team and their prize approached, the supporters were getting more excited, singing songs non-stop, and seeming to name every player who'd played in The Don's Leeds team. And then they entered the arena, on the cinder track surrounding the pitch, with Terry Cooper in a wheelchair, God bless him.

'Here they are, ladies and gentlemen, the one and only 1972 and centenary year FA Cup winners - super Leeds United!' The roar and the applause from the supporters all over the ground, shook the rafters and nearly raised the roof, I swear, even though it wasn't a capacity crowd. But then some of the fans got a bit too excited and decided to, uninvited, join the players. The *Evening Post* said about a thousand had tried to get on the pitch as the players paraded the Cup. I don't think it was that many but who knows? The disc jockey (probably Simon Peters with his Brains glasses) had to warn the fans to leave the pitch or Don Revie would take the team and the Cup off. The threat worked but for some of those who stayed put on the terraces, the occasion was spoiled by idiots thinking they had a right to get closer to their heroes than the rest of us.

There were shop and office windows all around Elland Road that were broken that night, including offices within the stadium. It was barmy, and course it caused a lot more unnecessary work for us over-worked and under-paid ground staff and casuals.

Chapter 13: 1972/3 - The defeated...are the victorious

13 i

May 1974, Andrews speaks to Revie and the watching world: 'You win the Football League and the Fairs Cup, the First Division Championship and one of your proudest moments comes when you make yet another return to Wembley in May 1972, this time as a manager when Leeds United take on Arsenal in the FA Cup Final.' ITV footage of Clarke's winning goal and then the Queen presenting the trophy to the captain of the team, with commentator Brian Moore announcing '...and the Cup goes to Billy Bremner and Leeds United,' to great cheers from the guests in that hotel dining room. 'And tonight of course, that victorious team of yours are here in your audience with your right hand man Les Cocker, the assistant manager Maurice Lindley and the man we saw holding the Cup aloft, Leeds skipper and Scottish international Billy Bremner.' Loud applause and cheering from the Queens Hotel gathering.

Although Revie smiles proudly, it is quite clear he prefers for his players, his sons, to receive the praise and credit rather than himself. The television camera focuses on Billy Bremner, sitting in the audience with his Leeds team-mates and coaches, all suitably attired for the occasion. What a fantastic player Bremner became, thanks largely to the foresight of Revie and the faith he had in the fiery Scotsman. And Bremner gets up from his chair, mistakenly thinking it's his cue to go on stage. Realising his error, he sits back down, embarrassed. Next to him, Peter Lorimer smiles knowingly at another gaffe from the notoriously forgetful team captain.

*

July 1972, Player Details.
Gary Sprake, born April 1945, now aged 27 - unhappy at missing Cup final.
David Harvey, born February 1948, aged 24.
Paul Reaney, born December 1944, aged 27.
Terry Cooper, born July 1944, aged 28 - out injured with broken leg.
Nigel Davey, born June 1946, aged 26 - also out with a broken leg.
Jack Charlton, born May 1935, aged 37 - looking to be a manager.
John Faulkner, born March 1948, aged 24 - has struggled with injuries.
Norman Hunter, born October 1943, nearly 29.
Paul Madeley, born September 1944, nearly 28.
Billy Bremner, born December 1942, nearly 30 - a concern.
John Giles, born January 1940, aged 32 - the main concern.
Mick Bates, born September 1947, aged 25.
Peter Lorimer, born December 1946, nearly 26.
Eddie Gray, born January 1948 - nearly 24, injuries have restricted him badly.
Allan Clarke, born July 1946, aged 26.
Mick Jones, born April 1945, aged 27 - knees aren't good; recovering from dislocated elbow.
Joe Jordan, born December 1951, nearly 21.
Terry Yorath, born March 1950, aged 22.
Trevor Cherry, signed from Huddersfield £100,000 - born February 1948, age 24.
Frank Gray, born October 1954, aged 18. He's not Eddie but has plenty to offer.
Roy Ellam, bought for £35,000 with Cherry - born January 1943, aged 29.

Soon after embarking on his management career, Revie had remarked that the best years for a professional football player '...are between 25 to 28'. By 1972, eleven years later, the matter was becoming more pertinent as each day passed. Player fitness problems and weaknesses increased and of course, age played a part too; naturally, the older the player, generally the less use he is to the team. Revie was the man blessed with the responsibility of deciding the Leeds men's futures, whether to extend or, effectively, cut short the careers of lads he had helped to bring up as his own. It was a responsibility he always hated, and that feeling grew as the end of certain current Leeds players' contracts approached.

Leeds were expected to tear out of the proverbial traps for the 1972–'73 season, fiercely determined to put the record straight and to give all opponents a sound beating. But in fact, Revie's team seemed subdued, almost unmotivated, as if their appetite existed only for the big games, the ones that really mattered. On August 12th, the new season began badly in a tough tie at Stamford Bridge in front of a crowd of over 51,000: Chelsea 4, Leeds 0. The scoreline however did not tell the full story. To begin with the United eleven had lined up without Hunter and Clarke, both suspended, plus the injured Charlton and Cooper. The new signings from Huddersfield came in for the injured duo - Roy Ellam at centre-half and Trevor Cherry at left-back. Ellam was a respected centre-half, good in the air, while Cherry was adept with both feet, and renowned for his hard tackling and versatility in defence. Around ten minutes before the half-hour mark and the score-line still 0-0, Leeds 'keeper David Harvey was knocked unconscious and striker Jones hurt with a twisted ankle, within two minutes of each other. Both needed to be carried off. Terry Yorath came on for Jones while Peter Lorimer went in goal. Down to ten men and a makeshift goalkeeper, with most of the match remaining, the result was just about a foregone conclusion. An Osgood goal put Chelsea 1-0 up by half-time, three more goals before the final whistle.

The upheaval endured by the team in that match would prove strangely ominous for the whole season, with not one Leeds player an ever-present in the side, only Lorimer and Harvey playing in more than forty League games. The team would also have to make do without Cooper for the entire campaign, his recovery complicated by a lack of calcium in his body. Meanwhile, Jack Charlton had been offered a two-year extended contract, but not just in a playing capacity - the club wanted him to help on the scouting and coaching side too, as well as 'spying' on future Leeds opponents. Charlton felt he still had plenty to give the team, playing-wise, and so turned the offer down.

By the end of September 1972, Leeds were not even in the top six. They had played eleven games, won five, drawn one and already lost three. In addition to the Chelsea defeat, they went down 2-3 at Newcastle and 1-2 at home to Liverpool. And the five victories had hardly been vintage Leeds either. During the same month, a *Sunday People* newspaper article insinuated that several Wolverhampton Wanderers players had been offered bribes to 'throw' that infamous Championship decider of last season against Leeds. Two days after that 'exclusive' came another allegation of attempted bribery, with Manchester City's Francis Lee claiming he had been approached before a match against a team fighting relegation, and asked to help fix the result.

13 ii

Another one for my bedroom wall, the **Footie Honours list for 1971-'72**. Half decent it was too. No, half great in fact, but I was fed up of halves.
Division One winners - Derby County, Ripped off runners up - LEEDS.
FA Cup winners - LEEDS, Runners up - Arsenal.
League Cup winners - Stoke City, Runners up - Chelsea.
European Cup winners - Ajax, Runners up - Inter Milan.
European Cup Winners Cup winners - Rangers, Runners up - Dynamo Moscow.
UEFA Cup winners - Tottenham Hotspur, Runners up - Wolverhampton Wanderers.
Football Player of the Year - Gordon Banks, Stoke City.
European Footballer of the Year - Franz Beckenbauer, Bayern Munich.
Leeds crowd average, home games = 35,636.
And only three years to wait for Clean Air.

Even though I didn't know anything about Watergate and I'd never been anywhere near Spaghetti Junction in 1972, this all felt more secretive than Watergate and more confusing than Spaghetti Junction. 'This' being what Ces and John were telling me, as well as a new friend I had by the name of Jim Lister, 'driver of the crown jewels'. Jim had been the players' coach driver for a while but I'd never really met him before. That was my loss too, virtually everyone said it, he was that popular was Jim. Anyway, 'this' is the matter I'd been made to swear to absolute, one hundred per cent, nailed on, sealed lips, mum's the word, watertight secrecy. Because that's what Don Revie had told them to do as well.

In the summer, after last season finished and before new pre-season training started, The Don took the three of them golfing up at the Sandmoor course, as a little bonus for all their hard work, along with a friend of Don's called Peter who was Harry Reynold's daughter Margaret's chap. If that makes sense. I don't know about Ray Hardy, whether he got some sort of gift or anything. I'm sure he will have done, The Don and the club were always generous to the full-timers, and not just with free turkeys for Christmas dinner. The coaches for instance, were given surprise holidays by the Gaffer a fair few times over the years. With this particular round of golf, The Don had much more than the game on his mind at the time, that's obvious, because he'd got the chaps together purposely to ask them their opinions on certain matters. I wasn't told everything but I found out what was worrying Don Revie the most, and that was the renewing of players' contracts. I didn't need to be a genius to work out *which* players, the ages of some of the first teamers and their injury records said enough. I didn't envy anyone having that on their mind, least of all Don.

For the 1972-'73 season, as well as buying Cherry and Ellam from Hudders', there were other new or newish faces coming into the first team squad. Mick Bates would be almost a regular this season, deservedly, plus Terry Yorath, Joe Jordan and Eddie Gray's younger brother Frank quite a lot, too. Jimmy Mann and Chris Galvin were on the fringe again, while young ones Billy McGhie, Gary Liddell and Peter Hampton would get an occasional look in as well. Frank Gray was very handy and had a sweet left foot on him but he was a different sort of player compared to Eddie. Eddie *danced* like Fred Astaire, while Frank was more a Gene Kelly! We signed a blond beanpole Scot too, who had so much hair it made his head look out-sized - Gordon McQueen, a centre-half from St

Mirren, for £30,000. He was recommended by Scottish talent scout John Barr. Funnily enough, Les Cocker had played in the same Accrington Stanley side as McQ's dad, who was in nets. Small world.

From what I saw of him in the Reserves, I thought McQueen had the lot to replace and maybe even be better than Jack Charlton - he was quick, tough, had good ball control for such a big fella, and was superb in the air. I once saw him walking up and down the corridor outside the players' changing rooms, juggling a ball. Somehow, every step he took he managed to flick the ball from that foot to the other at the same time, a bit like really good pinball machine players do with that ball and the flippers. I was no chump when it came to keeping a football up, but this wasn't normal, it was wizardry! The weird thing, for me any road, is that Charlton and McQueen played together in some Reserve games, so maybe he wasn't being lined up as a straightforward replacement for Jack after all. We were lucky to have got him, because he'd had trials at Rangers and Liverpool before joining us. Jack was preparing for retirement, it was obvious - it was a surprise he had any time for playing soccer, what with all his sideline businesses and hobbies. He'd run that souvenirs stall on Elland Road for some time now, opposite the main gates, and since then he'd started a few proper sports shops while the club opened its own sports & souvenirs shop this season.

Certain Leeds players didn't seem as 'up for it' this season, as if they just weren't that bothered, as if winning the FA Cup was their last hurrah almost. Maybe that was it, maybe some of them were bored of winning. Or maybe Don Revie's 'secret' worries about contracts weren't that secret after all, and were affecting player morale. I sort of knew about boredom or lack of motivation, with the St Anthony's side. There's only so far you can go until you get to thinking it's all a bit stale and humdrum, and you need new challenges. You didn't get new challenges in Sunday football, you were lucky if you got new pitch markings. And after the muscle tear in my calf, I'd put on weight again. I couldn't seem to shift it, even when I was training a load of times every week. My body seemed to have accepted the crap fact that my 'career' had gone as far as it could, and so it was going to enjoy itself by piling on the pounds. I still nearly always played well in a really good team but I couldn't take it as seriously as I should have, usually having a few too many pints the nights before games and after as well. Most of our games were walkovers, and there usually wasn't much pressure on me. If I'd been Passy I'd have probably dropped my arse to the sub's bench, giving it a good kick at the same time - the arse not the bench - as it was probably all I deserved.

It took ages for Leeds to properly get going this season, and we went out quite early in the League Cup to Liverpool, plus we looked like we'd caught a cold in the European Cup Winners' Cup, even though it was our first crack at the trophy. We'd scraped through the first round against some Turkish team, Ankaragucu, 2-1 on aggregate, and then made hard work of beating Carl Zeiss Jena of East Germany 2-0. Half the time the Leeds players couldn't seem to get out of first gear. And yet, despite the team's apparent sluggishness and in spite of all the grievances with their less than great form, by the end of November we had 26 points from 19 games and were second, with Liverpool top and Arsenal third. And our next League game was at Arsenal.

Elland Road crowds were slightly down compared to previous seasons, but that was happening all over Britain. The thing is, with the team playing not as well as in previous seasons, plus strikes and money worries and all that crap hitting people's pockets and peace of mind, I think the Leeds attendances - averaging well over 30,000 - proved how loyal the real and true supporters were, not how apathetic the stay-away ones were. I know The Don and the directors forever frothed at the mouth about low crowds, but when times really do get hard for normal folk, we should all be grateful there are so *many* Leeds fans turning up, not so *few*.

Something else was happening at Elland Road from 1972 as well, regarding crowds. It was to do with that film *A Clockwork Orange* directed by Stanley Kubrick. As well as there being a scene filmed outside Leeds University (some of the uni's grounds looked futuristic, apparently) some Leeds fans started dressing up like the mad characters in the flick: long white butcher's coats, bowler hats, big boots and even black make-up round one eye. It all probably sounded daft big time but I guarantee, those lads proper put the wind up people, me being one of them. Not as much as the skinheads did though, whoever's side they were on.

It was said that Stanley Kubrick demanded his film be banned in England because he was sick of all the criticism it got. But in fact it was revealed that he'd stopped it being screened here because him and his family had received death threats and the like due to violent content in the film. I eventually got to see *A Clockwork Orange* and it was alright, and I could see why some people got upset about it. But if you know a film is going to upset you, then don't go and watch it, how hard is that to work out? There was something ironic about people making death threats to a director for making a controversial film.

13 iii

October 1972 proved to be a better month for Leeds - since losing 2-1 at home to Liverpool at the end of September, they had won three League games and drawn one, including a 5-0 thumping of Derby and a solid 2-1 win at Everton. October also spelt the end of one particular footballing era.

Following a car accident and the resultant loss of sight in his right eye, Stoke City and England goalkeeper Gordon Banks announced his retirement. He would stay on as a coach at the Victoria Ground but his playing days had been cruelly cut short due to the crash. *Match of the Day* showed him receiving a magnificent send off by supporters of both teams at the Liverpool-Stoke match. Another goalkeeper was soon to make the news too, with Leeds' unhappy Gary Sprake submitting a transfer request, stating a need for regular first team matches as his reason.

On December 2nd 1972 at Highbury, third-placed Arsenal beat the team in second position, Leeds, 2-1, in a 'blood and thunder' game. Two penalties, one for each side, and a Radford cross apparently palmed into his own net by David Harvey decided the result. Referee Clive Thomas booked five Leeds players, plus Ball of Arsenal, and as a result Revie issued a statement advising that in future he would fine any Leeds player who argued with a referee. Only team captain Billy Bremner would be allowed to approach the referee and ask courteously for an explanation on any decisions. And, as in continental football, Bremner would wear an armband to indicate he was captain.

League Division One table (top), December 2nd 1972.

1 Liverpool	Played 20	Points = 30
2 Arsenal	Played 21	Points = 27

3 Leeds Utd.	Played 20	Points = 26
4 Spurs	Played 20	Points = 23
5 Chelsea	Played 20	Points = 22
6 Ipswich	Played 19	Points = 22

Leeds followed up the Arsenal defeat with a 1-0 home win over West Ham, a 4-0 win against Birmingham, and a creditable 1-1 draw at Old Trafford on Tommy Docherty's debut as Manchester United manager, 23rd December. Allan Clarke's equalizer was an early Christmas cracker for the many travelling Leeds supporters after Ted MacDougall had opened the scoring.

Former Leeds player Freddie Goodwin was in charge of Birmingham when they visited Elland Road that December, his first return to the ground since taking over as the Blues' manager in 1970. The stadium and its facilities had radically changed since his playing days there, including the repositioning of the pitch a few yards towards the north stand Kop. Before, the players' tunnel leading to the pitch had been level with the halfway line but now, as a consequence of the playing field being moved slightly, the tunnel was no longer aligned with the halfway line. Therefore, to some eyes, one half of the Leeds pitch looked bigger than the other. One owner of such eyes happened to be Freddie Goodwin; suspecting foul play and gamesmanship on Leeds' part, after the defeat he issued a complaint to the Football League.

At home to Newcastle on Boxing Day, Leeds had a Jordan goal to thank for settling the hard-fought match in front of over 45,000 spectators. Their seven points gained in December was no mean figure, by any standards, only that Liverpool clocked up ten points in the same period, albeit from one game more. January 1973 saw Leeds go unbeaten throughout, though four of their six games happened to be against the same opposition. Home wins over Tottenham 2-1, and Stoke 1-0, plus a 2-1 away win at First Division newcomers Norwich, gave them six points from the three League games, but two FA Cup replays against Norwich meant they were falling behind in League games played while the threat of fixture congestion rose. They already knew more than any other team about toiling in end-of-season fixture pile-ups, a recurrence was certainly not welcome.

Drawing 1-1 in their first FA Cup third round tie at Norwich, and the Elland Road replay producing the same result, the tie was finally settled at Villa Park on Monday 29th January, with a crowd of over 33,000. Goalkeeper Kevin Keelan had been in superlative form for Norwich but on this occasion, the yellow and green defence was finally run ragged. Billy Bremner summed the match up - 'We did not just beat them, we paralysed them' as a Clarke hat-trick in the first twenty minutes, followed by a Jones strike and a Lorimer thumper in the second half made it Leeds 5, Norwich 0.

*

Sunday, January 28th 1973, the Queens Hotel, Leeds - more controversial behaviour off the field of play, to upset the football world. Or at least the football world of Leeds United. It's another black tie affair at the popular but curious art deco-style hotel, and another banquet of fine food and drink. It's another awards evening, this time the annual Yorkshire Sportsman of the Year dinner which the hotel usually hosts. Famous men there include former Yorkshire and England great, cricketer Len Hutton, born in Pudsey; former England captain and footballing great Billy Wright who is not a Yorkshireman of course but is made most welcome anyway, and Labour's Huddersfield-born current Leader of the Opposition, Harold Wilson. And Middlesbrough-born Brian Clough, manager of Derby County, as a guest speaker.

Peter Lorimer was there to receive an award, his manager Don Revie allowing him to attend the event while the rest of the Leeds squad was in Wolverhampton preparing for their second Norwich City replay, at Villa Park, the next night. Lorimer received the Yorkshire Sportsman of the Year award earlier in the evening, from Harold Wilson, and then departed to rejoin his team-mates in the Midlands. He had gratefully accepted the small trophy, proudly thanked the audience and, with modest acknowledgement, praised the part played by his Leeds team-mates and manager in helping him win such an accolade.

By the time Brian Clough stands up at the long top table to address the privileged audience, Lorimer has long since left. And it is probably a good thing he has. *Clough* believes the audience is privileged, as they will have to listen to him, whether or not there is a feeling of privilege within the audience might be a completely different matter. Clough takes a deep breath, and then begins, with his left hand resting on his waist and his right eagerly accompanying most of his words, index finger animatedly leading the way. 'I have sat here now for approximately two and a half hours and I am *not* replying to anything or anybody until I have had a wee. And I'm being very serious, you get on your bloody feet, you go to the toilet, you get a beer and then, if you've not got to get up early in the morning, get back and *listen.*' And pointing good-naturedly at the people in front of him with that index finger, he sidles his way behind and past the other men seated at the top table, to go to the Gents' WC. It is all fairly friendly and reasonable, Clough's unexpected and perhaps less than respectful behaviour has not offended anyone. Not yet.

A few minutes later he returns. And he feels he has them all just where he wants them, just where they belong - he stands above them all, looking down upon them. He has the microphone and he's about to use it! He is the one they have waited for, so he will entertain them and surprise them, cause a bit of a stir. Not too much of a stir of course, he is just being Brian Clough, he does not necessarily want to hurt anyone's feelings. Talking slowly, drawling as only Brian Clough drawls, speaking with a nasal edge as only Brian Clough speaks, he reconvenes. 'I've come along to pay tribute to sport, I've come along to pay tribute to Peter Lorimer, who I didn't know had the award.' He pauses, like a gamekeeper setting his sights, and he even picks at his teeth for a moment. 'Despite the fact that he falls as many times, when he hasn't been kicked, despite the fact that he protests as many times when there is nothing to protest about...' Groans emanate from the seated audience, along with calls of 'Shut up!', 'Get off!' and 'Sit down!', all topped off with 'You're a disgrace!'

But he loves nothing more than speaking over people, being the loudest voice in the room, having the last word. Not such an unusual trait and probably typical of most football managers in the land, though most would surely choose their moments better. He continues to speak, offhandedly rejecting the objections, calling them 'mumblers' and complaining that the country is becoming a *nation* of mumblers. And he challenges anyone, everyone, to stand on their feet if they have anything to say, and to take his place if they think they can do any better. Claims surfaced later that Brian Clough also told the audience to 'Get off my bloody back, give me a bloody chance' and, finally, to 'Sod off.' A more professional and discreet response came from Clough's 'victim', Peter Lorimer. When informed of Clough's behaviour 'in his honour', he casually dismissed the Derby manager's behaviour as unimportant and that Brian Clough was just being Brian Clough.

*

After February victories over Plymouth Argyle and then West Bromwich Albion, Leeds steadily progressed through to the quarter-finals of the FA Cup. The month was not a good one for their title aspirations though, with a 2-0 defeat at Leicester on the 10th and a home 1-1 draw with Chelsea a week later. Liverpool stayed perched at the top. On March 3rd, Leeds travelled to Derby's boggy Baseball Ground and scraped a 3-2 win, with two penalties from Lorimer included, funnily enough. The following Saturday, another good 2-1 win over Everton gave them the double over the Merseysiders, and on the Wednesday in between, they showed their European pedigree with a 5-0 home win over Rapid Bucharest, a week later sealing the tie with a 3-1 win in snow-covered Romania. It was back to Derby's gluepot on the Saturday for the FA Cup quarter-final. The tie, between the all-blue hosts and all-red 'guests', was predicted to be a classic. Leeds fans weren't complaining at the inaccuracy of the prediction.

One goal settled it, scored in the first half of a tight affair. It came on the half hour mark for Leeds, and came from the one and only Peter Lorimer, a sweet volley after a Jones flick-on. The goal was fortuitous, as Allan Clarke stood offside as the ball hit the net. After consulting with his linesman though, the referee adjudged Clarke as not interfering with play. It prompted the often-asked question - if a player is on the pitch, how is he not interfering with play (especially if he is in the penalty area)? Despite Derby's grievances, Leeds had been the better side.

A 0-0 draw with Wolves, 1-1 with WBA and a 1-0 defeat at Manchester City, meant that by the beginning of April, third-placed Leeds had played 34 League games and earned 46 points while table-toppers Liverpool had played 36 games and won 53 points. The two sides were due to meet at Anfield on April 23rd, St George's Day, in what could well be another title-decider involving the two sides.

April was for Leeds a customary 'make or break' period, and this year continued the trend, with matches against Wolverhampton Wanderers in the FA Cup semi-final and, over two legs the Yugoslavs Hajduk Split in the Cup Winners' Cup semi-finals, plus seven League games, the fifth of which was that trip to Liverpool. A total of ten games within 28 days.

A rare goal from Paul Reaney won the Whites the two points at the Sky Blues of Coventry on April 2nd, to keep them within catching distance of Liverpool. But then came a disappointing 1-1 draw at West Ham and a disastrous 1-0 home defeat to Manchester United four days later. Three days after that, at home to Crystal Palace, first half goals from Bremner, Lorimer and Frank Gray on his full League debut, plus a late sniff from Clarke, earned them an impressive 4-0 win. The title dream was still alive, though only 31,000 and a few score seemed to share the belief. Two days later, on the Easter Monday afternoon, it was first versus third, Liverpool versus Leeds, while second-placed Arsenal travelled to Hampshire to face Southampton.

The first 45 minutes were even, the scoreline 0-0 between Liverpool and Leeds by half-time, but within two minutes of the restart, Peter Cormack put the Reds ahead with an expertly-taken low volley. And late on, a comedy of errors witnessed David Harvey drop the ball twice, the second time landing very nicely for Kevin Keegan to take advantage and finish the match. 2-0 and with main title rivals Arsenal - the only team to beat Liverpool at Anfield this season - only managing a draw at Southampton, bar mathematical improbabilities and a drastic loss of form by Shankly's team, Liverpool were champions. After the final whistle, the Leeds players formed a white 'guard of honour' to congratulate them off the pitch. Liverpool had occupied top spot in Division One for most of the season. In interview, Don Revie sprang no surprises, he knew how to conduct himself in times of both triumph and defeat, even if the sceptics seemed doubtful. 'I am far from broken hearted. Deep down I didn't really expect Leeds to finish top. Naturally we would have liked to have won the Championship but, next to ourselves, I think Liverpool are the side we would most like to see achieve it.' Shankly was also gracious, even in the knowledge that the brilliant white light of Leeds United had shone less brightly in this campaign - 'We have now beaten Leeds three times this season, and some teams haven't managed that in eight years.'

13 iv

And to think that there were people who actually wondered why Leeds fans adored Billy Bremner. Okay, he was suspended too many times but when he played he never ever gave in. He lived and breathed the *Keep Fighting* spirit and I truly believe there was no better captain in football, anywhere, ever. He *was* Leeds United - so what if he was an angel with a dirty face? He was *our* angel with a dirty face. With Billy it was never just football, it was war in the name of sport, with Billy fighting the good fight, the Leeds United fight. Keep Fighting!

This was our fifth FA Cup semi-final in eight years, and we'd only lost one of them, and that was more down to the referee and Cockney gangster bastards. This year's semi-final was against Wolves, the team who had nicked a draw in the League at our place to help spoil our title chances and the team who last season *killed* our chances of the title and the Double, and everything else that went with that crappy Monday night match. This was going to be a bit of a grudge match.

Getting to the final wouldn't be easy, Wolves were doing well and weren't far below us in the table. On the face of it, we were doing well too - third in the League, semi-finalists (so far) in Europe, current FA Cup holders and one match away from the final again - but I knew better, even if I was in the minority of Leeds fans. Quality-wise, we'd had a poor season in my book, and hadn't played well in too many games. Billy scored the winning goal in two of our previous FA Cup semi-finals, in 1965 against Man U and 1970 against Man U again (no wonder their fans hated him). Our Wolves semi-final at Maine Road turned out to be nearly as close as those two, though it was the Whites doing most of the attacking in this one, against desperate defending from the Old Golds. It was a nervy, dead close game, and it didn't take an expert to predict that one goal would settle it. That's exactly what happened, one goal settled it. One goal to us, thank chuff. And when Leeds United win an FA Cup semi-final by the one goal, who always scores it? Aye, Captain Marvel, Billy Bremner, that's who, this time with an excellent left foot half-volley in the penalty box. It wasn't all good news though - Jack Charlton had to go off with a hamstring injury. I couldn't see him playing many more games for Leeds, he was nearly 38 for God's sake.

The following Wednesday was the first leg of our other semi-final, the European Cup Winners' Cup, at Elland Road. We'd been drawn against Hajduk Split - Yugoslavian sides were always hard to beat they reckoned, and these proved it. 'Yogi' Yorath played alongside Norman at centre-half in place of Jack, as Paul Madeley was out injured too. The first leg was tough and had plenty of needle in it, mainly from the Yugoslavs. Allan Clarke was being kicked left, right and centre all night by whichever toerag was marking him - Boljat, however it was pronounced - yet the referee did sweet FA about it. The backs of Clarke's legs will have been a rainbow of colours, he got whacked that many times. But at least he was the one to smack in the winning goal for us. The trouble was, soon after scoring it, he was fouled by Boljat yet again. And badly - Clarke's legs were scythed away from under him this time. Clarke shouldn't have reacted, but he did, enough was enough, and he retaliated by kicking Boljat right in his *boljats* (bollocks, also known as) and then he got sent off for it. And a two European match-ban as a result. Don Revie said he was surprised at him getting a two-game suspension as it was normally just one for a sending off.

We went into the second leg with a 1-0 lead, so only needed a draw to go through. Except, the match was only two days after the Easter Monday Liverpool defeat. Those Leeds players who weren't injured *were* very tired. There wasn't a footballer on earth who wouldn't be done in after two games like that and so late in a season. What a joke it all was.

The Don called the Leeds team's performance at Hajduk Split as their equal finest European display, up there with the 1968 match at Ferencvaros. That had been during happier days for Gary Sprake, when he'd played like a superhero, keeping a clean sheet and winning us the Fairs Cup. We wouldn't have done it without him, everyone said it. Now, with David Harvey in goal, we drew 0-0 and made it to the final of the Cup Winners' Cup, to play AC Milan. But Billy Bremner got booked so he'd miss the final as well. In the run-up to the FA Cup final, we weren't exactly in top form in the League, losing 3-1 at Southampton and then 2-1 at Birmingham, on 28th and 30th April. It seemed obvious to me that Don Revie told the players to go easy in the games as there was nothing really riding on the results and we didn't want any more injuries. We ended up finishing third in the table.

May 5th 1973, FA Cup Final - Leeds versus Sunderland. I never meant to be disrespectful about it, but I'd hardly heard of any of the Sunderland players before. Of course, I knew who their manager was, Bob Stokoe with his silly hat and grubby brown coat that made him look like a part-time flasher, but the players were unknowns just about. *After* the final, well that was to be a different story.

The choice in my house was, watch it on BBC1 or ITV. No contest really, I couldn't stand television advertisements, they just interrupted and got in the way of whatever you were watching, so it was always the BBC for me. Besides, I could watch the highlights of the match on Sunday afternoon on ITV and listen to Brian Moore's hysterics then if I wanted.

As the two teams walked in to the arena of Wembley Stadium, Coleman was on his way and there was no stopping him - 'The sound is absolutely deafening, enough to stir even the most experienced.' Both teams looked dead smart, us in our white zip-up tracksuit tops, white shorts, white socks and brilliant blue and white sock tags. The Sunderland players had on red tracksuit tops over their red and white striped shirts, and black shorts and red and white socks. Coleman tells us that Trevor Cherry is the only team-list change from the 1972 final (at left-back) with Paul Madeley moving to centre-half in place of Jack Charlton. And Cherry is the only non-international in the Leeds side, and that includes our Welsh substitute Terry Yorath. Meanwhile, Sunderland have only one player, Ritchie Pitt (number 6), who has played at Wembley before, and that was as a schoolboy. 'Ritchie Pitt', what a name, it could be Cockney rhyming slang. Nearly as good as George 'Foo' Kinell not so long back for the same team. Coleman didn't tell us that, of course. Meanwhile, Billy Bremner at five foot five and Bobby Kerr five foot four are the smallest captains to appear in a FA Cup final. The referee is Ken Burns.

The skippers meet and shake hands in the centre circle. Kerr wins the referee's coin toss and decides the teams will change ends. There doesn't look to be any affection on show at all between the two captains or their teams, and the Sunderland players look like they are there to enjoy themselves whereas our lads look the opposite just about. In Wembley Stadium there are 45,000 spectators seated and 55,000 standing. The rain drizzles down and it is therefore quite cool on the pitch, with the playing surface looking top notch lush and green but very slippery. The match gets underway, three o'clock on the dot. It's a yellow ball which looks like the normal white gone off. Within two minutes the first foul of the afternoon's committed, Pitt chopping Allan Clarke down, midway in the Sunderland half. It's a bad challenge but 'the first is always a freebie' works for most football clubs and not just Leeds or our Norman Hunter! Clarke needs treatment from Les Cocker while Referee Burns gives Ritchie Pitt a firm talking to. Johnny Giles is set to take the free-kick, with Peter Lorimer hanging around ominously nearby. 'Leeds believe that Montgomery is suspect long range and they're hoping that Lorimer will prove that.'

Giles passes it square to Lorimer who connects well but his shot whizzes low a few yards wide of Jim Montgomery's right post. It's been described as underdog versus giant, David versus Goliath, but when it all boils down to it, it's just eleven men versus eleven men on an energy-sapping pitch, with those 'small fry' Sunderland players looking fresher and more energetic than ours. Without a doubt, Sunderland have had more time to prepare and relax for the big day than Leeds, and the most worrying thing is, they look more determined than us as well. It's fast and frenetic, there's hardly any time on the ball for the players in possession, and every time a man gets the ball, a challenge comes snapping in almost straight away, with the wet grass making the ball hard to control and cocking-up a lot of the passing. 'They're going in really like soldiers going over the top!' referring to Sunderland. There's nothing like melodramatic commentating to add to the occasion of Cup Final afternoon.

Giles has given the ball away more times already than he normally would in a full match, he seems distracted, troubled almost. Leeds look the tenser of the two teams but having said that, David Harvey's not had a save of note to make, while Montgomery has had just one cross to deal with, under pressure from Mick Jones. Although the quality of the match isn't as high as people hoped, it is exciting and end to end stuff. Billy Bremner, fed by a great Johnny Giles pass, puts in a good cross but Jim Montgomery gets there first to punch it well clear. It reaches Trevor Cherry a few yards outside the area. He controls it and sends it back in to Allan Clarke, on the prowl close to their penalty spot. He traps it, shimmies and then taps it away from the marking defenders to line up a clear shot on goal. But then he slips just as he's about to hit it. Sunderland clear it, three defenders lunging in to block and dispossess him. Twenty minutes gone so far, and there's nothing in it.

'There are no lost causes in this Sunderland side, they're chasing everything,' says Coleman. Sunderland are attacking again but Norman Hunter shows proper grace under pressure by classily dribbling the ball out of our area and beating their strikers. 'That left foot qualifies him for the Magic Circle.' There is no let-up, no challenge shied from, no responsibility shirked, every single player on the pitch is trying his hardest and giving it his all. But Sunderland's players have more to give, they're not as tired as our lads. And then Bobby Kerr wins the ball in the Leeds half on the right flank and hopefully punts a high ball into the Leeds penalty area. It's too close to Harvey, standing on his goal-line between the posts. But Billy Hughes is prowling nearby, watching the ball as it drops, watching Harvey as well, waiting for a mistake. He's hanging around like a bad smell, too close for comfort, so when the ball drops in just inches below the crossbar, Harvey has no choice but to tip the ball over the bar. Sunderland have a corner, their first of the match; we've had two so far.

More red and white stripes move up into attack, including Vic Halom and the bruiser centre-halves, Dave Watson and the big Pitt. Both those big sods pose a real aerial threat against us, especially as we've no great header of the ball in defence today.

Hughes takes the corner kick, and he's aiming for Watson. It's a long and high cross which floats over the penalty spot and lands near the edge of our area. Watson is great in the air but Hughes' corner-kick lands too low for his head and the ball just seems to hit his left shin and then bobble away before he can control it. It bounces forward, waist-high in the direction of our goal, in front of Sunderland's Ian Porterfield who's standing side-on to the net. He controls it on his thigh and then swivels to whack a half-volley on goal. He's set it up so invitingly that the ball just begs to be thumped as hard as possible, it's one of those shots that are so well hit that you don't even feel anything as it rockets off your boot. Just like the best golf shots, it just happens, it's pure, it's smooth and it's natural almost. I hate it but it's a great goal, hitting the roof of our net. 32 minutes gone, Leeds 0 Sunderland 1 and I want to puke, I really feel sick and hurt and upset and jealous and evil. The television screen shows all the Sunderland players and supporters going crazy while Coleman's going on and on and on about it.

Half time. I'm just numb and I don't know where the time goes, and then it's the second half. The lads have come out clearly more attack-minded for this half. Coleman's noticed as well - 'And now Leeds appear to be asking the questions.' Allan Clarke jumps for the ball as a cross comes in but he collides with and fouls Montgomery who has caught the ball but then dropped it. Cherry nets but the goal isn't given. Soon after, Bremner darts into the Sunderland area with the ball. He shapes to hit it with his left foot but then cuts in, deceiving the defender who dives in and seems to catch Bremner and swipe his feet away. Bremner hits the deck with a dramatic fall, but it seems to be *too* dramatic for the referee's liking and he waves play on, intimating that no contact was made. Me, I think it's a foul, there might not have been that much contact but there definitely was *some*, Billy couldn't have jumped backwards in that position, there had to be some sort of impact to knock his feet out of the way. I don't care if he did overdo it or if he took bloody acting lessons in his spare time, it was a definite infringement and we should have had a penalty. Jesus, Francis Lee gets penalties in his own half he dives that much. Billy never dived and he wasn't acting.

65 minutes gone and it's all pretty much the same as the first half, every ball fought for, every player grafting non-stop, no chickening out or shirking of duties. How Sunderland are in the

Second Division is beyond me. Leeds are trying to cut loose a bit and there's good build up play occurring, we're definitely dominating the play now even though there's still very little time on the ball. Yorath comes on for Eddie Gray. Eddie's not really been involved throughout. He looks injured to me, even though I don't think he was limping or anything. No disrespect intended to 'Yogi', but he's not likely to create any sparks for us in attack like Eddie can. He can't half tackle though.

Mick Jones receives the ball on the edge of the Sunderland penalty box but he's being tightly marked and so can't turn with the ball as he'd lose it, so he lays it out wide to Paul Reaney on the right flank. Reaney crosses, long in to the area. It's a great pass and the ball is dropping just a yard or so in front of the on-running Trevor Cherry. He brilliantly dives full-length to try and reach it with his head. And he manages it, connecting with the right side of his head - the ball spears towards goal. It's a fine effort and looks like it will deceive Montgomery but somehow he then twists his body to dive left instead of right, parrying the ball out. It rebounds straight to Lorimer standing on the six-yard line. He hits it decently, though it's not a one of his trademark lashes. It's on target and looks like the equalizer, until Montgomery somehow lifts himself off the ground to dive backwards and left. And somehow bloody well reach the shot, pushing the ball up into the air; it hits the crossbar and bounces out. Mick Jones raises his arms in celebration, thinking we've scored, unable to comprehend that Montgomery has actually saved it. Lorimer meanwhile can't believe what he has seen with his own eyes, that his shot didn't go in. Cherry, who dive-headed the first attempt on goal, is still lying on the ground, and as the ball ricochets off the bar it bounces gently towards and *by* him, and he can only wave his right sodding calf at it as the chance trickles away. What drama, what tension, and what a holy pain in the arse, if only he'd been able to get back to his feet.

Five minutes left and the sun comes out, as if the heavens are smiling in approval on the Sunderland team as they close in on an almighty victory. Leeds, pressing forward desperately to get the equalizer, are tiring and leaving gaps at the back which Sunderland try to exploit. Nerves seem to get the better of them though and they waste two decent chances of nabbing a second goal. Regardless, Jim Montgomery's brilliant performance is really what's stopped us getting the goal back, he should have had a red cape on, the bugger. And then the referee blows the final whistle and Sunderland have won, supposedly against all the odds, but that team has battled so well there is no way they belong in Division Two and, even though it makes me sick as a dog to say it, they deserve to win the Cup. There's hardly any difference in class judging by today.

Years later I might be able to watch the match without feeling too bad or sickened, and give credit where it's due (to Sunderland) but on this particular May 1973 afternoon, not only do I really vomit in the kitchen sink but I'm beefing at the same time as well. 23 years old and I'm crying and puking because of a game of football, I bloody well hate Sunderland, I hate 'Porterfield, one-nil!' and I hate red and white stripes even more now. I hate their supporters and I hate Stokoe's lack of sportsmanship after the final whistle, the classless old codger.

Club chairman Manny Cussins was in the royal box along with other 'dignitaries' and rich farts and snobs and he personally congratulated each and every Sunderland player very sportingly as they collected their Winners' medals and the Cup. When it came to the Leeds team getting their Losers' medals, Billy Bremner looked quite philosophical about it all, as if he'd expected it and was thinking 'We gave it our best shot but it wasn't quite good enough on the day' and immediately I felt a bit better about it all - if Billy could take losing the FA Cup on the chin as well as he did, then so could I. Mind you, the rest of the players looked pretty upset, despite Manny Cussins consoling them and trying to lift their spirits. A long time after, Norman Hunter said he thought it possible that the defeat hurt Don Revie more than he ever let on, partly because he was even more worried that the Super Leeds team was close to past it. It sounded a probable to me, not just a possible. Revie himself could well have been thinking along those lines when he made a speech at the after-match banquet - 'It's a bit unusual for me to stand but I feel our players have done enough in ten years to walk in to your applause, even without the FA Cup. We never tried to cheat, we tried to be honest, and I would be less than honest if I did not ask you to salute the most consistent side that ever lived.' That sounded more like a farewell speech to me. He admitted later too, that when all the Leeds guests were leaving the banquet, he'd slumped into his chair and cried like a baby.

Don Revie often cried when he was manager and he hadn't been afraid to cry in front of the players too. He'd seen plenty of harder men than himself in tears, and he felt there was no shame in it. He cried in 1965 when Bobby Collins had suffered that shocking leg-break and he cried after losing to Liverpool at Wembley, he cried in 1970 when Paul Reaney broke his leg at West Ham and when Chelsea beat us at Old Trafford, and he cried again, in 1972, when Terry Cooper broke *his* leg, at Stoke. It was all so much more serious than just losing matches, limbs being broken and careers being damaged, they were lethal blows to the lives and the futures of men he regarded as his own sons. And to think, there were people who said football was just a game, and not an important or meaningful game at that.

Our last League game of the season was the Wednesday after Wembley, at home to Arsenal. I must admit, I was expecting a decent but not spectacular match, but we absolutely slaughtered them, it was like the players were desperate to prove something or even exorcise the ghost of the Saturday past. 6-1 we won, 6-1, against the second best team in the League. Reporters were calling it one of the most important results in Don Revie's reign as Leeds manager, even Revie talked of it that way. Me, 'too little too late' is what I thought it.

There were rumours which were increasing the closer we got to the Cup Winners' Cup final in Greece. At first I thought someone in the media was taking the piss so I asked Ces and John, was it true that Don Revie was leaving Leeds for Everton? Neither of them replied, and that said more than enough for me. John just raised his eyebrows and gave a sad 'Sometimes life disappoints you' sort of smile, and Ces wouldn't even look at me, as if he was too upset for words.

'The city has carped and cribbed, grumbled about admission charges and generally shown itself quick to criticise and slow to praise. Perhaps thoughts like this are passing through Don Revie's mind as he basks in sunny Greece. If so, who can blame him?' is what the Yorkshire Evening Post was saying just a few days later. I don't know which bit annoyed me the most, their blaming the people of Leeds if Don left the club or suggesting that it would be understandable if he did. What a load of crap, on both counts. Okay, so attendances were never as high as we'd all hoped they would be, but those Leeds supporters who turned up week in, week out, always backed the team and the management to the hilt. If he was to leave Leeds, the club he had grown up as a manager with, then he'd need better reasons for doing it; it would be like abandoning the family. *If* he wanted to go then it had to be for other reasons, and the only one I could seriously think of was his stressing out over players' contracts.

Everton were looking to replace Harry Catterick who'd had to retire for health reasons after having a heart attack in January '72. They were cash-loaded, money wasn't a problem, so they assumed Don Revie would be tempted to accept their job offer and be able to take over quickly. They were half right with their assumptions. Tuesday 15th May, 1973, the day before the AC Milan game, Revie was planning on having breakfast at the home of John Moores, the Everton chairman. Moores' home was called 'Freshfields' and Revie, driving in his unmistakable yellow Mercedes, realised he was lost and so called upon a passer-by for directions. That passer-by went yapping to the press. *Don Revie lost in search for Freshfields!* sort of summed it up for me. It was all coming out now, no one knew what to believe. Some reports said Everton were offering him a £50,000 signing-on fee and an eight year contract worth £250,000 before tax. Others were saying that money was an issue, the major issue - to do with government employment rules, the Pay Board and the tax office - companies weren't allowed to pay more wages to new people hired to replace employees who'd done the same jobs.

Not surprisingly I suppose, Revie took plenty of stick from various quarters for his 'lousy timing' and for neglecting team preparations for the match, but to be fair to him, the players did know of his intentions to leave and he'd told them to make the European final a match to remember as it was probably his last as Leeds manager. He'd even told Norman Hunter that if he took the Everton job he would be his first signing.

13 v

BBC Television images appear on screen, of charming monuments and a busy, pretty harbour awash with sunshine and swish white yacht sails. Then, in contrast to the picturesque scenes, the voice of commentator Barry Davies emerges, mentioning a football match soon to be played. Something in his tone is untoward, his voice stern, foreboding even, as if trying to deter from rather than attract the public *to* the coverage. 'Tonight on BBC One at ten-forty, the final of the European Cup Winners' Cup competition, Leeds United versus AC Milan, played in Thessaloniki in north east Greece.'

Most Greeks at the United-Milan match are said to be 'Leeds daft', and a crowd of 45,000 is expected in the new Kaftatzoglio Stadium. It's a big occasion for football and a huge occasion for the people of Greece. They hope to impress the world of football with the friendly reception and fine hospitality and sports facilities. The Greek match referee and his two linesmen are probably anxious to please as well. Barry Davies confirms the team line-ups as the names appear on screen at the same time, each team's players numbered from one to eleven, plus the substitutes at twelve. AC Milan: Vecchi, Sabadini, Zignoli; Anquilletti, Turone, Rosato, Sogliano, Benetti, Bigon, Rivera, Chiarugi. Sub: Dolci. And Leeds United: Harvey, Reaney, Cherry; Bates, Yorath, Hunter; Lorimer, Jordan, Jones, F.Gray, Madeley. Sub: McQueen.

The weather has changed dramatically, while Davies' mood appears not to have brightened at all - dark and gloomy like the evening sky, as if he is there under duress, a sports commentator forced to report on matters he does not want to report. The match *should* come with an X certificate, and Mary Whitehouse, if she watched, would feel there was genuine cause to complain. Viewers are informed that AC Milan could be the first team to win the Cup Winners' Cup twice, and that they are probably their country's League Champions for this season, too, one point ahead with one game to go.

'Whether this was or this wasn't the last match Leeds United played under the managership of Don Revie, only time will tell,' comes Davies' rather unimpressed comment. 'An enthusiastic welcome and a pretty wild night to greet the two teams as they come into the Kaftatzoglio Stadium. It's threatening to rain, there's quite a strong wind and we've had claps of thunder and the odd flash or two of lightning...'

The teams enter the arena, walking on the running track while a nearby brass band plays lively music. Two men in traditional Greek costume walk in front of the two side-by-side, single-file teams. One leads AC Milan carrying the Italian national flag, swaying in the breeze, and his compatriot carries the Union flag aloft in front of the Leeds team. The two lines of footballers bear the national flag of Greece between them, like a huge stretcher. 'Leeds United on the right in their all-white strip, being captained tonight by Paul Reaney.' Reaney is skipper due to Bremner being suspended, along with striker Clarke, and injuries to Giles and Gray and of course Cooper have caused them to miss the match too, and Jack Charlton had recently retired from playing. Conversely, this will be Frank Gray's full Leeds debut in Europe.

'The referee in the centre, Christos Michas of Athens. And the two linesmen both come from Salonika.' It is raining quite heavily, proven not so much by the television cameras but by the frequent, bothersome tip-taps of sizeable raindrops dripping on to the commentary box roof. 'Leeds United battling for a trophy which has been won four times by English clubs... Leeds United in the all-white strip defending the goal to our left. AC Milan in their black and red stripes and white shorts...' In comparison to Milan's shirts, and set against the murky surroundings, despite the floodlighting, Leeds' white shirts stand out brilliantly, almost glowing in the dark. The players consequently look bigger, more muscular than Milan's - the Leeds men are near god-like!

'And as the game gets underway, I suppose one of the questions being asked is how much Leeds United will be affected by the strong rumours of the impending departure of their manager Don Revie from Leeds United to Everton... Here's Norman Hunter, one of the senior professionals who would miss him most... The pitch in very very good condition. '

The opening couple of minutes of the game are keenly contested, played at a quick pace with both teams aiming to play attacking football. In the second minute, near the half-way line, the referee adjudges Madeley to have fouled his opposite number as they challenged in the air to win Vecchi's incoming goal-kick. Not one player on the pitch claimed a foul had been committed, the referee is the only person present to have seen a supposed infringement. Already, protesting whistles sound from the crowd but fortunately, for Leeds at least, nothing comes of the free-kick. Seconds later, Hunter receives the ball and switches the play from the left side to the right with a lofted pass, midway in the Leeds half, to Lorimer, with the time to bring the ball under control before choosing his pass, a low diagonal arrow to the feet of Bates in the centre circle. Bates begins to run with the ball, only to be challenged by the outstretched leg of Sabadini, Milan's number 2. Sabadini fails to reach the football but he does clip the Leeds number 4's trailing foot and Bates tumbles to the floor. Perhaps not done deliberately but Sabadini, nonetheless, has committed a foul and the referee, less than five yards away, cannot miss it.

But 'No free kick given,' states Barry Davies, as the referee waves play on, as if there has been no infringement. Shocked, Bates gets to his feet and protests to Referee Michas who ignores him. And Milan's Benetti escapes with the ball in to the Leeds half. Madeley challenges him but is pushed away by the Italian, illegally. And another foul by Milan against Leeds, another foul dubiously missed by the referee.

Barry Davies - 'Benetti finding Bigon, trying to set himself for the shot...' but Madeley is still in pursuit, and he is too fast and too strong for Bigon, easily overtaking him, causing the Italian to lose control of the ball without being touched, close to the D of the penalty area. Curiously, the referee now sees a foul. 'And the free kick given against Madeley,' declares Davies. 'Well that's the second decision given, one after the other. The first the decision *not* given then the one given. Both of them going against Leeds....' Terry Yorath, with two minutes gone and aghast already at the poor refereeing, remonstrates furiously with the match official while Paul Reaney claps his hands, as if imploring the referee to improve his performance which has been grossly inadequate already. Leeds players hastily form a defensive wall, between where the alleged foul took place and Harvey's goal.

The free-kick is over and done with in short time and the Leeds defence has had little time to organize their wall efficiently. What's more, its component defenders seemed to break ranks just as Chiarugi's direct shot was fired in. Leeds have defended poorly against a well-struck shot which pierces the wall and spears through a crowd of players to smack the base of Harvey's left-hand post and then ricochet into the net. Bad luck on Harvey's part as he saw the ball late and it took at least one deflection on the way, taking it a crucial inch or so away from his desperate attempt to finger-tip it away.

'Three minutes of the match gone and AC Milan in the lead.'

And from the kick-off, Leeds give the ball away almost immediately. AC Milan are on the offensive again, progressing dangerously down the left wing. It's an indication of what a fast, tough and skilful side they can be when they want purely to play football, there ought to be no need for refereeing decisions to assist them.

'Milan really dictating things at the moment. Sogliano is in the middle...' as a dangerous cross whips in to the Leeds area, 'There he is!' but it's just past the far post and is a goal-kick for Leeds. 'Sogliano got up well, he wasn't picked up as he made the run on the near post.' It could easily have been 2-0. 'And Paul Reaney's got a lot to do to lift this Leeds team at the moment... It's always easy to say that one goal counts for a lot but in Leeds' present situation it does count for an awful lot.'

Leeds fight back though and get in to more of a rhythm now, taking the game to their opponents. A Mick Bates free-kick near the Milan left corner flag is passed short to Peter Lorimer. He places a good cross in to the goal mouth, straight to Norman Hunter who has a free header on goal but can only direct the ball straight at the goalkeeper.

As the rain continues to fall, and the number of black umbrellas continues to increase, chants of 'Leeds! Leeds! Leeds! Leeds!' sound from crowd, trying to lift and spur on the men in white. A few yards outside the Milan penalty area, centrally, Lorimer receives the ball again. He has a good, clear sight of goal ahead of him, and he is never a man in need of thinking twice about taking a pot shot. He hits it, on target, low and of course, hard. In goal, Vecchi scrambles on his line and blocks it but he can't keep the ball in his grasp. It rolls a few inches away before he snatches it back securely, and just before Reaney and then Cherry get there. Reaney jumps harmlessly over Vecchio but Cherry, a half second later, arrives in the hope of taking advantage of any handling error. He does not get the ball or even touch it, nor does he make any contact with the goalkeeper. Unwisely though, instead of running back to his position, he stays put to stand over Vecchio, perhaps in hope of intimidating him. It doesn't work, as the calm Vecchio remains on the ground with the football safe and sound in his hands. Cherry's actions however, have seemingly incensed three other Milan players - number 2 Sabadini, 5 Turone and 4 Anquilletti. Suddenly, Turone is the ringleader, cursing Cherry and then kicking him hard on the back of his right ankle, with the referee merely feet away. And then Anquilletti and Sabadini hassle Cherry, threatening him, trying to get him to react as well as incriminate him, waiting for the slightest encouragement to inflict a sly strike or two of their own on him. They tell the referee that Cherry has committed a bad foul. He hasn't. As Cherry begins to walk away, Mr Michas calls him back, to give him a stern talking-to, as well as Anquilletti who pleads absolute innocence.

A few minutes later, blatant cheating incidents occur in the Milan penalty area. Barry Davies needs to watch replays of the events for them to sink in - 'Lorimer doing the protesting bit with the referee... and he's been booked for it... Jordan, who made the break and Rosato nearly fouled him then... Jones, getting pushed and shoved all over the place. He tries to turn. Is he tripped?' Oh yes he is definitely tripped, and gouged, and kicked, and dragged, and barged. Mick Jones endured at least three fouls while in possession of the ball for ten or so seconds, and the referee was there, right on the spot and perfectly positioned, to witness the series of Milan misdemeanours. 'Well he certainly looks as though he was that time...' Davies says, answering his own question. But to the incredulity of players and spectators, referee Mr Michas decrees that not one single foul had been committed within a whole chain of assaults on Jones. And so, soon after, retaliating to the scandal of the refereeing, Yorath inflicts a horrendous, shinbone-jarring foul on Sogliano near the half-way line. His violent reaction is understandable but inexcusable, and he is lucky the referee really did miss it. 'The match at the moment no great advertisement for European football.'

Joe Jordan receives the ball at his feet on the edge of the Milan box. He turns with it quickly, deceiving his marker Anquilletti who stretches a leg out to kick the ball or the man but succeeds in missing both, but he doesn't miss the chance of tugging Jordan's shirt to stop him getting far. The referee does miss that sneaky little foul though. Nonetheless, Jordan has earned himself a chance to shoot on goal. He does so, and had it been on target then Milan would have been in trouble, but he skews the shot yards wide. It's a disappointingly poor effort from the young Scot, after such promising play. Shortly after, a towering and strong Jordan header brings a fine save from Milan's 'keeper. The corner-kick leads up to a left-foot stinger from Lorimer - yes, his left foot - only to see another acrobatic save prevent the equalizer. Seconds later, and a low drive from Norman Hunter outside the area is again well saved, while Frank Gray has a dangerous cross-cum-shot narrowly miss the goal, also.

'Leeds perhaps, missing the knife up front - Allan Clarke.' Early in the second half, the pitch is even wetter and greasier. Leeds take the initiative and attack from the off. Bates slips and misses an opportunity to shoot in the Milan area, he is beaten by rainwater of all things. The next minute, Cherry stumbles in the Leeds half to leave a gap for Milan's Bigon to hit a sharp shot which flies beyond the despairing Yorath but brings about a fine stop from Harvey. The chants of 'Leeds! Leeds! Leeds!' grow in frequency and fervour, the vast majority of the crowd urging the English side to win the final - 'The Leeds supporters who have made the trip - and there are quite a few of them - trying to get behind their team.'

Peter Lorimer has the ball at his feet on the right wing, he jinks and swerves with it, and gracefully slinks and curves through two Italian defenders to strike a rasping shot towards goal. But it fizzes a disappointing few yards wide and doesn't trouble Vecchi.

Not one of the Leeds officials at the side of the pitch is enjoying the occasion. The older Leeds men there have other issues on their minds too, personal, more important issues.

Frankly, their concerns *are* more important than the result of the Cup Winners' Cup final because word has already reached them that the outcome of the tie has been pre-determined. In other words, it has been fixed - Leeds will not be allowed to win. Someone from the media and close to UEFA had advised Leeds officials that the name engraved as 'Winners 1973' on the Cup Winners' Cup would be an Italian team's. And as if that wasn't enough, the confusion over manager Don Revie's career intentions was affecting the Leeds backroom team also. Revie's backroom team, the men who had been with him from the very start of his managerial career, all those years ago, who are now unsure of their Leeds futures and their careers in football altogether. If Don Revie leaves the club, what happens to them? Even Maurice Lindley, normally the most relaxed and easygoing of Leeds men, looks unhappy.

Seated on the bench, Revie grinds his chewing gum ardently but he is tired, irritated, bemused. For all manner of reasons - his mind is annoyingly cluttered. Next to him, Dr Adams has his hands to his face, as if he can't bear to watch any more. Bespectacled Bob English too, expects nothing but bad from the night. Syd Owen stares at the pitch, in a daze, like he is in shellshock. Agitated, nervous Cyril Partridge is furiously chewing too - his fingernails - and disliking intensely this whole sorry affair, hating being there. In front of them, seated on a cushion, Les Cocker can hardly keep still, like he is playing in the match himself. The players out on that pitch are his immediate responsibility, everything else can wait, even his job prospects.

The strong, lanky Gordon McQueen has entered the fray in place of Frank Gray, and makes an impact almost straight away. A free-kick, taken by Hunter, finds McQueen's head and he connects with the ball firmly and on-target. It is so nearly the equalizer but Vecchi contrives to push it out and away for a corner. The corner-kick is safely cleared by Milan but Leeds continue to attack and are awarded another free-kick near the Italian penalty area. Lorimer places the ball on the ground... 'Lorimer prepares to have another crack...' but something has happened in the Milan penalty area... 'And a Leeds player has gone down in the wall.

Quite clearly an incident off the ball... it's Yorath who's down. I doubt very much that the referee saw that, quite frankly because I didn't.'

Yorath appears to have been struck, in the face, by a Milan player. Leeds captain Reaney and striker Jordan try to inform the referee that Yorath has been punched. Yorath sits up, rubs his face, shakes his head while referee Michas brushes off the protests and physically pushes Paul Reaney away. The referee appears more aggravated than the badly done-to Leeds players. Lorimer takes the free-kick and it's a hard, low and accurate shot, but straight at the 'keeper who saves comfortably. Seconds later, back in the Leeds half, as they successfully defend a Milan move, Jordan runs with the ball on the left wing but is tripped by Sabadini in a pointless and spiteful foul. Yorath clips Sabadini's foot to return the favour and Hunter dashes in too to remonstrate with the Italian. The referee books Sabadini.

Gordon McQueen makes a marauding run in to the Milan half, his long strides swallowing up the yards. He looks a fine prospect to replace the great Jack Charlton. McQueen coolly passes the ball to his right, to Reaney on the wing. The captain traps the ball and then tries crossing it into the area - the ball's flight is blocked within five yards, inside the Milan penalty area, by a defender's outstretched arm. It did seem too, as though the defender deliberately handled it and a penalty to Leeds should therefore be awarded. The referee however, indicates it's just a corner. Mick Jones, normally a quiet man who rarely complains to match officials, regardless of the rough treatment dished out to him, rushes up to Mr Michas, animatedly demanding he do the honourable thing and give the penalty kick. But the referee ignores all the protests, from the players and the numerous spectators. The corner-kick floats in and Jones is accidentally floored for his troubles.

'But Leeds have got to keep their heads in this situation, it's becoming a physical battle.' A deflected Mick Bates pass veers across the Milan area, with Jones in close pursuit of it. But his progress is halted abruptly yet again, as an Italian defender hauls him down to the ground, unfairly. The ball goes out of play and

Jones stands up, already expecting the referee to give anything but the penalty-kick. Still, Jones throws his arms up in exasperation and questions the Referee Michas, standing just a couple of feet away. Again the referee pays him no heed and turns his back on the player. Jones' exact words are not known, but will probably have been along the lines of 'Do they need to murder me before you give the penalty?'

It is not all Leeds attacking - in the 85th minute, goalkeeper Harvey stretches and just manages to push a Milan shot wide. Straight back down to the other end of the pitch, Jones controls the ball well, close to the Milan area. He taps the ball to Lorimer inside the box, near the dead-ball line. Lorimer runs at the defender Zignoli, knocks the ball by him and is then brought down by the despairing defender's sliding challenge. Although Lorimer's fall is dramatic, there is little doubt that it is yet another foul against his team and that a penalty-kick should ensue. As the end of the match approaches, Norman Hunter tries to commence another Leeds attack - he beats number 11 Chiarugi to the ball but then feels a stab to his lower left leg - Chiarugi has kicked Hunter with a malicious jab. Despite the nickname, 'Bites Yer Legs' and his being no stranger to hard tackling, Hunter is not considered to be a violent or dirty player, and he is incensed by the Italian's pernicious behaviour. He turns back to run at Chiarugi and then push him. Chiarugi theatrically sprawls away to the floor, as if hit by a knockout punch. He wasn't, he wasn't even pushed with much force. And then, from a few yards away, Milan's Sogliano races towards Hunter and aims a high kick at him. Seemingly overreaching himself though, he falls comically flat on his back on the ground. Mick Bates, one of the mildest of men in football, immediately stands over him, incensed and fists clenched at the ready. Fortunately, Joe Jordan intervenes to steer Bates away from the hotspot. Officials from Milan, Leeds and UEFA enter the stage, trying to get involved, but after a while relative calm is restored and the referee decides to send Hunter and Sogliano off.

A minute or so of uneventful football then takes place while the bemused Barry Davies, with disgust in his tone, remarks 'The two players who were sent off have just shaken hands.'

The final whistle is blown and AC Milan have 'won' the 1973 European Cup Winners' Cup. Any cheers for the Italian side are vociferously drowned out by booing, jeering and whistling from the crowd. 'And listen to what the crowd feel about it, not appreciating in any way the way AC Milan have won this match. The absence of Giles, Bremner and Clarke proving too great for Leeds United who had the will but in the end not the subtlety or perhaps, one should say, the genius to break down this Italian defence. A match which became a physical battle of push and shove, trip and punch, which was no advertisement for football.'

The AC Milan players walk up the stand steps to the platform to be presented with the trophy, the dignitaries and UEFA officials seemingly gushing with praise but with scant applause or cheering from the paying public. 'The cup to be presented by an Italian to an Italian...' and jeered by most of the spectators. 'And it's not being well-received... European football has been done no service by this match... Leeds United now, coming up once again, to accept the runners-up award. They've won the League Championship once, the FA Cup once, the Fairs Cup twice, the League Cup once. But eight times, now nine, have they been runners-up in a major competition during the reign of Don Revie. It must be a bitter feeling for them. 'Super Leeds' says the banner. They've certainly tried their hardest, there can be no doubt about that... but what must they be feeling? Third in the League, runners-up in the FA Cup, runners-up in the Cup Winners' Cup. As in 1970, everything they have tried for has eluded them.'

'But although Nereo Rocco has once again a European trophy in his hands, and it goes once more to Italy, the feeling of this packed crowd in the Kaftatzoglio Stadium in Salonika, is for the Leeds United team. Being applauded there by Bob Roberts, a member of their board - but Leeds United once again finish as runners-up, here in Greece...' The closing shots show the brilliant white of the Leeds team together on the stadium running track, making their way back to the changing rooms. The defeated, in the eyes of the crowd, are the victorious. The pride of the fallen is wounded but not mortally so, in this a bitter-sweet end to a bitter, bitter season.

'And that's it from Thessaloniki, as the whistles greet the referee. And Leeds United doing a lap of honour and getting tremendous applause from this crowd.'

*

Don Revie had declined Everton's offer, or so went the *official* version of events at least. Unfortunately for most Leeds fans, those reports claiming he had been willing to ditch the club did have substance. Following the AC Milan defeat, Revie stayed on in Greece for a family holiday, a holiday occasionally interrupted by business matters involving prospective new employers, but this time those employers were Greek. So now, not only were Leeds fans unaware of Revie's intentions, so were the Leeds chairman and board of directors.

During his visit, Revie had been a guest on the yacht of Nikos Goulandris, the president of Olympiakos FC, while the president of the Greek Football Association was also hopeful of luring Revie's services, to manage the Greece national team - for a salary rumoured to be £20,000 tax free a year. Panathinaikos were also said to be interested and willing to pay Revie £28,000. However, one early June morning, Revie telephoned the club's secretary Keith Archer, from his hotel room, to advise that he wanted to remain as Leeds' manager. Although it was never officially confirmed, he was expected to stay on at Elland Road until the 1979-'80 season. By then he would be 52, the age he had vowed would be his retirement year.

Chapter 14: 1973/4 - Revie was better than them all

14 i

Eamonn Andrews - '...the name Don Revie is known in every corner of the world where soccer is played. In your career you've won a Cup final medal, six England international caps, become Player Of The Year, three times Manager Of The Year, and for your services to football, the OBE.' Rapturous applause and then Andrews introduces more surprise guests: former players of the Middlesbrough Swifts team in which Revie played as a young teen. The Leeds manager meets and greets them all, one by one, exchanging pleasantries, shaking their hands, telling them how pleased he is to see them all again.

Andrews - 'That was Don's team of over thirty years ago. Your team of today is, as we know, here tonight. And skipper Billy Bremner. Billy, you have another surprise for him haven't you?' Bremner enters the tiny stage area, loud applause greeting another hugely popular Scot on this mild late-April evening. Andrews holds the microphone out for the Leeds captain to speak into - 'Well we have a surprise for him Eamonn but the memory like I've got...' he chuckles, 'I've left it down in the safe down the stairs!' amid roars of laughter all around. Andrews, ever happy to pounce on such an opportunity, toys with him, 'The next best thing you can do, as you're a real Scot, is *tell* us what it is!' More merriment.

'Well we thought like, tonight, there were so many honours going on the boss, that we felt that we couldn't be left out, for all he's done for us. So we bought him something that we think will be worthwhile to him. It's a little gold cup and on it it's got TO THE BOSS, THE GREATEST IN THE WORLD, FROM THE PLAYERS AT ELLAND ROAD.' Although Don Revie is more relaxed now, once the initial shock of the surprise party has passed, he still looks uncomfortable and rather embarrassed. Eamonn Andrews however, intends to enjoy himself as well as make the occasion as entertaining as possible for the viewers. And he has more surprise guests lined up.

The signature tune arises once again - 'Fellow managers are here to pay tribute too... Your old friend and great rival Bill Shankly...' The camera follows Liverpool boss Shankly as he walks from his chair near the front of the room, to a huge round of applause, to centre stage with Revie and Andrews. His black dinner jacket looking slightly too big for him, he hitches up his trousers just as he's asked a question. 'Thanks Bill,' Revie says, off microphone.

Eamonn Andrews - 'Now Bill, you're the manager of Liverpool and right now your teams are battling it out for the First Division title. You and Don are great mates.' The famous Shankly growl, capable of sandpapering wood panelling within twelve yards, responds - 'Yes, we're the greatest of enemies,' to loud laughter. 'Again we're battling it out... ay... When the... ay... media talk about flair and skill and things like that, but Leeds United and Liverpool have got more flair and skill and guts than any other team and they're a credit to England.' Now cheers from the audience. 'Don... ay... is a household name throughout the world in football and I mean, you can't take his achievements away from him.'

'How would you sum him up, Bill?'

'Well... ay... he goes down in history as one of the greatest managers of all time.'

Eamonn Andrews - 'What better than that? Thank you Bill Shankly.'

Shankly shakes hands with Revie again, and then kisses Elsie Revie on the cheek before returning to his seat. He raises a hand to the audience in acknowledgement of the fine reception.

Andrews - 'Don, you turned to one man for advice. That man was then Britain's most famous manager.' The programme's theme tune airs once more as Sir Matt Busby emerges through the curtain, met by another rousing reception from the appreciative audience. Busby, former manager of Manchester United, the club Revie openly aspired to emulate all those years ago, is wearing a light brown suit, brown tie, cream shirt with brown stripes, and quite spectacularly large spectacles which could come from the Nobby Stiles range of eyewear. As the applause fades, Eamonn Andrews asks, 'What advice did you give Don?'

Busby is thin, gaunt even, but when he speaks, his strong Scottish voice contradicts his age and build - 'Well actually I started off by saying, if you're going to be a successful manager you're going to have to have a successful team. That was number one...' As he speaks, Revie looks up at him, solemnly, respectfully. '... Can I tell you what Don's first question was? 'Can you enlighten me Matt, about the snags in the game?' And I thought to myself that that's a very good quick thinker - he wants to know the snags before he meets them... I got the tremendous impression that here was a man bursting to build, bursting to succeed and bursting to build a great side. And this, the world knows, Don Revie has done.' Loud applause from the audience. 'And again, in keeping with Bill Shankly - it's a wonder he didn't kick you, Bill, er Don! - in keeping with Bill Shankly, may I say that ... one of the great all time football managers.'

*

The 1972-'73 season saw discipline in football generally decline, and Leeds' record was not at all good - termed 'above average misconduct' - with Trevor Cherry and Norman Hunter being the worst United offenders. In July 1973, manager Revie and chairman Cussins were summoned to a FA disciplinary hearing at Lancaster Gate, London where they were adjudged to have brought football into disrepute for 'permitting players to violate the laws of the game'. The club was given a £3,000 suspended fine - if the team's record did not improve by the new season's end, they would have to pay the fine. A hefty punishment, though not hefty enough for some critics. After the meeting, Leeds called a press conference in which Revie promised that the players' behaviour would improve. Later, he would request that the FA send referee assessors to Leeds' away games as seventy per cent of their bookings last season had been made at opponents' grounds. The club also hired a public relations manager, Peter Fay, to improve their image. Possibly a forlorn hope.

In early August, in customarily forthright fashion, Brian Clough wrote of his disgust at the FA's leniency shown to Leeds - 'The men who run soccer have missed the most marvellous chance of cleaning up the game in one swoop,' adding that he believed Leeds should have been kicked out of Division One and that Revie deserved a personal fine for his part in the club's disciplinary record. Revie ignored the jibes. Meanwhile, the President of the Football League, Len Shipman, called for the return of corporal punishment, specifically public birching - not for Leeds United or Revie but for football hooligans who were increasingly harmful to the game's image.

A new feature in Leeds United match programmes was a 'manager's column' in which the thoughts and opinions of Don Revie would appear. In the Leeds v Everton edition, the first of the 1973-'74 season, he commenced in forceful manner - 'The name of Leeds United has once again been sullied, blackened by critics and writers even before the new season has started. Once again we have been branded by sour tongues, mercilessly lashed by others. We begin our latest quest for success cast in the role as music hall villains... The guns have all been trained on Elland Road. We have become the butt of everyone's bad feeling. At a time when we felt we had at last thrown off that clichéd old tag of being a 'dirty' side, BANG, off go the guns again and we have to run for cover. But then our critics - and what club has had more criticism than us? - have always been quick to regularly point out that our slip is showing. This hoary old chestnut has been roasted and re-roasted so much that we have grown an extra layer of thick skin to combat it... In 1973-4 we will be doing everything in our power to improve our conduct record. The situation is not helped by the fact that ahead of us lie nine months of highly personalized limbo. We live under threat of suspended sentence - a nice situation to be in indeed for the club who have become a household name for soccer success... make no mistake, however physical a team is, trophies are only won in football by sides with skill, flair and artistry.'

Desperate to motivate and win back the affections of his players and personnel, and fans, Revie decided on a new strategy for the team. 'We're going to win the title and we're not going to lose a single game' he declared to the squad. He had said similar to them a few years before but the challenge then, not surprisingly, had been too steep. This time around, he approached the situation differently, primarily because the situation itself was much different now. For one thing, this time he was only interested in winning the League title, and winning it well. He was aware too of the need of fresh ways to motivate the players, due to some of them having been dismissed by the media as too old or injury prone for the team to be a force again, even though most of the side were younger than 30. Combine those player weaknesses, said the sceptics, with Revie's obvious unrest at the club and there you had the proof that Leeds United were on the wane, on the brink. The Sunderland Cup final defeat delivered conclusive evidence that they were finished. The negative press articles went up on the dressing room wall for the players to see, while copies of the less than flattering television pieces were recorded and replayed to them.

It was believed that Revie blamed himself for the Sunderland defeat, because he had restricted the players from playing attractive, attacking football all season. This time around, he was intent on putting it right - 'From now on they have freedom of expression,' he declared. 'I'm letting them off the leash so that they can show the world what they are capable of. I believe Leeds United are as talented a club side as British football has ever seen. Now my lads have my blessing to show what they can do with all that skill, imagination and passing.'

14 ii

The Honours 1972 - '73.
League Division One winners - Liverpool, Runners up - Arsenal.

3rd - LEEDS.
FA Cup winners - Sunderland, Runners up - LEEDS.
League Cup winners - Tottenham Hotspur, Runners up - Norwich City.
European Cup winners - Ajax, Runners up - Juventus.
European Cup Winners Cup - AC Milan, Robbed, ripped off runners up - LEEDS.
UEFA Cup winners - Liverpool, Runners up - Borussia Monchengladbach.
Football Player of the Year - Pat Jennings, Tottenham.
European Footballer of the Year - Johan Cruyff, Ajax.
Crowd average, home games = 35,831.
Clean Air – less than three years.

Honours? That was taking the piss and not subtly either, thank you not very much. There wasn't any honour coming this way last season. We'd been embarrassed, dishonoured, humiliated even, by Sunderland at Wembley and ripped off ultra-dishonourably against Milan in Salonika thanks to that bastard in charge, plus we'd had to endure the prospect of Don Revie leaving for Everton or Greece or bleeding Timbuktu for all we knew. 'Honour' wasn't a word you could associate with Leeds last season.

That corrupt cash-grabbing cockroach Greek referee who'd cheated us out of the Cup Winners' Cup was banned from refereeing ever again *and* he was jailed for match fixing, I heard. I hope he thought it was all worth it, the bastard. So that meant a tiny bit of justice had been done but it still didn't give us our rightful trophy or motivate UEFA in to thinking about awarding it us or banning the Ities from European football. No, did it hell as like, there was no honour within UEFA, that was for sure. It all smelt as crooked as a John Poulson deal but at least you got something for your money with him, his ugly buildings. What did Leeds get for being robbed? Nothing but Losers' medals and sympathy. What sort of bent organization lets a major football final be refereed by the crappest and most crookedest sack of shit you're ever unlucky enough to set eyes on? That's right, it can only be UEFA.

I'm not sure whether the world knew at first of Don Revie's target of going unbeaten in the League but we all knew it at Elland Road, once the players had been informed of course. I'm sure it was more than just an incentive to the players, I'm sure he had other reasons in mind as well. When it had looked like he really was leaving, I must admit it reminded me in a strange way of the spineless slug who abandoned me just after I was born, leaving my poor grandma to look after me completely on her own. Not that I would ever compare that coward with Don Revie OBE, they were miles and miles apart, it's just that I'd been in a state of shock just about, I couldn't believe Don had been set on leaving. I'd even wake up in the middle of the night thinking 'He won't go, he just won't', I was that sappish. Eventually though, I *expected* him to leave, and sooner rather than later, in spite of mentions that he had a contract to stay with the club till round about 1980.

I knew someone who *definitely* would be moving on in the next few years - me, and all the other poor buggers living in the Hoxton streets. The council wrote to us to say that we were all, at some stage or other, going to be shipped out of our homes and re-housed. Our houses were to be knocked down and replaced by much nicer new houses not too far away. Oh, ta very much, do we kiss your backsides now or once we've been turfed out? Like Leeds United in some ways, they had big plans for the city did Leeds council, and that was fair enough. But they should never forget, the both of them, what, *who*, their biggest assets are - it's us, the public, the rate payers, the paying customers, the workers, the voters. Leeds United were going to take their spending on the stadium up to nearly a million pounds by revamping the south end, the Scratching Shed, of the stadium, plus putting up three absolutely massive floodlights. But the main thing that the fans love to see is big money being spent on the team, and that didn't seem to be happening, not really. It was obvious to most supporters that the Leeds first team squad needed strengthening, sooner rather than later at least. There were some great youngsters coming up through the ranks, but not enough of them. McQueen looked good enough to replace Jack, but where were the next generation Billy Bremners and Johnny Gileses?

14 iii

Match 1 - Saturday 25th August, 1973 - Leeds 3, Everton 1, the opening day of the new season, a vociferous crowd of nearly 40,000, a warm sunny afternoon and a rousing performance from the Whites, with Billy Bremner running the show against an unlucky Everton, unlucky because they faced a Leeds team raring to prove something to the football world. With this being Bremner's testimonial year too, the captain was desperate to show the supporters what they and the club meant to him. The new yellow and blue LU badge decorated the Admiral-made Leeds shirts too, some of which were short-sleeved like Bremner's who also wore white sweat bands on his wrists. He opened the scoring in just the third minute, riding one tackle, exchanging a one-two with Clarke and then squeezing through into the box to smash a left-foot shot high into David Lawson's net. The second came courtesy of a Giles medium-range missile with the outside of his foot, and the third from Jones, receiving the ball with his back to goal, flicking it behind him to fool his marker before coolly placing the ball into the corner of the net.

Match 2 - 28th August, Arsenal 1, Leeds 2. Arsenal dominated the first half and took a second minute lead through Blockley but Leeds responded perfectly after the break with early goals from Madeley and Lorimer. Don Revie - 'Having the London supporters applaud us for our second half football was like music in my ears. I have been saying for years we have players in our side with world class footballing skills. People have refused to believe me.'

Match 3 - 1st September, Tottenham Hotspur 0, Leeds 3. This match was effectively over as a contest after just thirty minutes, the first goal coming on four minutes when a Lorimer free-kick was met by the smallest man on the pitch Bremner, unmarked at the near post, to nod it into the net to Pat Jennings' left. Ten minutes later, from open play, Lorimer hit another perfect through-ball for Bremner to run on to and steer home, in off the post. The third goal comes from another defence-splitting cross which Clarke takes full advantage of. After the match, referee Roger Kirkpatrick praised Revie and the team in person, telling the media - 'I had to say something, if this is what Leeds intend to do in every game, on behalf of my fellow referees I had to say thank you in advance. I wish all matches were played in the same spirit.' On a less happy note, Clarke was carried off in the second half with a leg injury.

Match 4 - 5th September, Leeds 4, Wolves 1. A superstitious man might have expected a defeat tonight, given that Don Revie had been laid low with a stomach complaint and Les Cocker with mild blood poisoning after accidentally cutting his foot. Two goals from Lorimer, one a third minute penalty, and one each from Bremner and Jones saw Leeds coast home though. Derek Dougan had made it 2-1 near half-time.

Match 5 - 9th September, Leeds 3, Birmingham 0. Rumours circulated that Terry Cooper's career was over due to the broken leg suffered in 1972, so, as if to quell such talk, Revie arranged for Cooper to present prizes to certain Reserve and Junior players before kick-off. Although he had not played a first team match for over a season, the England left-back looked fit and healthy. Award recipients included Frank Gray, Billy McGhie, Glan Letheran, Gary Liddell, Peter Hampton, plus Byron Stevenson, Derek Loadwick, Keith Parkinson and David McNiven. Revie's programme notes mentioned other lads too, like Bobby Shields, Neil Parker and Billy McGinley - 'These are all boys you're going to hear a lot of in the not too distant future.' In the match Leeds made relatively short work of Birmingham thanks to a hat-trick from Lorimer. Two goals were scored in the first half - one a penalty - and a trademark rocket past City 'keeper Paul Cooper finishing off the very satisfying win.

Match 6 - 11th September, Wolves 0, Leeds 2. The hosts put up a much more resolute display but were undone by the classic 'hammer and blade' partnership, Mick Jones scoring on eleven minutes and Allan Clarke near the half-hour mark in a majestic Leeds display. Leeds' sixth League win in a row, equalling the club record.

Match 7 - 15th September, Southampton 1, Leeds 2. Two more typical strikes from Clarke, one in each half, took the points and broke their record; O'Neill pulled one back for the Saints at the death. *The Guardian*'s John Arlott wrote, 'Wearing the white strip of a blameless life, Leeds moved in a ceaseless flow, back in a packed defence, competing for the midfield, and sweeping forward with backs overlapping. Yet it was all so controlled, almost amiable... so free from the aura of violence they used to generate.'

Match 8 - 22nd September, still unbeaten but the winning sequence is ended in this thriller. Leeds 0, Manchester United 0. Bad news too with Eddie Gray suffering another serious injury causing him to miss the rest of the season.

Match 9 - 29th September, Norwich City 0, Leeds 1 - another gritty display and a well-taken goal from Johnny Giles saw Leeds depart Norfolk with two more points. Giles scoring was perfectly apt as Sir Alf Ramsey had recently called him the complete footballer.

*

In October, Birmingham manager Freddie Goodwin bid £100,000 for former team-mate Gary Sprake. Leeds accepted the bid. Sprake, who had played just one first team match the previous season, felt out in the cold and his resentment was not helped by not yet being offered a testimonial season for his ten years-plus service to the club. In fairness to Leeds, Sprake would not have been the first in line for such a benefit year. The club held a farewell party for him, and Don Revie commented, 'I have looked on Gary like a son,' and would wax lyrical about two incredible Gary Sprake saves - against Ferencvaros and Liverpool respectively - describing them as the best he had ever witnessed. Business is business though, and Leeds sign 'keeper David Stewart from Ayr United for £30,000 the day after Sprake's departure.

*

Match 10 - 6th October, Leeds 1, Stoke 1 - another point dropped though Leeds remain firmly placed at the top of Division One with 18 points out of a possible 20. A 41st minute Jones strike is cancelled out by Stoke defender Denis Smith in the last minute of the match. Burnley occupy second spot, three points behind the Peacocks.

Match 11 - 13th October, Leicester 2, Leeds 2 - the hosts give Leeds a fright in a pulsating battle, leading 2-0 after only twenty minutes through Frank Worthington and Alan Birchenall, but well-taken Jones and Bremner strikes square matters by half-time.

Match 12 - 20th October, Leeds 1, Liverpool 0 - in the 33rd minute a Lorimer cross expertly put away by Jones wins the points against the current champions, in front of a near 45,000 crowd. No Leeds player is enjoying their game more or in better form than Mick Jones, he looks quicker and keener than ever before. Unfortunately, Giles aggravated a long-term calf injury while warming up, it will seriously restrict his first team appearances this season. Coincidentally, he will soon be offered the Eire player-manager job.

Match 13 - 27th October, Manchester City 0, Leeds 1 - no unlucky number thirteen as a rare Mick Bates strike fifteen minutes from time deservedly earns the victory. A corner kick had been headed clear but only to Bates who whipped a right-foot volley straight back in, hard and low, and into the corner of the net.

Match 14 - 3rd November, Leeds 4, West Ham 1. Were under pressure England boss Sir Alf Ramsey to resign, Hammers manager Ron Greenwood is widely tipped to take over. In today's match programme, Greenwood praises Leeds and Liverpool for playing football 'the way it should be played'. Mick Bates hit the first goal with a left-foot snapshot in a crowded penalty area; Jones prodded home the second and *his* second is a deft lob over the advancing 'keeper. Bates caps a splendid performance by setting up the fourth goal with a perfect cross for Clarke to head home. Ted MacDougall scored a late consolation goal for the visitors.

Match 15 - 10th November, Burnley 0, Leeds 0 - a tough match and no love lost between the clubs off the pitch too, due to 'disrespectful' behaviour in the transfer market from outspoken Burnley chairman Bob Lord and manager Jimmy Adamson towards Don Revie and the Leeds directors.

Match 16 - 17th November, Leeds 3, Coventry 0 - 'The last fifteen minutes of the game were sheer poetry, and the third goal was one of the finest I have seen. It began with David Harvey and ten men touched the ball before it went in,' beamed Don Revie. Leeds at their devastating best again, even without Giles, Jones and Gray. Mick Bates involved in all three goals, from Clarke, Jordan and Bremner. Coventry manager Gordon Milne remarked that the season was already just a race for second, third and fourth places due to Leeds' superiority.

Match 17 - 24th November, Derby 0, Leeds 0. Derby are managed now by Dave Mackay following Brian Clough and Peter Taylor's shock departure. Presently eighth in the table, a draw at the Baseball Ground is no mean feat and so Leeds remain in top spot.

Match 18 - 1st December, Leeds 2, Queens Park Rangers 2 - although QPR were a creditable seventh, it's a disappointing result for Leeds who had Jones and Bremner to thank for the one point. Dave Thomas, a Revie target when at Burnley, scored QPR's first (Burnley sold him for less than Leeds had offered) and the enigma that is Stan Bowles snatched the late equalizer. The early kick-off (2-15pm) due to industrial disputes, the government's state of emergency and the energy crisis - affected the attendance, with less than 33,000 there. Leeds need just one more undefeated game to equal Liverpool's record.

Division 1 table (top), December 1st 1973

1 Leeds	Played 18, Points = 30
2 Liverpool	Played 18, Points = 24
3 Newcastle	Played 17, Points = 22

Match 19 - 8th December, Ipswich 0, Leeds 3. All the goals came in the second half of a generally one-sided affair, the first a looping Terry Yorath shot from the edge of the area, sneaking in just under the crossbar. Yorath sets up the second too - a fine right-foot cross to Jones to head in, and the third is a wonderful virtuoso effort from Clarke, dribbling the ball from thirty yards out on the right wing, beating all before him and then finishing with a left-footed arrow. Ipswich manager Bobby Robson describes the Leeds performance as the finest team display he has ever seen - 'Leeds United are the yardstick - Ipswich Town should aspire to better them.'

Match 20 - 15th December, Chelsea 1, Leeds 2. A superb win, and Leeds overtake Liverpool's record of unbeaten games from the start of a season. This scoreline barely skims the surface of Leeds' superiority and even the partisan Chelsea crowd applauds the quality of the Northerners' win. Sir Richard Attenborough, a Blues director, made a special point of personally congratulating the team on their fine victory. Nonetheless, Revie suspects the Leeds team's performances are becoming less fluent, maybe even blasé. Peter Osgood had equalized Jordan's 44th minute strike before Jones sealed the tie in the 68th minute with a superb half-volley from a Jordan knock-down. Many had predicted the match would be Leeds' first League loss.

By this stage of the season, Leeds had been knocked out of the League Cup by Ipswich and, more surprisingly, the UEFA Cup by Portuguese side Vitoria Setubal. Revie though seemed concerned only about the League Championship, and his selection of Roy Ellam, Jimmy Mann, Peter Hampton and Frank Gray for the away leg in Portugal supported the theory.

Match 21 - 22nd December, Leeds 1, Norwich 0. Before kick-off, nearly 35,000 see Billy Bremner presented with a silver salver for his 500th Leeds League game. Terry Yorath notches the all-important goal in the 56th minute. The team display was far from perfect but the win keeps them on course for glory: fifteen wins and six draws so far.

Division 1 table (top), 22nd December, 1973.

1 Leeds Played 21, Points = 36
2 Liverpool Played 21, Points = 29
3 Burnley Played 20, Points = 26

Match 22 - 26th December, Newcastle 0, Leeds 1. Over 54,400 crammed into St James Park to watch the Boxing Day battle, most of them hoping and many expecting Leeds' unbeaten run to end. It wasn't to be, as Madeley slammed home his second of the season with a belter from 25 yards late in the first half to seize the win.

Match 23 - 29th December, Birmingham 1, Leeds 1. A hard but not nasty game with five bookings, City belied their lowly status in the table by giving Leeds a real fright before another

50,000-plus crowd. Leeds are the team most people want to see beaten, purportedly the men they love to hate, but they are usually the main attraction too. Bob Latchford scored City's goal on 21 minutes but a late pounce by Jordan salvaged Leeds a share of the points.

Match 24 - 1st January, 1974 - Leeds 1, Tottenham 1. A holiday crowd of 46,000 sees Jones net for Leeds on 21 minutes to help ensure the fantastic sequence continues, topping Sheffield United's record set in season 1899-1900. Spurs' winger Chris McGrath levels the scores in the 77th minute though Martin Peters was Spurs' main threat throughout. In his programme notes, Revie remarked on the school-leaving age being raised to sixteen and the consequent lack of good young players emerging, while the club announced its plans to replace the Scratching Shed with a luxurious new two-tier stand containing sixteen executive boxes, dining facilities and the like, plus three sky-high floodlights which would be the tallest in Europe and possibly (some said) even the world.

An impressive 43,000 crowd watches the FA Cup third round replay at Elland Road between Leeds and Wolves, with a Jones goal sealing the Wednesday afternoon tie after the 1-1 draw at Molineux the previous Saturday.

Match 25 - 12th January 1974, Leeds 2, Southampton 1. Back to the quest for the title with goals from Jones (21 minutes) and Jordan (55) winning the points against a hard-working Saints side who replied with a late Mick Channon strike.

Match 26 - 19th January, Everton 0, Leeds 0. Another 55,000-plus crowd at Goodison sees a tight game which eighth-placed Everton probably deserved to have won, though there were few goal scoring chances for either team.

Match 27 - 2nd February, Leeds 1, Chelsea 1. A cold and wet afternoon brightened by United's welcome inclusion at left-wing of Terry Cooper, making his first full League start for nearly two years. He had played well in Saturday's 4-1 FA Cup fourth round win at Peterborough and his experience undoubtedly boosted the side in the absence of Eddie Gray. Chelsea stood too close for comfort to the relegation zone but Sexton's men put up a valiant fight and may well have even deserved to win rather than draw. They had taken the lead just before half-time with a header from Bill Garner and fended off the majority of Leeds' subsequent attacks with relative ease, it took a defender to net the equalizer, a dive-header from Trevor Cherry on 68 minutes.

Match 28 - 5th February, Leeds 3, Arsenal 1. Before this Tuesday afternoon game, Billy Bremner spoke of a team meeting in which Don Revie asked the players why their form had dropped, with four draws in the last five games. 'The team wasn't performing professionally enough - we agreed we were a little slack at throw-ins and free-kicks and we were not challenging strongly enough when opponents are in possession.' Arsenal, who were having a mediocre season anyway, were outplayed by an improved Leeds, despite Alan Ball's goal separating the sides at half time. A Simpson own-goal plus two fine goals from Jordan brought the hosts a comfortable win.

Match 29 - 9th February, Manchester United 0, Leeds 2. Over 60,000 saw the second-bottom hosts put up a gritty fight against the table-toppers, emerging with plenty of credit but no points. 57th and 87th minute goals from Jones and Jordan - on in place of Reaney for a matter of minutes - after great probing work by Madeley and Hunter respectively, sorted the men from the boys and left the Reds at the foot of Division One. Now Leeds could relax a little and look forward to their FA Cup fifth round tie at Bristol City next Saturday.

Across the city of Manchester, Leeds were lining up a move for City right-winger/forward Mike Summerbee. However, for reasons unstated, the transfer falls through and Summerbee stays at Maine Road. Meanwhile, Celtic defender David Hay, reportedly also a Revie target, stayed put too.

14 iv

Because of the power cuts, we had to stage the Bristol City FA Cup replay on a Tuesday afternoon. And what a crowd - 47,128 attended. I saw Bill Shankly, sitting in our Directors' Box. Even though he was about my height, he definitely stood out in a crowd. Always did, in any crowd, just like Don Revie. Anyway, I bet Shanks left the ground in good spirits after the Cup replay, seeing as somehow we managed to lose to Second Division Bristol City and went out of the Cup, with our FA Cup tail well and truly flopping between our legs again. Not that Bristol were lucky, because they weren't, they beat us fair and square and by rights probably should have beaten us at Ashton Gate in the first place. Billy had popped up with the equalizer in that one, when we hadn't really deserved it. From absolutely loving the FA Cup just a couple of years before, I now hated the sight of it and wanted nothing to do with the competition any more. There was one saving grace to the Cup matches this term - Terry Cooper got a run out and was looking like his old self again, a silver lining (with white boots on) if ever there was one.

We had been drawn against Hibernian in the UEFA Cup second round, the first leg here late October, and as well as everyone at the club knowing Europe was a low priority this season, low crowds sort of proved it too. Don Revie had said all along that the League Championship was the target and nothing else, even the FA Cup, would get in the way. Winning the League was *the* proof you were the best team, not some or other cup competition. In that respect, I couldn't fault him.

That Hibs game here ended 0-0 which was about the fair result. I don't remember one thing really notable about the match itself, though three or four of the Reserves got to play. For the away leg, The Don intended resting Billy Bremner but 'Chalky' really wanted to play so he could meet up with friends and family up there. And so Revie picked him as sweeper, usually the easiest, least energetic place to play, besides goalie of course (and that was no disrespect to nutters who played in goals). There was a little rumour that some of the Leeds players had money riding on Hibs winning, but we fielded a strong line up, no doubt about that, even with young 'keeper John Shaw playing and then replaced in the first half by even younger Glan Letheran. It was 0-0 again after ninety minutes so had to go to thirty minutes' extra time. Even after that it stayed scoreless so it would be penalties to decide it. And this is where Hibernian made asses of themselves. Not on the pitch or at that specific time but later.

When the penalty kicks were being taken, Don Revie and Les Cocker were on the pitch talking to their players. This, apparently, was against the rules even though the referee didn't seem bothered. So the next day, two Hibs directors only went and flew to Zurich to officially protest to UEFA about Leeds' 'illegal coaching'. I could just imagine the vital, intensive, match-winning coaching given to the Leeds players by our Don and Les - 'Right lads, put the ball on the penalty spot, take a few paces back and wait for the referee to blow his whistle. When he does blow that whistle - listen to me son, because this bit is very important - you run up to that football and you kick it and you make sure it goes in the net past that chap in the goalkeeper jersey who's trying to stop it doing so.' Anyway, we won the penalties 5-4, obvious we won really, those directors wouldn't have gone to all that trouble to complain if *they'd* won. In the next round we were drawn against some Portuguese lot called Vitoria Setubal. It seemed blatantly clear we weren't bothered about getting through, even though we beat them 1-0 at home in the first leg (with less than 15,000 watching). Over there we lost 3-1, and the Leeds players played golf in the afternoon of the match, more concerned about who won *that* game.

The Saturday after the Bristol City FA Cup loss we were at Stoke in the League and two goals up after only eighteen minutes, so it looked like a 'normal service has been resumed' situation. And when Joe Jordan had a goal disallowed for offside – I reckon he was actually *on*side - then it was obvious we were going to chalk up another win and our thirtieth League game without losing, no problem. But, almost straight after the disallowed goal, Mike Pejic pulled one back for Stoke and it didn't take long before they scored again, Alan Hudson hitting the equalizer. To be blunt about it, our second goal from Billy Bremner's quickly taken free kick goal (with no Stoke players ready or even looking when he hit it in) was asking for trouble. It worked, Stoke were riled big time. The second half was a right battle but it wasn't a major shock when Stoke scored again, Denis Smith getting their third about twenty minutes from time. That was it, the winning goal, 3-2 to Stoke. Our brilliant run was over, and people reacted to it like we'd lost a cup final or even been relegated, it was dead weird. I was a bit peed off but I got over it soon enough, after all it was only one match and we were still top of the table by a mile, what was there to worry about?

Well, it didn't matter whether I was worried or not, it was how the manager and the players were feeling that was important, how they reacted to the defeat. Problem was, they *were* worried and all of a sudden it looked like they'd lost their confidence, judging by most of the games after the Stoke one. First there was Leicester at our place, on 26th February - I mean, fair dos, they were sixth in the table so obviously no pushovers, but still, we should have been beating teams like this easily enough. We were one up at half-time from a Peter Lorimer penalty, but we were still edgy, so whenever a move broke down or a shot didn't go in, the players looked less sure of themselves while the supporters, thirty thousand of them, got more and more impatient even though we were still winning the match. Leicester had got a good spirit about them, they reminded me of Leeds in the mid sixties when we were new to Division One - 'side not self' and 'fight together till the end' sort of stuff. Keith Weller in midfield was having a very tidy game and it was him who equalized quite late on. I'd heard that we'd been checking out Weller and might try to sign him - he'd have fit very nicely, in my opinion - he had good skill, looked quick and could hit the ball sweetly.

He was interviewed after the match and said that the Leeds supporters have nothing to worry about, the League title is virtually Leeds' already. Nice of him to say it but you shouldn't be talking like that while Liverpool are anywhere nearby, for chuff's sake! We were still top with 49 points from 31 games, whilst Liverpool were second with 42 points from 30 games. Derby were third but nowhere near really. As long as we didn't lose any more games, I thought, we'd be alright. Draws wouldn't be that bad as long as we won our home games. The big nagging doubt though was the fact that we had to play Liverpool at their place yet - the number of times the League title is decided at Anfield late in the season is bizarre. Whatever that result would turn out to be, there was some good news for Leeds, as Liverpool could be heading for a fixture backlog due to still being in the FA Cup - they were playing Bristol City in the sixth round in fact - and had done better than us in the League Cup too. Didn't take much doing, like.

14 v

On 2nd March, while Leeds United were drawing 1-1 at home with a plucky Newcastle side, Liverpool were beating Burnley 1-0 at Anfield, therefore keeping alive their hopes of retaining the title. Seven days later, as Liverpool were at Bristol City in the FA Cup, Leeds were hosting one of the season's under-achievers,

Manchester City. A Peter Lorimer thirtieth minute penalty proved to be the decider. Despite the penalty award being a controversial one, they were good value for the win and their inability to score a second hadn't been for want of effort. Sighs of huge relief were breathed around Elland Road when the full-time whistle was finally blown.

The match to possibly decide the '73-'74 First Division title outcome would take place on 16th March at Anfield. Liverpool versus Leeds United, the two high-quality heavyweights of the English game. Lose or even draw and Liverpool could probably wave farewell to the Championship trophy. Not that they or their supporters were in any such defeatist mood, and with a fervent crowd of 56,003 watching the match, the home side had most of the possession. Ultimately, the tie needed just one goal to settle it, arriving in the 82nd minute with Steve Heighway exploiting confusion in the Leeds penalty area. After the match, Billy Bremner said, 'We planned to attack but Liverpool's pressure was so great we just could not get going. In short we were cuffed and we deserved to be.' The gap in the table had narrowed again.

Division 1 table (top), 16th March 1974.

1 Leeds Utd.	Played 34	Points = 52
2 Liverpool	Played 32	Points = 46

On 23rd March, Leeds were at home to Burnley while Liverpool were visiting Wolverhampton Wanderers. Relations between Leeds and Burnley were already strained, to put it mildly, and subsequent comments from Burnley chairman Bob Lord merely exacerbated the matter. During financial negotiations between the Football League and television companies over screen rights and pricing, Lord - never one afraid of being outspoken - had said, 'We have to stand up against a move to get soccer on the cheap by the Jews who run television.' As a consequence of the remark, Leeds' Jewish chairman Manny Cussins responded by banning Lord and his directors from Elland Road unless an apology was issued. No apology arrived, and the Burnley board claimed they were boycotting the game anyway. A gesture they might well have regretted, seeing as the team went on to trounce Leeds 4-1.

Brian James of the *Sunday Times* accurately summed up the match - 'Leeds were haunted by doubt, undermined by misunderstandings... their reputation was on the verge of destruction.' Burnley had taken advantage of a sluggish all-round Leeds display and inept defending, and whilst it was a shock result, it was a thoroughly deserved win nonetheless. Worse for Leeds was Liverpool's 1-0 victory at Wolves, thanks to a first half Brian Hall goal.

Division 1 table (top), 23rd March, 1974.

1 Leeds Played 35, Points = 52
2 Liverpool Played 33, Points = 48

For the match at West Ham on 30th March, Revie made a surprise change to the line-up by dropping Peter Lorimer and replacing him with less than fully fit John Giles. The change looked to be working for the better as Leeds took the lead on 32 minutes through Allan Clarke. A few minutes later and Clarke had an apparently fair goal ruled out for offside. He earned himself a booking for arguing about it. In the second half, the hosts bucked up their ideas and scored the equalizer through Clyde Best on 49 minutes, then goals from 'Pop' Robson just past the hour and finally Trevor Brooking in the 85th minute meant another disturbing and depressing defeat for the Peacocks. Liverpool could now leapfrog them but after the match Revie, perhaps with more optimism than realism, remarked, 'I had the feeling that we turned the corner at Upton Park. We gave one of our best performances of the season, particularly in the first half, and we only had ourselves to blame for the goals we conceded.'

Four days later, England had a friendly international against Portugal scheduled. To the chagrin of manager Ramsey and the FA, Revie withdrew Paul Madeley and Norman Hunter from the squad, not wanting to risk the already tired players getting injured, especially for a match of scant importance. Both players appeared in Leeds' next match on the Saturday against Dave Mackay's Derby County.

Revie's optimism after the West Ham defeat was justified after all, his side putting in a decent performance to see off third-placed Derby 2-0. The Leeds players seemed more relaxed, especially after the rejuvenated Lorimer opened the scoring with a lob over 'keeper Colin Boulton in the 17th minute. It was his first goal from open play since September. Their second came after half-time, Bremner volleying home a poorly headed clearance. Not the most spectacular of strikes but delivered with perfect technique by the Leeds skipper. It is possible that Mackay's pre-match comments were more a help than a hindrance to Revie's cause. Almost as if reciting from the Clough book of tact and diplomacy, he remarked, 'Leeds have something of an inferiority complex because of missing out on so many trophies in the final weeks of the season, and I think we can win.' No let up in the race for the crown though, with Liverpool beating QPR 2-1 at Anfield on the same afternoon.

Leeds could rest for six days now as their next match was away at Coventry on Saturday 13th April. Liverpool meanwhile, were away to Ipswich Town on that date, plus they had games at Sheffield United and away to Manchester City before it, almost incredibly the City game taking place on Good Friday, 12th April, 24 hours before the Ipswich game.

Joe Jordan, Gordon McQueen and David Harvey - a trio of Scotsmen even though Yorkshireman Harvey had a distinctly un-Scottish accent - had a good feeling about Liverpool's match at Sheffield United, so good that they attended as spectators. They had an even better feeling afterwards, having watched the Blades win 1-0. And Good Friday brought more favour Leeds' way as Liverpool only drew with Manchester City 1-1 at Maine Road. And the day after that, Ipswich earned a point against the Reds with the same score-line, while Leeds drew at Coventry, 0-0. Leeds could and possibly should have won it but in the end they were thankful to come away with a share of the points as Coventry began to dominate the later stages.

Division 1 table (top), 13th April, 1974.

1 Leeds	Played 38, Points = 55
2 Liverpool	Played 37, Points = 52

The advantage was back with Leeds but the jitters seemed to have returned in the Coventry match and advanced into the Bank Holiday Monday 0-0 draw with Sheffield United too. Although, Lorimer had seen a screamer of a goal ruled out for offside it had been a dour tussle. And the very next day the teams met again, at Bramall Lane, and those first 45 minutes also passed uneventfully, while at Anfield, Liverpool were in front against Manchester City by an incredible 4-0 score-line. At that stage the title race was again hanging in the balance, with disaster seemingly looming for Leeds. Yet a Leeds United strongpoint, possibly their strongest over the Revie years, was resilience in the face of adversity. 'Keep Fighting' was their dictum, and a Don Revie team might be often be down but rarely were they out until the end. Underestimate them at your peril: the Liverpool-Manchester City score stayed at 4-0, while two Lorimer goals, the second a penalty, helped reignite the White spirit.

Their next game was at home to the division's top scorers, third placed Ipswich, while Liverpool had a derby match with Everton, traditionally the toughest of ties. The Elland Road game was tense but exciting, watched by 44,015 tense and excitable spectators. Goals from Lorimer (16 minutes) and Bremner (22) put Leeds two up and helped the crowd relax, but Brian Talbot soon pulled a goal back to make it 2-1 by half-time and matters were soon to get worse as Bryan Hamilton hit the equalizer in the 54th minute. Leeds desperately needed a spark to win the two points, regardless of what was happening at Anfield. In the 70th minute, such a spark arrived in the form of Allan Clarke, detecting a chance and putting it away coolly and expertly to make it 3-2 and eventually win the match. Even better news was the Merseyside derby producing no goals and so another point dropped by Liverpool.

Division 1 table (top), 20th April, 1974.

1 Leeds	Played 41, Points = 60
2 Liverpool	Played 39, Points = 55

*

Eamonn Andrews - 'Now Bill, you're the manager of Liverpool and right now your teams are battling it out for the First Division title. You and Don are great mates.'

'Yes, we're the greatest of enemies.'

Tuesday 24th April, 1974, millions tune in to ITV's pre-recorded *This Is Your Life* show, with Leeds boss Don Revie the unsuspecting recipient of all the, frankly, unwanted attention. Many of those viewers will have switched on the radios soon afterwards to listen for news of a Division One football match taking place at Liverpool's Anfield stadium between the Revie and Shankly dynasties.

*

On May 3rd 1971, Arsenal's Ray Kennedy had scored the solitary goal in the crucial match against Tottenham Hotspur, three minutes from full-time, to seal that year's League title for Arsenal and dump Leeds in to second place at the same time. On April 24th 1974, Arsenal's Ray Kennedy - who would sign for Liverpool within a couple of months - again had a vital say in determining the destination of the Championship trophy, this time by scoring the only goal of Arsenal's game at *Liverpool*. This 1-0 scoreline left Liverpool stranded in second place, simultaneously wrapping up the title for Leeds United. For all the stress and anxiety they had endured in recent weeks, from times of ecstasy sinking to virtual agony, Leeds' winning of the League came without their actually kicking a football. Commenting on what had undoubtedly been a memorable period for the Gaffer, Les Cocker said, 'A great week for Don Revie: the Championship, *This Is Your Life* and he even beat Val Doonican at golf!'

Liverpool, who never gave up the chase despite Leeds' fantastic early unbeaten run through to late February, earned great credit for their efforts and for making the season a fascinating one. Manager Shankly was bitterly disappointed at the weak finale to their pursuit of retaining the title but he showed good grace in defeat, 'My congratulations. I know Leeds care about everyone, from the cleaning ladies right through, and that's how it should be.' And with a May 4th FA Cup final victory over Newcastle United, their disappointment would soon fade. The week before that was Leeds' final League game of the season, at Queens Park Rangers. The Loftus Road club rolled out a red carpet on to the pitch to congratulate them on the title win, and Rangers' players presented Leeds' with a bottle of champagne each. A second half Allan Clarke strike won Leeds the two points. Three days later, Sir Alf Ramsey's reign as England manager was brusquely ended by the FA who had spent months prevaricating on his future, and not very discreetly either. The national team's failure to qualify for the 1974 World Cup decided Ramsey's fate, though his employers' actions were hardly impressive or respectful to the only home nations manager to ever win the World Cup.

14 vi

Leeds United, champions, again – oh yes, oh yes, oh yes! But the good feelings didn't last very long, our bonfire was definitely being aimed at with some or other liquid matter. A week after we'd bagged the title and Don Revie had been on *This Is Your Life*, Sir Alf Ramsey got booted out of the England job. The writing had been on the wall for ages for him but the (Sweet) FA had made him sweat for ages like the thoughtless gits they were. And once his leaving was confirmed, then there was more writing on the wall - for us - at least from where I was looking.

There was really only one man suitable and good enough to replace Ramsey, and that was Don Revie. I reckoned it was just a matter of whether he actually wanted the job or not. I prayed he didn't but I really suspected he did, even though he'd said he would rather stay with Leeds to have another crack at the European Cup. The fears came true, as he finally admitted he did want to be the new England manager. I felt hurt and that's no exaggeration, I was stewing inside about it all. I'd had enough of being left behind by family members, this was nearly as much of a shock as my grandma's death. So, not long before Don Revie was set to leave Elland Road for good, I let him know my feelings. He was the man who mattered to me the most, after all.

One specific June 1974 morning, I had the ultra-important job of sweeping the Home and Visiting Team dressing rooms, plus the tunnel area. Even without training or any matches being played

- most of the players were on holiday and five of them were in the World Cup with Scotland - the muck gathered on the lengths of black lino like no one's business. There was plenty of work going on at the stadium: a new stand, three mountainous floodlights plus undersoil heating for the pitch, so a lot of hard graft was going on virtually every day. Sweeping up was important too, I kept telling myself. That day, I'd just about finished the corridor when Don Revie came sauntering by towards the reception area door. I felt a bit awkward and a bit embarrassed, not sure what to say or do, just knowing that I should do *something*. So I just said 'Hello' to him at first. And he said the same back, but with hardly a glance my way. I'd seen him hundreds of times over the years and often exchanged pleasantries (and more often not) so there was nothing unusual about this particular time, except I *had* to speak to him, even if I'd regret it later on. One thing was for sure, I'd live to regret it even more if I just kept my mouth shut. I wanted to say 'Please don't leave Leeds' to him but couldn't muster the nerve to do it. I did though manage to say, 'No one wants you to leave, Mister Revie…' and it took him aback a bit I think. He wasn't walking now, he stood still. And because he'd stopped walking and I knew I had to keep on talking, I said, 'You *are* the club, you are The Don of Leeds United, don't you realise?'

Then he turned around and said, 'Yes… I'm a bit busy at the moment but I won't forget you said that. Thanks John,' and off he walked, up the corridor and through the door to the reception area. *Thanks John.* Don Revie had just bloody called me John and then he'd gone, all as quick as that. But then the door opened again and he popped his head round, and with a shy smile on his face, 'I've a lot on my mind… I meant to say 'Jim'. Sorry.' I told him it was alright, and he disappeared again. And I suddenly had this good feeling inside me that everything was going to turn out alright, too, that I'd actually done something good and significant. The crap you believe when you're in your twenties.

July 4th 1974 arrived, Independence Day for the septic tanks and a sort of independence day for Don Revie too. I'll never forget it, it was a day I could have really made a name for myself, on television, so the whole country could have witnessed my heroic actions. I could have gone down in folklore as 'The man who tried to save Leeds United'. July 4th 1974, was officially the day the news was announced that Revie was leaving Leeds to take over as

England manager. The TV cameras were at Elland Road as the Football Association's Ted Croker arrived at the stadium to sort it out with the Leeds board of directors. I'm there on film, as Croker walks towards the glass doors of the club reception, and that's when I reckon I had the chance to make a name for myself, to get my point across to him and those chumps at the FA. I wouldn't have sworn or got physical but I would have said it in the most forceful manner I could. Him being there was like a burglar knocking on your door and asking if it was alright if he popped round later to rob you. I should have told him to sod off out of Leeds and look elsewhere for another manager, in front of all those cameras and in ear shot of all those microphones. England would have known what Don Revie meant to us all at Leeds then. The fact I did nothing still taunts my mind even now, I just wish I'd had the nerve to do *something*.

Various comments and opinions were expressed as to why Don Revie left Leeds. Most of them wrong, I reckon. That's football for you, millions of opinions with every single person thinking somehow that they know better. He was accused of running out on the club like a coward, scared of his responsibilities, especially with regards to the players' and coaches' contracts. Some said that the team and manager were past it, that Revie was getting out before being 'found out', even though we were current League Champions and up for the next European Cup. And some even said he went just for the money, even though England didn't pay that well.

It was all a lot simpler, I was sure of it. It was the England job after all, the England job! The *top* job, no self-respecting Englishman could turn the chance down. And no one was better suited for it than Don Revie, even though Jimmy Bloomfield of Leicester, QPR's Gordon Jago and Coventry's Gordon Milne were supposedly short-listed for it. I'm sure loudmouths Malcolm Allison and Brian Clough would have loved a crack at it, too, but they'll have talked themselves out of the reckoning ages ago. Don Revie was better than them all.

At one time I did think he was leaving the club in the lurch, due to the seven or eight player contracts needing sorting out, but it turns out he tried to help Leeds by recommending the man he thought best to succeed him, and that was Johnny Giles. Giles was one of those players near the end of his contract, so who better to pass on the dilemma of new contracts to than the actual main dilemma himself? Everyone knew he was clever, everyone respected him at the club and everyone trusted him; he'd do things the right way, like Don Revie had always tried to do. I suppose it always looked like Don's 'favourite son' Billy Bremner was being groomed to be the manager, but Billy had more games left in him than Giles as he was younger and he'd been luckier with injuries. It seemed obvious Billy wanted the job, but a fantastic captain wouldn't necessarily make a fantastic manager. That was my opinion anyway.

Don Revie left Leeds United for England with a clear conscience, he wanted and expected the board to give John Giles the job. I've never accepted the accusation that Revie would just leave so many of the Leeds 'family' worrying about whether they were going to get new contracts or not, as if he didn't give a damn about anyone but himself.

I was never really one of those so-called inverted snobs who resented people just because they had more money than me. Had I been then I'd have resented most of the bloody country. So, I genuinely had nothing against the Leeds directors, all of them wealthy men. I *had* to respect them anyway, they paid me a wage after all, as weakly as my weekly wages were. But when Percy Woodward was quoted with 'It's not for the manager who is leaving to invite his successor' my respect for those directors was severely tested, I suspected they were plotting something. And that *something* was bound to be stupid, bound to be. Because they were annoyed with Revie for having the audacity to recommend his successor, they'd decided that his opinions on the future of the club were worthless, despite everything he'd done for it. I only wish someone had asked Harry Reynolds for his thoughts on the matter or even just left it to chairman Manny Cussins to decide on his own.

The week after Don's departure, Bill Shankly only went and left Liverpool too. And in September, Bill Nicholson packed in Tottenham Hotspur too. Shankly didn't retire, he just wanted a break because his wife was worried he was under too much stress in the job, whereas fed up Nicholson was finished with football forever. Jesus, I wished we'd persuaded Shanks to take over here, looking at who those jokers on the Leeds board finally chose. I wondered what planet were they on. The arrival of the new manager happened pretty fast, the oddest, maddest, most stupid, idiotic appointment made in football, ever, by directors who seemed to have taken leave of their sodding senses. I really, *really* wish they hadn't bothered. I mean, Brian Clough... Brian shithousing Clough!

*

Early in September, Harry Reynolds died, outside the Leeds boardroom, soon before a Leeds Reserves match. God bless him. Had he had a choice, I bet he wouldn't have minded dying there, at Elland Road. God bloody bless him, he was a proper man, and none of this would be what it is without Harry Reynolds. Our *city* wouldn't be what it is without him, I mean it. And even if the Dirty Leeds myth carries on, those who've lived it know the truth and what's been achieved. So stuff 'em all, anyone who is that dim to believe it. Calling Revie's team 'Dirty Leeds' is like calling Michelangelo a simple painter & decorator. Reynolds and Revie. Harry and Don in 1961, thirteen years ago. Thirteen, unlucky for some, but not for us, not for Leeds.

About the Author

Robert Endeacott was born and bred in Leeds and still lives in the south of the city and still manages to afford a season ticket despite being a 'dissident' and a 'moron'. *Dirty Leeds* was his third novel and *After Extra Time* is the extended version of that.

Other books by Robert Endeacott

- and for more information see www.dirtyleeds.net and all the books are available from good bookshops, etc.

One Northern Soul, 2002 Route - an acclaimed, cult classic.

If that goal in Paris had been allowed then everything that followed could have been different. For young Stephen Bottomley something died that night. *One Northern Soul* follows the fortunes of this Leeds United fan as he comes of age in the dark days of the early eighties with no prospects, no guidance, and to cap it all off, his beloved football team suffers relegation to the Second Division.

No More Heroes, 2004 Relish Books – the sequel to *ONS*.

Following fast on the heels of J.R. Endeacott's first novel, *One Northern Soul*, it is a moving, home-grown tale about friends, faith and football and an amusing coming-of-age story which charts the experiences of Leeds youth, Steve Bottomley, during the 1980s.

It is an uplifting, touching but fun story of friendship, flirtations, family, football fanaticism, faith and other words beginning with 'F'!

Fanthology, with Graeme Garvey, 2005 Relish Books

Whatever you say about Leeds United FC, it's very unlikely the words 'boring' and 'mundane' would be used. The life & times of this famous club, the fortunes & misfortunes and the trials & tribulations are unparalleled in world football.

Here, Leeds fans all over the world tell of their emotions, their tears of joy & their tears of misery in good, bad and downright ugly times with the world famous Whites. And fans of all ages reveal 'WHY' they're Leeds fans, what it is that makes them so loyal and give their reasons for nearly losing all sense of reason watching Leeds play the beautiful game.

Dirty Leeds, 2009 Tonto Books' best-selling novel

Dirty Leeds is the 'cut' version of *After Extra Time*, telling of Revie's thirteen year reign as Leeds manager, entwined with the tale of Jimmy O'Rourke, a local lad with the rare ambition of playing for his favourite, his only, football team Leeds United. And he is good enough.

DisRepute - Revie's England, 2010 Tonto

Recounts Don Revie's torrid time after taking over the England job from the sacked Sir Alf Ramsey in 1974.

Numerous reports and theories abound about Revie's time as England manager: the players he selected or dropped, the tactics, the dossiers, money, why he resigned and if he was pushed, and the 'deceitful' manner of his leaving. *DisRepute* addresses the myths and rumours and allegations, to paint a clearer, more honest picture. Truth is stranger than football!

Jimmy O'Rourke should be returning quite soon, with ***Scandal FC***

What is Candlelighters?

Established in 1976, it is a charity formed and run by parents of children who have or have had cancer, ex-patients and the medical staff who treat them. Based in Yorkshire, Candlelighters provides essential services and support to children with cancer and their families.

It funds the extras that make life on the ward and clinic easier. It funds holidays for families during treatment, family grants, sibling groups, special trips and days out. It also funds research posts and extra play workers on the wards.

'CANdlelighters – together we CAN help!'

You can find out more about Candlelighters at;

http://candlelighters.org.uk/DesktopDefault.aspx